W9-AQN-929

Molecular Structure and Biological Specificity

Molecular Structure and Biological Specificity

A Symposium sponsored by the Office of Naval Research and arranged by the American Institute of Biological Sciences. Held in Washington, D.C., October 28, 29, 1955.

EDITED BY

LINUS PAULING

AND

HARVEY A. ITANO

PUBLICATION

No. 2

1957

AMERICAN INSTITUTE OF BIOLOGICAL SCIENCES
WASHINGTON, D.C.

THIRD PRINTING, 1961

Library of Congress Catalog Card
Number: 57-11004

PRINTED IN THE UNITED STATES OF AMERICA
BY WAVERLY PRESS, INC., BALTIMORE

Table of Contents

Participants

Chairman

Linus Pauling, California Institute of Technology, Pasadena, California.

R. A. Alberty, University of Wisconsin, Madison, Wisconsin.

C. B. Anfinsen, Jr., National Heart Institute, National Institutes of Health, Bethesda, Maryland.

Jerry Donohue, University of Southern California, Los Angeles, California.

Felix Haurowitz, Indiana University, Bloomington, Indiana.

J. Hirschfelder, University of Wisconsin, Madison, Wisconsin.

Harvey A. Itano, National Institute of Arthritis and Metabolic Diseases, National Institutes of Health, Bethesda, Maryland.

Herbert Jehle, University of Nebraska, Lincoln, Nebraska.

J. G. Kirkwood, Yale University, New Haven, Connecticut.

I. M. Klotz, Northwestern University, Evanston, Illinois.

Robert R. Redfield, National Heart Institute, National Institutes of Health, Bethesda, Maryland.

K. S. Pitzer, University of California, Berkeley, California.

David Pressman, Roswell Park Memorial Institute, Buffalo, New York.

Herman Schroeder, Jackson Laboratory, E. I. duPont de Nemours & Co., Wilmington, Delaware.

I. B. Wilson, Columbia University, New York City, N. Y.

Molecular Complementariness in Antigen-Antibody Systems

David Pressman

Roswell Park Memorial Institute, Buffalo, N. Y.

IN MANY EXAMPLES of biological specificity there appears to be a close complementariness of fit of the active site of the receptor molecule about its substrate, so that enough of the various weak, short-range forces, such as the van der Waals forces, charge interaction, hydrogen bond, dipole interaction and so forth, can be effective in holding molecules together (Pauling, Campbell and Pressman, 1943; Pressman, 1953).

Specificity arises from the fact that only certain configurations can fit the site; other configurations are blocked sterically so that they cannot fit.

The study of hapten-antibody interactions permits the determination in a particular specific system of just how close the fit is, and what forces are acting. This is so because antibodies can be formed against simple chemical substances of known configuration and the contour of the antibody's specific site can then be determined more or less precisely, or felt out, by the interaction of that site with substances of known configuration.

The studies of hapten-antibody interactions discussed here stem from the voluminous pioneer studies of Landsteiner (1945) on chemically altered proteins and the antibodies dervied therefrom.

The extent of combination of a hapten with an antibody which is directed against it can be determined either by partition of the hapten between an antibody solution and a control solution, as was first carried out by Dr. Haurowitz, (1933) our next speaker, and by Marrack and Smith (1932), or by the ability of the hapten to combine with the antibody and inhibit the precipitation of that antibody by the homologous antigen, as in the extensive studies by Landsteiner.

The studies which I shall be reporting here were carried out initially under Dr. Linus Pauling's direction at the California Institute of Technology and subsequently at the Sloan-Kettering Institute and now at the Roswell Park Memorial Institute. Some of the work reported here, as yet unpublished, was done by Dr. Nisonoff, who is now at Roswell Park with me.

An antibody acts as though it were formed against the antigen as a template. It is important to realize that the orientation of the hapten with respect to the antigen surface during antibody formation is a prime factor. Fig. 1 shows three such orientations for a hapten, *p*(*p*'-azobenzeneazo) benzoate, attached

Fig. 1a

FIG. 1. Possible orientation of hapten with respect to antigen during antibody formation. a. Extended from surface of antigen. b. Lying flat on surface. c. Lying perpendicular to surface.

to the tyrosine of an antigen. In the first case (Fig. 1a), the hapten extends normal to the surface of the protein and an antibody formed against this portion of the antigen might have a long invagination, about 12 Å long, to accommodate the hapten. There are two other possible orientations, each with the hapten lying along the surface of the protein. One is with the faces of the benzene ring lying flat on the surface of the antigen (Fig. 1b) and the other is with the benzene rings lying perpendicular to the antigen surface (Fig. 1c). In the first case, an antibody formed against the haptenic portion of the anti-

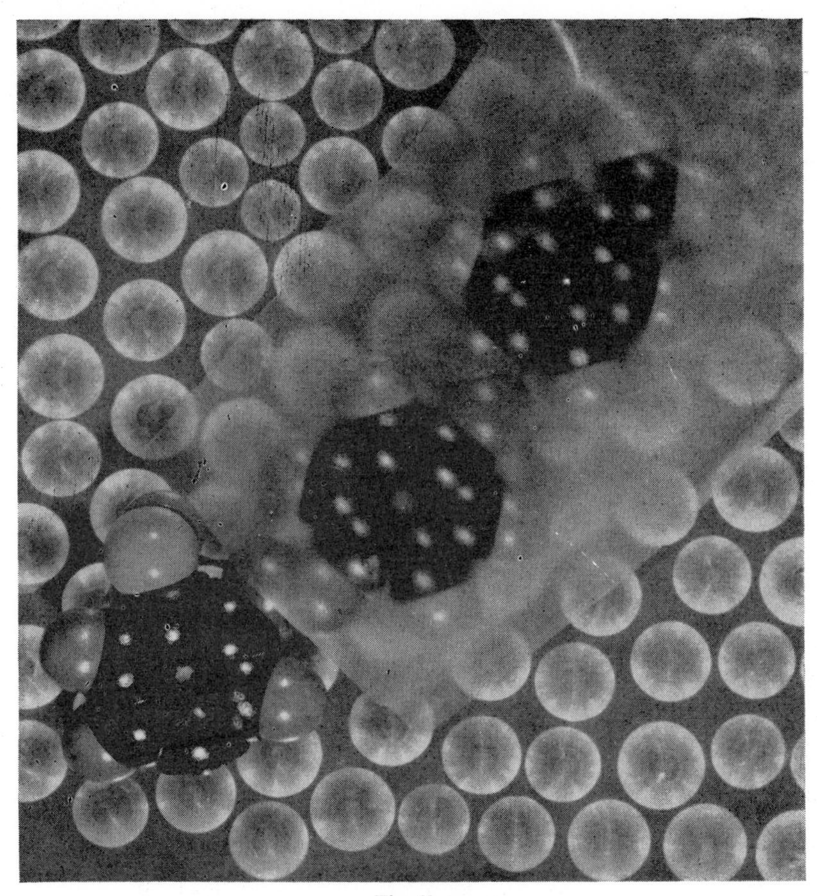

Fig. 1b

gen would have a long invagination to accommodate the hapten. The fit would be all around the hapten but perhaps not very close in view of the length of the invagination, ca. 12 Å. In the second case, the antibody would be formed against the face of the hapten group, and in the third, the antibody would have a slit trench type of anti-hapten region with one side open to accommodate the hapten. Evidence is available that indicates that these three types of antibody do exist.

Another point to bear in mind is that the antibody is quite heterogeneous. An antiserum formed against even a simple hapten contains a mosaic of different antibody molecules, each having specificity directed toward particular portions of the hapten. Thus Landsteiner and van der Scheer prepared antiserum against a hapten containing two different groupings, 5-azoisophthalyl-

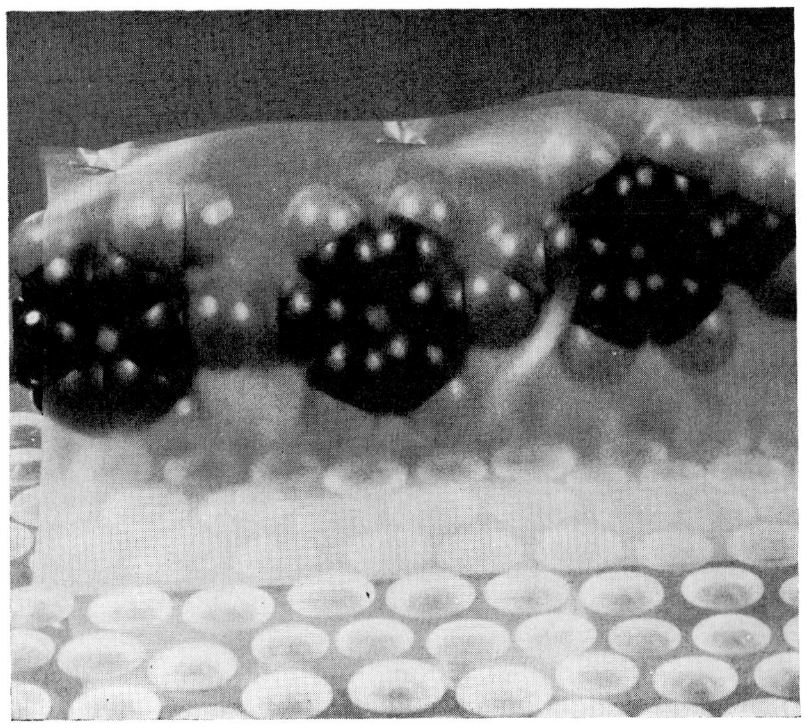

Fig. 1c

glycine-leucine, which contains 1 glycinate residue and 1 leucinate residue (1932).

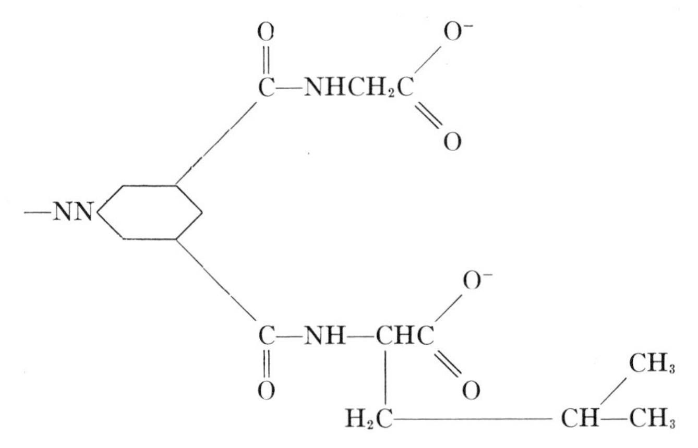

Among the antibodies formed, there could be found antibodies with specificities directed against either one or the other of the two groups as well as

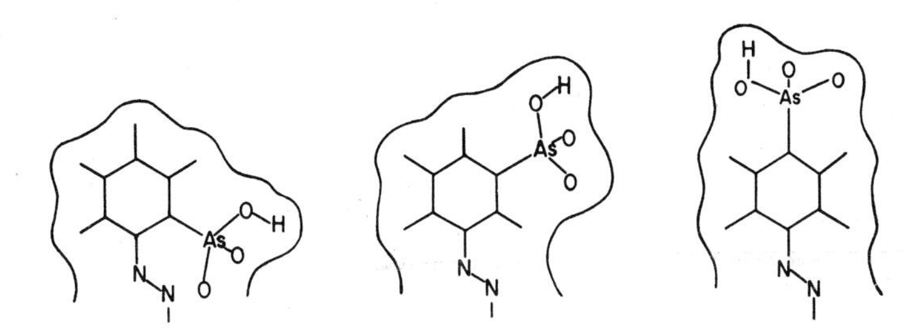

FIG. 2. Van der Waals outline of *ortho*, *meta* and *para*-azobenzenearsonates

antibodies directed against both groups. Thus, even though both determinants are present in the antigen in close juxtaposition and in equal quantities, individual antibodies are formed against individual parts.

For an example of an antibody formed against a simple substance, let us look first at antibodies formed against the azobenzenearsonate ion (Pressman and Siegel, 1953). Fig. 2 shows the *para*, *meta* and *ortho* azobenzenearsonates. The outer line is the van der Waals outline of the molecule.

When antibodies are formed against any one of these, they act as though they were formed against the van der Waals outline of the hapten as a template. They can also combine with an unsubstituted benzenearsonate ion. Substituents on the benzenearsonate decrease the extent of combination when they interfere sterically.

Thus, for antibodies to the *p*-azobenzenearsonate group, substituents in the *ortho* or *meta* positions decrease combining power generally. If we place a substituent in the *para* position, we might expect an increased combination of the hapten with the antibody, because the antibody would have a region which has been formed against the azo group and this region can also accommodate some other substituent.

In the case of antibody to the *meta*-azobenzenearsonate, there would be steric effects observed for substituents in all positions except the *meta* position. In the case of antibody to the *ortho*-azobenzenearsonate, there would be observed steric effects of substituents which are in the *meta* or *para* position. Substituents in the *ortho* position, however, would fit in the region of the antibody which was formed to accommodate the azo group.

The results of studies obtained from these three systems are shown in Fig. 3. Values are listed for the relative combining constant, K_0', which is the combining constant of the substituted benzenearsonate relative to the combining constant of the unsubstituted benzenearsonate in these various systems (Pauling, Pressman and Grossberg, 1944). The various substituents used are listed, and it can be seen that with the antibody against the *ortho*-azobenzenearsonate we get the best combination with the *ortho* substituted compounds, interme-

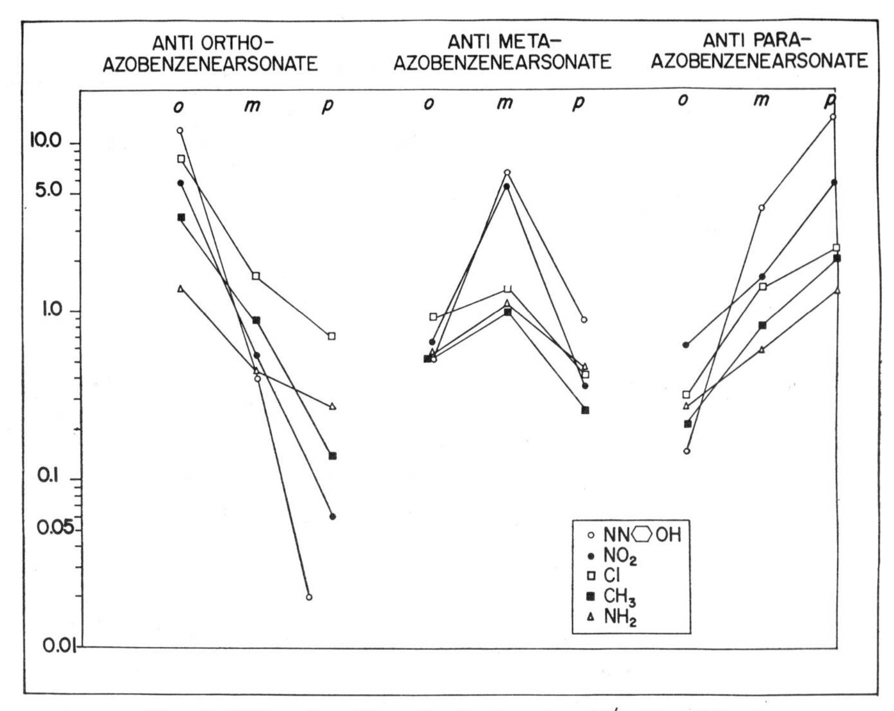

FIG. 3. Effect of position of substituent on K_0' value of hapten

diate combination with the *meta*, and least combination with the *para*, indicating steric interference of the substituent in the *meta* and *para* positions.

In the anti-*meta*-azobenzenearsonate system, we find the greatest combination with haptens with the substituent in the *meta* position, where there is no steric interference, and less combination when the substituents are in the *ortho* or *para* position. Similarly, with the antibodies specific to the *para*-azobenzenearsonate system, greatest combination takes place with *para* substituted compounds.

In order to determine more precisely how closely antibodies fit around the hapten group, we have carried out studies with the *ortho*, *meta*, and *para*-azobenzoate ions. We prepared the *o*-, *m*-, and *p*(*p*-hydroxybenzeneazo)benzoates and all of the monochlor derivatives (except one) of these compounds with the chlorine in the benzoate ring. We then measured the interaction of the chlor-substituted haptens with the antibody against the *ortho*, *meta*, and *para*-azobenzoate ions (Pressman, Siegel and Hall, 1954).

The results are shown in Fig. 4. Here I have indicated the van der Waals outline of the injected hapten by the dotted lines and the van der Waals outline of the chlor-substituted hapten by the solid lines.

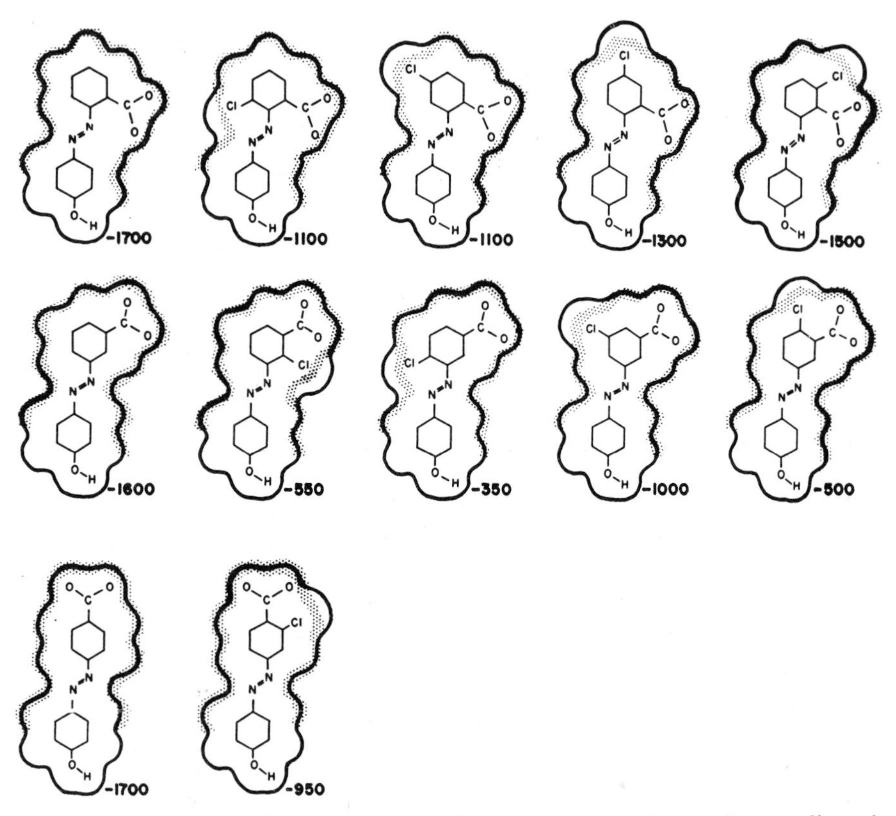

FIG. 4. Van der Waals outline of inhibiting hapten superimposed on outline of an injected hapten group. Numerical values are for ΔF(relative). (Reproduced from the Journal of the American Chemical Society, *76*, 6339 (1954) with permission of the Editor.)

There are listed the free energies of combination of these substances with homologous antisera relative to the combination of the unsubstituted benzoate ion. You can see that, depending on which position the chlorine occupies, there is a steric interaction which contributes to the decreased interaction of these substances with the specific antibodies.

The free energies involved when the chlorine is in the various positions are summarized in Fig. 5.

In the case of the antibody against the *meta*-azobenzoate group, we find that there is a large effect of a chlorine in either of the *ortho* positions. There are two possible reasons for this large effect. There may be a steric effect of the chlorine in interfering with the combination of the antibody or there may be an effect of the *o*-chlorine to tilt the carboxylate ion out of the plane of the

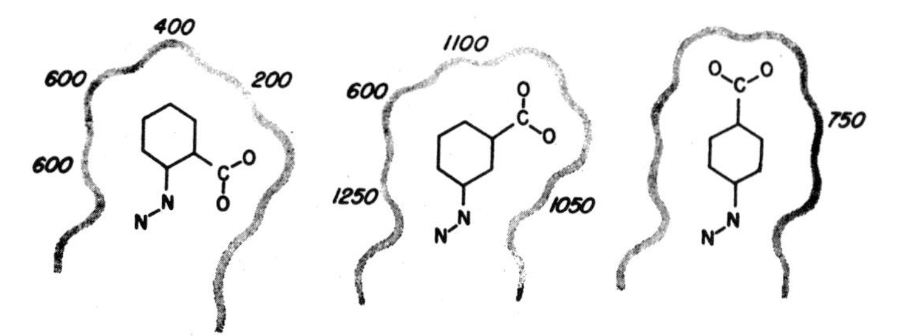

FIG. 5. Effect of chlorosubstituent in indicated position on the free energy of combination of (p'-hydroxyphenylazo)benzoates with antibody. (Reproduced from the Journal of the American Chemical Society, *76*, 6339 (1954) with permission of the Editor.)

benzene ring so that the carboxylate group no longer fits the antibody site as it did in the original hapten.

In correlation with this tilt effect, we find that antibodies against the *ortho*-azobenzoate ion show very low interference with substituents in the *ortho* position. This is presumably due to the fact that the carboxylate in the hapten against which the antibody was formed is already tilted out of the plane of the benzene ring, so that the antibody formed against this nonplanar carboxylate can accommodate a chlor-substituent in the *ortho* position.

So far, I have discussed substituents which exhibit a steric interference on the combination of hapten with antibody. What happens if a substituent is placed on the hapten in the position occupied by the azo group of the injected hapten (position of attachment of hapten with antigen)? Since the antibody was formed against the azo group, it can accommodate other substituents in this position. Indeed, a substituent in this position almost always increases the combining power of the hapten.

In the case where no hydrogen bonds are formed, one might well expect the greatest interaction to take place with those radicals which have the greatest van der Waals interaction, and this is actually the case.

Fig. 6 shows the increase of combining power with van der Waals attraction in several systems for the case where the substituent is in the position of attachment of the hapten group to the antigen. It can be seen that for each system, the order for strength of combination is methyl $<$ chlorine $<$ bromine $<$ iodine, which is in the order of the polarizabilities of the groups and indicates an attraction of these groups for the part of the antibody directed toward the azo group.

The order holds throughout except in the *ortho*-azobenzoate system, where there is the problem of tilt. As the substituent becomes larger, there is a tendency toward decreased combination due to increased tilt of the carboxyl on the one hand and a tendency toward increased combination due to polariza-

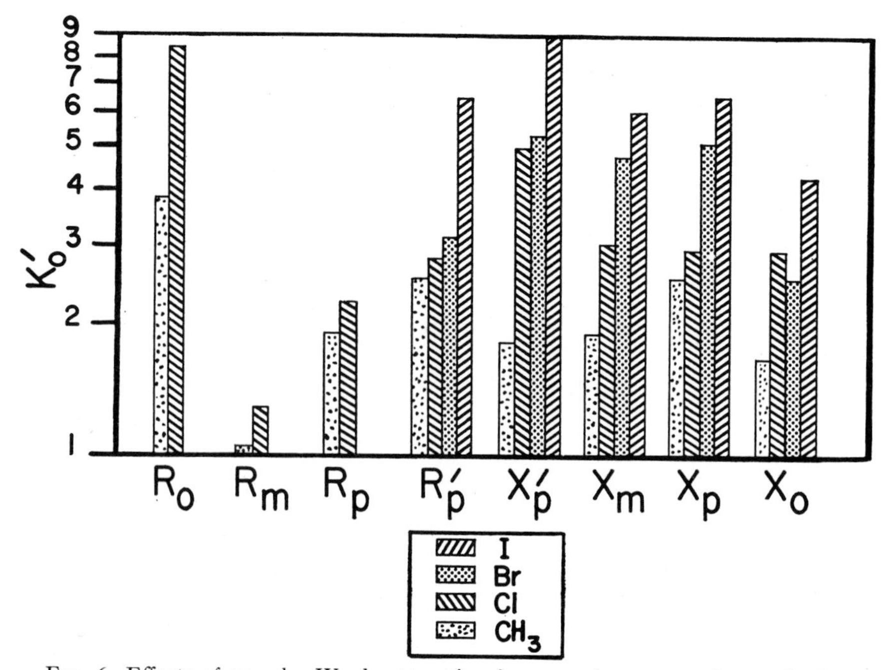

FIG. 6. Effects of van der Waals attraction for several systems where substituent is in position of attachment.

bility on the other. The order observed in the anti-*ortho*-azobenzoate system is CH_3 < Br < Cl < I. Apparently, the increased tilt due to the bromine over that induced by chlorine due to size is not compensated for by the greater polarizability of bromine, while for iodine the greater polarizability wins out.

Table 1 is a summary of some other *para* systems investigated (Pressman and Siegel, 1953; Pressman, Grossberg and Pauling, 1943; Pressman and Siegel, 1953a; Pressman and Siegel, 1953b). Antisera were prepared against the various haptens indicated. The asterisk represents the homologous charged group as indicated. The values are the relative combining constants of the homologous hapten with antibody. The benzene derivative has the value of 1 in all cases. A *para*-methyl substituent increases the constant in all cases. The methyl group fits into the part of the antibody site directed toward the azo group in the position of attachment and thus, exhibits a greater van der Waals attraction than the hydrogen of the benzene derivative without any steric effect. The relative constants for the *meta*-methyl, *ortho*-methyl and *alpha*-naphthyl derivatives are an indication of the tightness of fit of antibody around the hapten group. For a tightly fitting antibody we would expect the constant to be decreased; the tighter the fit, the greater the decrease (taking into account also the tilt of the carboxylate out of the plane of the benzene

TABLE 1

Closeness of fit in various *para* systems

System	*	Hapten: *	* CH$_3$	* CH$_3$	* CH$_3$	*	*
		K_0'					
 NN⟨ ⟩	N(CH$_3$)$_3$	1.0	1.45	0.86	1.05	2.0	
 NN⟨ ⟩NN⟨ ⟩	AsO$_3$H	1.0	2.7	1.1	1.0	2.9	3.9
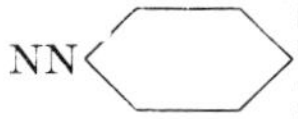 NN⟨ ⟩	AsO$_3$H	1.0	1.9	0.78	0.21	0.52	6.0
 NN⟨ ⟩NN⟨ ⟩	C(O–)O	1.0	1.8	.21	.03	.03	1.98
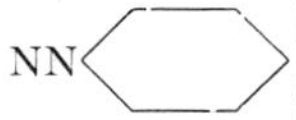 NN⟨ ⟩	C(O–)O	1.0	3.0	.66	.08	.18	10

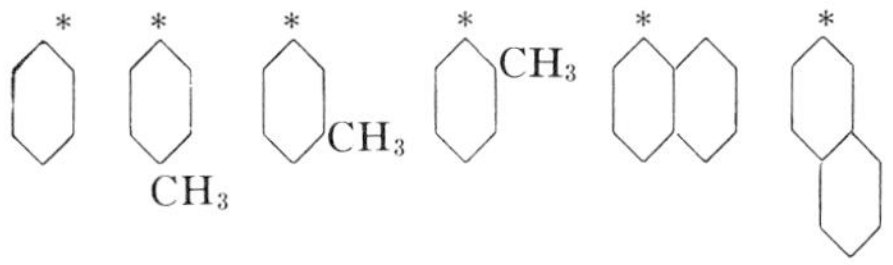

ring). It can be seen that the fit is much closer in the last three systems than in the first two. The fit around the positive charged hapten and the azobenzene-azobenzenearsonate hapten is loose enough along one side so that the extra benzene ring of the naphthyl or the *ortho* or *para*-methyl groups can be accommodated. This is taken as an indication that the antibodies formed here are of the slit trench type. The antibody presumably was formed against one side of the hapten leaving the other side free.

Table 2 shows how closely anti-*ortho*-azobenzoate antibody fits around the 4 position of the benzoate ion. The combining constants of the antibody with the *para*-fluoro, -chloro, -bromo and -iodobenzoates are listed. The hapten can fit into the antibody site in only one way. Fluorine, which is not much larger than hydrogen, decreases the relative constant to a value of 0.6. Chlorine decreases it somewhat more, and bromine still more. The differences are significant. Iodine shows a slightly increased combining constant over that of bromine and is about the same as that of chlorine. This order is an example of balance between steric effect and van der Waals interaction. As the size increases there is a greater steric interaction, but frequently the van der Waals attraction increases in a compensating manner, as occurs here with iodine.

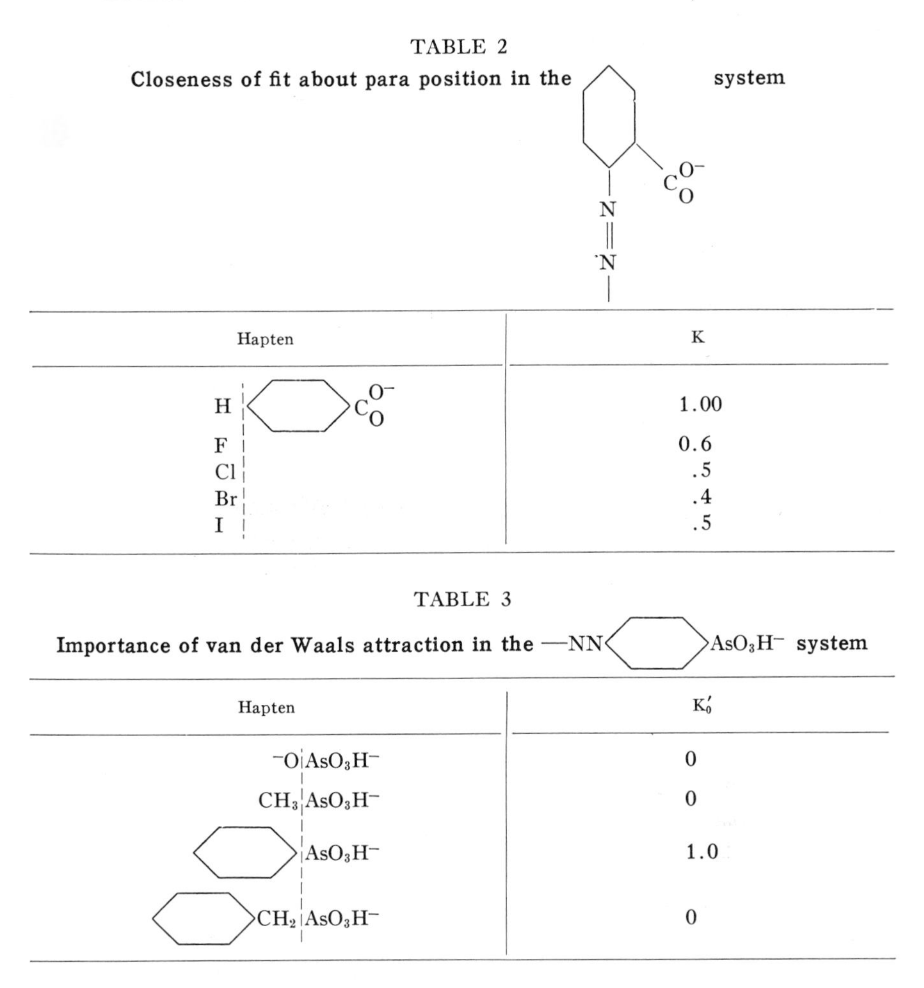

TABLE 2

Closeness of fit about para position in the [structure: benzene ring with $-COO^-$ and $-N=N-$] **system**

Hapten	K
H [benzene ring]$-CO_2^-$	1.00
F	0.6
Cl	.5
Br	.4
I	.5

TABLE 3

Importance of van der Waals attraction in the $—NN$[benzene ring]AsO_3H^- **system**

Hapten	K_0'
$^-O \mid AsO_3H^-$	0
$CH_3 \mid AsO_3H^-$	0
[benzene ring] $\mid AsO_3H^-$	1.0
[benzene ring]$CH_2 \mid AsO_3H^-$	0

The relative position of components of a haptenic group is important. This is shown in Table 3, where we have relative constants for the interaction of various substances with anti-*para*-azobenzenearsonate antibodies. It can be seen that it is very important for the benzene ring to be right next to the arsonate group, since separating the benzene from the arsonate by the CH_2 group, as in the case of benzylarsonate, decreases the combining constant markedly. This indicates that the fit of the antibody around the hapten is so close that the displacement of the ring essentially destroys combining power. The benzene ring is very important here as is shown by the fact that neither the arsonate ion itself nor methylarsonate combines with the antibody. This relation is not unique for the benzenearsonate system but holds also for several other systems,

TABLE 4
Van der Waals attraction due to benzene ring

System	Hapten		
	C_6H_5-	H_3C-	$C_6H_5CH_2^-$
		K_0	
$-NN-C_6H_4-AsO_3H^-$	1.00	0	
$-NN-C_6H_4-AsO_3H^-$	1.00	0	0
$-NN-C_6H_4-AsO_3H^-$	1.00	0	0
$-NN-C_6H_4-NN-C_6H_4-AsO_3H^-$	1.00	0	0.05
$-NN-C_6H_4-COO^-$	1.00	0	0
$-NN-C_6H_4-NN-C_6H_4-COO^-$	1.00	0	0
$-NN-C_6H_4-COCH_2CH_2COO^-$	1.00	0.12	
$-NN-C_6H_4-CONHCH_2COO^-$	1.00	.01	

as is shown by Table 4 (Pressman, Bryden and Pauling, 1948; Pressman, Maynard, Grossberg and Pauling, 1943; Pressman and Siegel, 1953a; Pressman and Siegel, 1953b; Pressman, Siegel and Hall, 1954; Pauling, Pressman and Grossberg, 1944).

In the several systems listed, the benzene derivative gave good combination; the methyl derivative gave essentially none, except in the case of the benzoyl propionate system and the phenyl-trimethylammonium ion system, where there was a slight combination with the methyl derivative. Moving the benzene ring over by one methylene group also decreased combination, except for the phenyl-trimethylammonium ion system. The fit around the latter

TABLE 5

Specificity of charged groups in the NN⟨⟩AsO_3H^- **system**

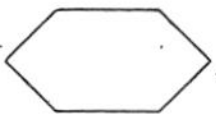

Hapten	K_0'
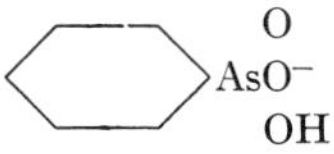 ⟨⟩$AsO(O)(OH)^-$ (O / AsO⁻ / OH)	1.0
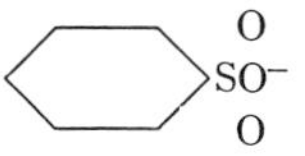 ⟨⟩SO_3^- (O / SO⁻ / O)	0
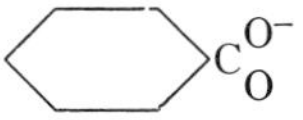 ⟨⟩CO_2^- (C, O⁻, O)	0
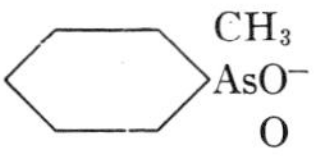 ⟨⟩$As(CH_3)O_2^-$ (CH₃ / AsO⁻ / O)	0
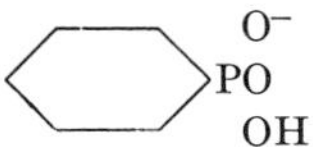 ⟨⟩$PO(O^-)(OH)$ (O⁻ / PO / OH)	1.0
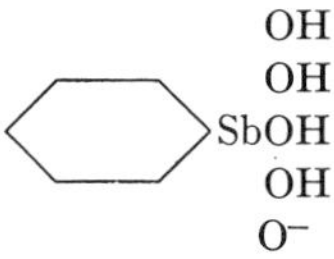 ⟨⟩$Sb(OH)_4O^-$ (OH / OH / SbOH / OH / O⁻)	0

system has already been described as being loose with the antibodies essentially of the slit trench form.

The specificity of the antibody with respect to the nature of the charged group is very important; this is illustrated in Table 5 (Pressman, Pardee and Pauling, 1945). Antibody specific to the *para*-azobenzenearsonate group was studied and it was found that the phosphonate group was essentially as effective as the arsonate group. However, other charged groups, some of even smaller size, were unable to replace the arsonate group effectively. Thus, sulfonate, carboxylate, methyl arsonate, and stibonate did not combine.

In a carboxylate system, i.e., antibodies against the benzoate ion, similar specificity is observed in that antibody will not combine with sulfonate ion or arsonate ion, but requires the carboxylate ion for combination.

I should like to mention at this time that it is not necessary to have a charged group for specificity to exist against haptens. Specificity against uncharged groups also occurs (Landsteiner, 1945).

Just how closely antibody fits around the charged group was determined by experiments involved in combination of antibody to the *para*-azobenzene-trimethylammonium group with two haptens of identical configuration, except that one has the trimethylammonium group and the other a *tertiary* butyl group as shown below (Pressman and Siegel, 1953a; Pressman, Grossberg and Pauling, 1943).

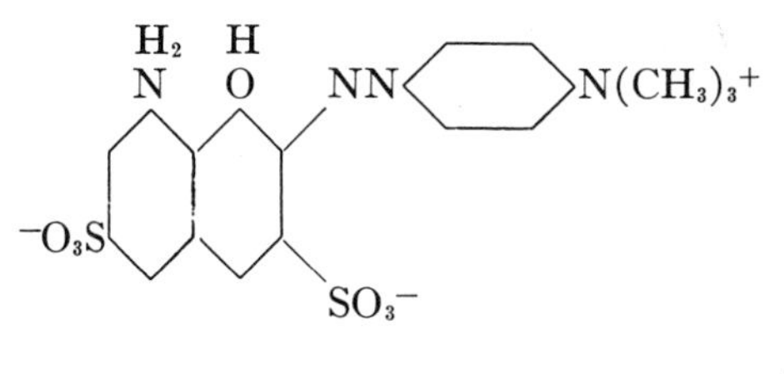

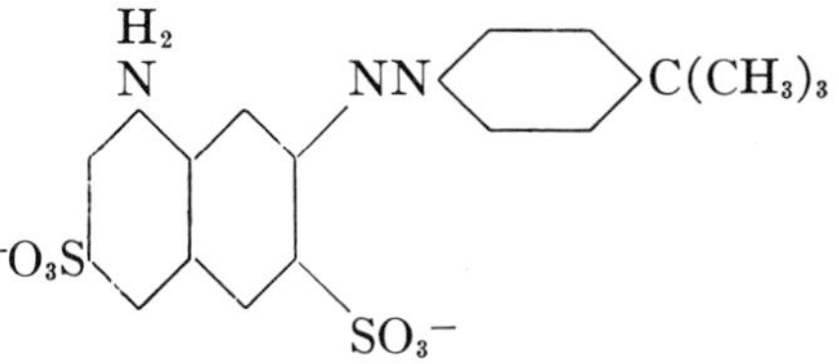

The compounds were prepared by coupling *para*-azobenzene-trimethylammonium ions and *para*-azo-*tertiary*-butylbenzene to "H acid." The *tertiary*-butyl group has the same configuration and size as the trimethylammonium group but lacks the charge. Experimentally we observed a factor of 8 between the relative combining constants of these two haptens with the antibody. This factor of 8 represents a free energy of interaction due to the positive charge of about 1100 cal., assuming that the van der Waals interactions for the two groups are the same. On calculation of the distance between the positive charge on the hapten and the corresponding negative charge on the antibody which would give an energy interaction of this magnitude, we find that the two charges approach within about 3 Å. of the distance to the closest possible approach. The calculation is made on the basis of Schwartzenbach's evaluation of the dielectric constant of water for relatively small distances between charges. This is indicated in Fig. 7.

Table 6 shows the effect of increasing the size of the positive ion by replacing the trimethylammonium group with either the trimethylarsonium group or the triethylammonium group. We find that the combining constant decreases directly with the increasing radius, and we conclude that the decreased combination may be attributed to a greater distance between the charge of the central atom and the negative ion of the antibody in the complementary position.

Since antibodies in general seem to fit closely about certain particular substances and the closeness of fit can be determined by detecting substances of known configuration, information can be obtained about the steric configuration of systems in aqueous solution. An interesting example of this is the case

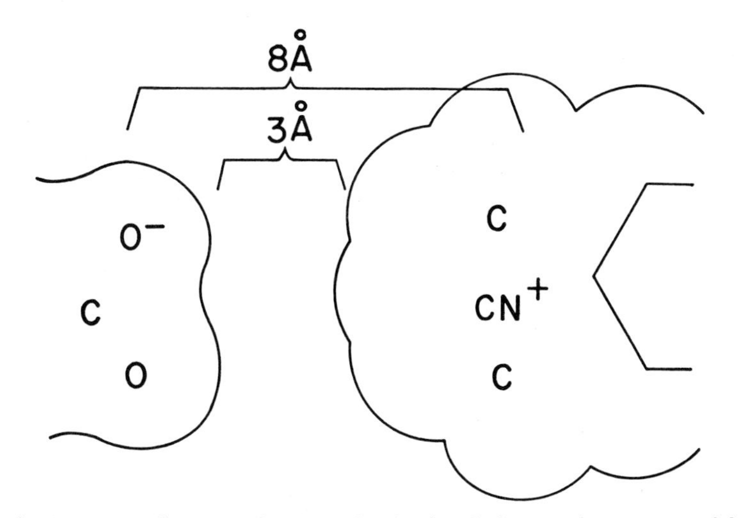

FIG. 7. Apparent distance of approach of trimethylammonium group of hapten to carboxylate of antibody.

TABLE 6

Effect of ion radius in $\langle\bigcirc\rangle N(CH_3)_3^+$ **system**

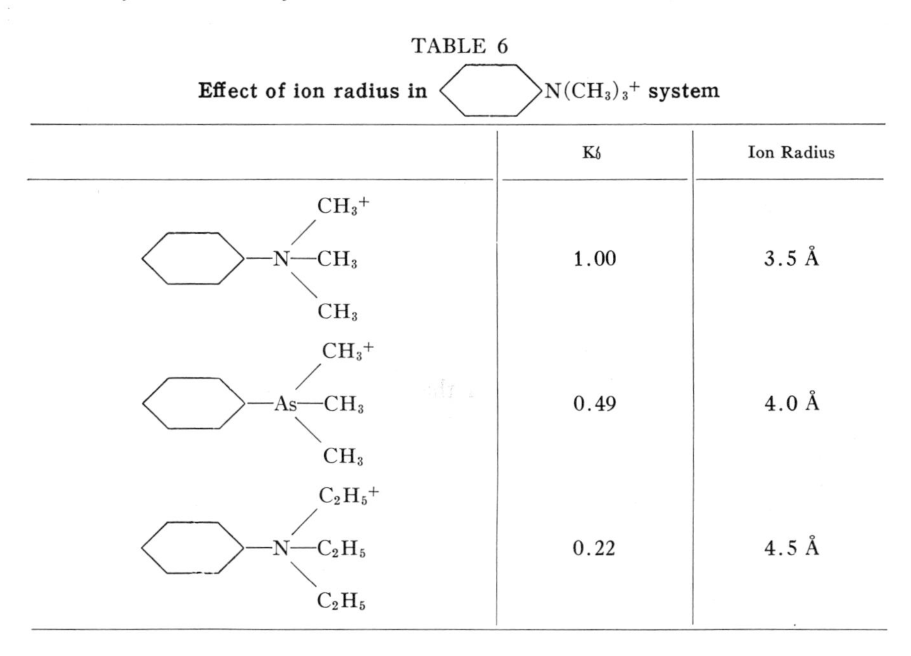

	K_0'	Ion Radius
—N—CH_3 (CH_3^+, CH_3)	1.00	3.5 Å
—As—CH_3 (CH_3^+, CH_3)	0.49	4.0 Å
—N—C_2H_5 ($C_2H_5^+$, C_2H_5)	0.22	4.5 Å

of pyridinecarboxylate ions. From the extent of combination of nicotinate, *iso*-nicotinate and picolinate ion with antibodies prepared against the azobenzoate ions, it appears that the position occupied by the nitrogen atom in the ring acts as though it were a carbon of a benzene ring connected to a large steric substituent. The nitrogen atom, instead of acting smaller than the CH of a benzene ring, acts as though it were a CBr or some other large grouping. This apparent steric effect of the nitrogen atom in the ring fits in with the concept that the nitrogen is hydrated in aqueous solution in these compounds and the hydration is strong enough to affect the interaction of these molecules in biological systems.

Since in nearly all biological systems the reactions take place in aqueous solution, the hydrated configuration of various ions is of extreme importance and may be the determining factor in molecular specificity in these systems.

In conclusion, I want to point out that antigen-antibody systems resemble enzyme-substrate systems and other systems of biological interaction in which there are rigorous requirements of configuration and charge for specificity, and that they are being used to yield information about the configuration of substances of biological interest in aqueous solution.

References

Haurowitz, F. and F. Breinl. 1933. Chemical investigation of the specific binding of arsanic-protein and arsanilic acid to immune serum. Z. physiol. Chem. *214:* 111–121.

Landsteiner, K. 1945. The Specificity of Serological Reactions. Rev. Ed. Cambridge, Mass. Harvard University Press. 310 pp.

Landsteiner, K. and J. Van der Scheer. 1938. Cross reactions of immune serums to azoproteins. II. Antigens with azo components containing two determinant groups. J. Exper. Med. *67:* 709–723.

Marrack, J. R. and F. C. Smith. 1932. Quantitative aspects of immunity reactions: The combination of antibodies with simple haptenes. Brit. J. Exptl. Path. *13:* 394–402.

Pauling, L., D. H. Campbell and D. Pressman. 1943. The nature of the forces between antigen and antibody and of the precipitation reaction. Physiol. Rev. *23:* 203–219.

Pauling, L., D. Pressman and A. L. Grossberg. 1944. The serological properties of simple substances. VII. A quantitative theory of the inhibition by haptens of the precipitation of heterogeneous antiserums with antigens and comparison with experimental results for polyhaptenic simple substances and for azoproteins. J. Am. Chem. Soc. *66:* 784–792.

Pressman, D. 1953. Antibodies as specific chemical reagents. Adv. in Biol. and Med. Physics *3:* 99–152.

Pressman, D., J. H. Bryden and L. Pauling. 1948. Reactions of antiserum homologous to the p-azosuccinanilate group. J. Am. Chem. Soc. *70:* 1352–1358.

Pressman, D., J. T. Maynard, A. L. Grossberg and L. Pauling. 1943. Serological properties of simple substances. V. The precipitation of polyhaptenic simple substances and anti-serum homologous to the p-(p-azophenylazo) phenylarsonic acid group and its inhibition by haptens. J. Am. Chem. Soc. *65:* 728–732.

Pressman, D., A. B. Pardee and L. Pauling. 1945. Serological properties of simple substances. XI. The reaction of antiserum homologous to various azophenylarsonic acid groups and the p-azophenylmethylarsinic acid group with some heterologous haptens. J. Am. Chem. Soc. *67:* 1602–1606.

Pressman, D. and M. Siegel. 1953a. The binding of simple substances to serum proteins and its effect on apparent antibody-hapten combination constants. J. Am. Chem. Soc. *75:* 686–693.

Pressman, D. and M. Siegel. 1953b. The steric configuration of 3-benzoylpropionate ion in aqueous solution as determined by immunochemical means. J. Am. Chem. Soc. *75:* 1376–1379.

Pressman, D., M. Siegel and L. A. R. Hall. 1954. The closeness of fit of antibenzoate antibodies about haptens and the orientation of the haptens in combination. J. Am. Chem. Soc. *76:* 6336–6341.

Siegel, M. and D. Pressman. 1953. The reactions of antiserum homologous to the p-azohippurate ion. J. Am. Chem. Soc. *75:* 3436–3439.

CHAIRMAN PAULING: (Repeating question from audience) I would like to ask Dr. Pressman if he has examined the specificity and how far the specificity which he has determined with respect to antigen antibodies in hapten combination occurs over other systems? For example, he pointed out combination constants where he has substituted benzoic acids with respect to his haptens. What happens with sulfonate in the system? Would you expect highly substituted sulfonic nitrogen to inter-react with one of your benzoic acid haptens, or not, or with inhibitors?

DR. PRESSMAN: The question is whether or not the acid is an inhibitor in the sulfonylamide system. We measured the extent of combination of antibodies prepared against para-azobenzoate with sulfonylamide and found no combination. Now, our antibody was directed against the azobenzene carboxylate ion, and the question comes up as to how the receptor site for sulfonylamide or the receptor site for a paraminobenzoate ion in the appropriate enzyme systems is oriented toward the ion?

It may well be that the para-amino group is the more important group with the charge group oriented in opposite direction from that in our study. This is a problem which I have wanted to investigate for some time to see if I can discover how the receptor for the para-aminobenzoic acid and the sulfonylamide compare with each other. This would require orienting the para-amino benzoate molecule in the antigen in various ways for the preparation of antibody or in orienting with sulfonylamide molecules in various ways, in its attachment to a prospective antigen, to form a proposed antibody which could subsequently be studied. I think that this is a very important problem which might well yield results with further investigation.

CHAIRMAN PAULING: I might mention another example. In the serological experiments the methyl group and the chlorine atom are not exactly identical but quite similar in their functions. Their shape is nearly the same; they differ significantly in polarizability, it is true. You will remember that a hydrocarbon analogue of DDT, was synthesized as a result of the application of just this argument. The substance in which a methyl group is introduced in place of every chlorine atom is used now as an insecticide. It does not go after just the same insects as DDT does, but still it is effective.

Nature and Formation of Antibodies

Felix Haurowitz

Indiana University, Bloomington, Ind.

THE HIGH SPECIFICITY of serological reactions, that is, of reactions between antigens and antibodies, was recognized at the end of the last century and wide use was made of these reactions for the diagnosis of certain diseases. However, there was no satisfactory scientific explanation for the bases of this specificity. Paul Ehrlich, the famous German immunologist, assumed complementariness in shape between antigen and antibody (Ehrlich, 1906), although it was not clear at that time whether complementariness of cellular shape or complementariness of subcellular particles or smaller units was meant. One has to keep in mind that "antigen" at that time meant, in general, a bacterium or a red blood cell and that only later was it found that protein molecules also can act as antigens. Nothing was known of the nature of antibodies. Many immunologists attributed antibody function to an unknown physical-chemical state of the immune serum rather than to definite antibody molecules.

Our present views on immunochemical reactions are based mainly on the fundamental experiments of Landsteiner (1946), who discovered that serological specificity is *chemical* specificity. Landsteiner introduced into serology the coupling of proteins with diazotized aromatic amines and amino acids. He proved that injection of proteins substituted by *o*-, *m*-, and *p*-azophenylsulfonate groups gave rise to the formation of three different types of antibodies and that antibodies differentiated not only between *o*-, *m*- and *p*-, but also between *cis*- and *trans*- or *d*- and *l*-compounds. It became clear by these results that serological specificity is not directed against the antigen molecule as an entity but against a definite chemical group of the antigen molecule.

A deeper insight into the problem of specificity was obtained by quantitative analyses of the precipitate. The first analyses of this type were done by Hsien Wu (1927). Shortly thereafter Heidelberger (1929) in this country and myself with Breinl (1932) in Prague analyzed various antigen-antibody systems. It became clear from these analyses that antigen and antibody combine according to definite ratios and that antibodies are proteins. It had been known for many years that the antibody function was linked to the globulins of the immune serum. The general belief was, however, that these globulins were contaminants of the true antibodies just as enzymes at that time were considered as unknown substances contaminated by proteins. In 1930, Breinl and I came to the conclusion that antibodies were not "contaminated" by globulins but that they were indeed globulins; we attributed their affinity for the respective antigens to complementariness in shape. We imagined that this complementariness arose by the influence of antigen molecules which orient the amino acids *during the process of globulin formation*; we assumed originally that antibodies might differ from normal serum globulins by the number and sequence of amino acids in their peptide chains. Similar views were proposed shortly thereafter and independently by Jerome Alexander (1931) and by Mudd (1932).

In 1940 Pauling took up the problem of antigen-antibody relation and modified our view by assuming that the complementariness in shape was due *to changes in the mode of folding of the peptide chains* rather than to changes in the amino acid composition or in the sequence of amino acids. This view is strongly supported by analyses (Haurowitz, 1954; McFadden and Smith, 1955) which show that the amino acid composition of antibodies is almost the same if not the same as that of normal serum gamma-globulins and also that the sequence of the first five or six N-terminal amino acids is the same (Porter, 1950; McFadden and Smith, 1955). Although it is dangerous to extrapolate from a sequence of 5 or 6 amino acids to a chain of about 1500 amino acids, it is quite possible that the sequence of the amino acids in an antibody molecule is the same as in a normal gamma-globulin molecule of the same species. According to this view, the antibodies produced by an animal species differ from each other merely in the mode of folding of the common peptide chains. This folding, evidently, occurs in such a fashion that the combining group of the antibody is a negative print of the determinant group of the antigen. At this meeting Dr. Pressman has discussed the methods for measuring complementariness in quantitative terms.

In my own talk I would like to discuss the mechanism by means of which this complementariness is brought about. The first question which arises is whether *complementariness* is achieved by the rearrangement of preformed proteins or whether it *arises in the moment in which amino acids combine to form the protein molecule.* The latter view was proposed by Breinl and myself (1930) and was included by Pauling in his theory of antibody formation (1940). Pauling and Campbell also presented evidence that artificial antibodies can be produced *in vitro* by mild denaturation and renaturation of normal serum globulins in the presence of an antigen; efforts to repeat the conversion of normal globulins into antibodies made by Morrison were in the main unsuccessful (1953). When isotopically labelled amino acids are used it can be shown that they are incorporated into antibody molecules at the same rate as into other serum globulins (Heidelberger, Treffers et al, 1942). This supports strongly the view that antibodies are formed like other globulins by direct synthesis from amino acids and not by rearrangement of preformed globulins.

What is the role of the antigen in this process? The simplest idea is that the antigen molecule acts as a template, a kind of mold, and that antigen and newly formed antibody are related to each other like punch and coin. According to this view, each antigen molecule can act repeatedly as a template, and thus can induce the formation of numerous antibody molecules. Although this view seems reasonable to chemists, serious objections have been raised by immunologists. These objections have been formulated very clearly by Burnet (1949).

Burnet bases his objections on the well established fact that antibody formation, in some instances, continues over many years or during the whole life. Burnet considers it as impossible that molecules of protein antigens can persist such a long period of time in the sensitized organism. He assumes that the injection of an antigen elicits the production of antibody-forming enzymes and that antibody formation goes on after elimination of all of the antigen. If this view were right, we would have to postulate the formation of enzymes which are able to produce antibodies to strange artifacts of the chemical laboratory such as azophenylarsonate or azophenylsulfonate groups. Burnet admits that this is hardly possible. He assumes that in these instances antibody formation proceeds by means of another mechanism for which he has no satisfactory explanation.

Both the template theory and Burnet's theory agree that the antibody molecule is complementarily adjusted to the determinant group (hapten) of the antigen molecule and that this adjustment takes place during the enzymatic synthesis of the antibody molecule from amino acids. According to the template theory, the presence of the hapten portion of the antigen molecule is indispensable during the formation of antibody; it remains undecided whether the hapten is present in the unchanged antigen molecule or whether it is incorporated into the synthesizing enzyme or other molecules of the antibody-forming cells. In contradiction to these views, Burnet postulates continued antibody formation after elimination of all of the antigens.

The reason why I discuss Burnet's view so extensively is that many, if not most, immunologists are inclined to accept it, or to "combine" it somehow with the template theory. Such proposals of combination are based on a misunderstanding of the basic ideas of the two theories. One of them postulates the presence of the antigen (or its hapten), the other absence of the antigen during the enzymatic process of antibody synthesis. I do not see how these two postulates can be combined.

The attractiveness of Burnet's theory for bacteriologists and serologists is due to the particulate nature of most of the pathogenic antigens. There is no doubt that bacteria disappear rapidly from the organism. This does not mean, however, that the true antigens, i.e., their antigenic molecules, disappear. It has been shown very impressively by Felton (1949) that pneumococcal polysaccharides, injected into mice, persist there for many months if not for years. Similarly, McMaster et al, (1955), using serological methods, have proved the persistence of protein antigens. This persistence of antigens is the principal postulate of the template theory of antibody formation. During the past few years we have attempted to prove it by chemical methods and to measure it quantitatively.

In our first experiments we used antigens labelled by large amounts of I^{131}, of S^{35}-azophenylsulfonate or C^{14}-azobenzoate groups (Crampton and Haurowitz, 1950; Crampton, Reller and Haurowitz, 1952). We found that the radioactivity of these substances persisted in the tissue proteins of the injected rabbits for many months. Nine months after injection a liver or spleen cell of the rabbit still contains an average of several hundred antigen molecules. In rabbits injected with S^{35}-azo-proteins we found most of the protein-bound S^{35} in a fraction of the hydrolysate which, on chromatography, behaved like a phenylsulfonic acid derivative (Haurowitz and Walter, 1955). Cystine and methionine contained only a small fraction of the radioactivity.

We have repeated these experiments with proteins containing S^{35}-amino acids in their molecules. They were prepared by injecting animals with the hydrolysate of yeast raised on S^{35}-sulfate. Some of these S^{35}-proteins were then coupled with I^{131} or with diazotized anthranilic acid containing C^{14}. These doubly labelled proteins were used as antigens. We found again persistence of the injected radioactivity. Indeed, the internal label, i.e., the label of the amino acids, persists much longer than the externally attached I^{131} label, indicating incorporation of S^{35}-amino acids or loss of fragments containing iodine (Friedberg, Walter and Haurowitz, 1955a; Idem, 1955b). When we injected proteins internally labelled by S^{35} and externally labelled by diazotized C^{14}-anthranilic acid, both labels persist in the organs and the ratio of S^{35}/C^{14} increases much less (Haurowitz, Ellenbogen and Walter, unpubl.). This indicates that many of the antigen molecules persist as such.

I see no reason, therefore, to invoke the formation of enzymes which form antibodies in the absence of antigen, but I prefer to consider the antigen molecule or its hapten as a template which persists for many months or years in the organism and thus can give rise to the formation of many generations of antibodies. This does not mean, however, that the antigen persists as such, i.e., as easily soluble free antigen. We know from our own experiments that considerable portions of the antigen are bound to the tissues and cannot be extracted by isotonic saline solutions. Evidently, the antigen combines with some of the cellular constituents (nucleic acids, lipids, polysaccharides or other proteins) to form insoluble complexes; the antigen molecule in these complexes is masked in such a manner that it does not react with added antibody (Haurowitz, Ellenbogen and Walter, unpubl.).

The extent of complementariness can be estimated from the affinity between antigen and antibody. One of the methods has been described by Dr. Pressman. Another method can be applied when we are dealing with antigen-antibody precipitates. They can be washed repeatedly without losing too much of their weight. Using precipitates in which either the antigen or the antibody was radioactive, we found that only antibody is removed by washing and that the so-called solubility of the precipitates is not true solubility but loss of antibody (Haurowitz, Crampton and Sowiski, 1951). In the experiments in which radioactive antibody was used, it became possible to measure the very low concentrations of antibody in the washings and to estimate the apparent association constants of the antigen-antibody complex. This constant is called apparent because it increases on repeated washing from an initial value of approximately 10^6 to values of about 10^8 and more, thus indicating that the precipitate first gives off loosely, later firmly bound antibody molecules. The difference in affinity may be caused either by sterical factors which affect the combination of antigen with antibody or by differences in complementariness. That such differences exist, that each immune serum contains a variety of well and poorly adapted antibodies is quite clear from serological experiments (Haurowitz, 1942).

How many different types of antibodies can an animal form? At first sight this seems to be an unanswerable question. However, if we investigate the specificity of antibodies formed in response to antigens which carry different determinant groups, A and B, separated from each other by more than about 15 Å, we find that either anti-A or anti-B is formed, but not anti-AB; evidently, the determinant area of an antigen molecule is not larger than about 100–200 $Å^2$. If the antigen is a foreign protein, this area cannot contain more than about 3 or 4 amino acid residues. We know at present of 16 types of amino acids occurring in most proteins. A simple calculation shows that there are about 5000 possible permutations of 3 and about 60,000 permutations of 4 amino acid residues. Many of these permutations may not occur at all in nature; others may not be serologically active. There may not be more than a few thousand serologically active permutations of 3 or 4 amino acids; accordingly, the number of possible antibodies against proteins may not exceed a few thousand. This agrees with the well known fact that antibodies against proteins of closely related species such as hen and duck show serological cross-reactions. Likewise, antibodies against the carbohydrate of blood-group A combine with the polysaccharide of pneumococcus type XIV (Goebel et al, 1939). Evidently, the number of antibody types which can be formed by an animal is not indefinite but of the order of 10^3 to 10^4.

Determining the amount of injected antigen and of circulating antibody, we can calculate the number of antibody molecules formed per injected antigen molecule and the maximum time required for the formation of an antibody molecule. As a basis for such a calculation the figures of Cohn and Pappenheimer (1949) can be used; these authors, after injection of a single dose of diphtheria toxoid, observed formation of approximately 2 g. of antibody per microgram of injected toxoid during a period of three weeks. Taking into consideration the molecular weights of diphtheria toxin and antitoxin, this gives approximately 1 million antitoxin molecules per molecule of toxoid in three weeks, or approximately two antibody molecules per second. This is a minimum value based on the assumption that all of the injected toxoid molecules act as templates. Many of the toxoid molecules are excreted, others are destroyed by the action of enzymes or deposited in tissues where antibodies are not formed; the number of serologically active toxoid molecules is, therefore, smaller and the number of antibody molecules formed per toxoid molecules much higher than two, probably about 10–20 per second. Accordingly, the time during which complementariness is accomplished is less than about 0.05 to 0.1 second.

How should we imagine formation of a complementary antibody molecule in such a short time? We cannot do more than speculate when we try to answer this question. We can assume that formation of globular proteins quite generally takes place in two phases, the first of these consisting in the formation of an extended, threadlike peptide chain, the second in its folding. One of the reasons for this assumption is that the amino acid composition of the peptide chains of all antibodies formed by an animal seems to be the same, independent of the nature of the antigens involved in their formation; evidently, the amino acid composition and their sequence are determined by the genes and are inherited from mother cell to daughter cell. In contrast to the constant amino acid composition, the complementariness of antibodies is *not* transmitted to the next generation. Acquired immunity is *not* inherited. Evidently, the folding pattern, which is the basis of complementariness, is not under the control of the genes. We have all reason to assume, therefore, that formation of the peptide chain and its folding takes place in two phases, the first of them controlled by the genes, the second independent of the genes.

We can imagine that the extended peptide chain is unstable, that it collides, after its formation, with the template and, on collision, folds up to form a complementarily shaped globular molecule. This globular form is stabilized by numerous cross-links such as H-bonds and salt-bridges, possibly also by dithiobridges (Karush); the folded globular antibody molecule is then detached from the template. We know from *in vitro* experiments that dissociation of the antibody from the antigen can be accomplished by acidification, by increasing the salt concentration and by other changes in the physical-chemical conditions. Similar changes may suffice to cause removal of the globular antibody particle from the template immediately after its formation and may lead to its passage into the blood stream, thus making the template available for collision with other extended peptide chains. Accepting this two-phase process of protein formation, we have to remember that the period of less than 0.1 second at which we arrive is the time of the second phase only. The first phase, the formation of the peptide chain from amino acids, may last much less than 0.05 seconds. It can last longer, but not very long since radioactive amino acids injected into sensitized animals are incorporated very rapidly into the antibody molecules (Humphrey and McFarlane, 1954).

If all these ideas about formation of antibodies are accepted, the question may be raised, "What happens if there is no antigen present? What happens in normal cells? Are the normal gamma-globulins of the serum complementarily adjusted to some normal templates?" The answer is not quite simple. First, we do not know whether there is anything like a normal gamma-globulin. We know that the blood serum of new-born animals is either devoid of or very poor in gamma-globulins. It is quite possible that all gamma-globulins are formed in response to some foreign material entering the body through the mucosa of the gasto-intestinal or the respiratory tract. If this is so, then all gamma-globulins are antibodies. However, we are not forced to make this assumption. It is quite possible that globulin formation, quite generally, takes place in two phases, as outlined above, and that the normal blood serum proteins, albumins as well as globulins, are complementarily adjusted to some cellular constituent which acts as a template. Tyler (1948), who proposed similar views, called proteins of this type autoantibodies. The possibility has to be considered that all proteins of the globular type are autoantibodies formed under the influence of normal cellular constituents which act as templates. There are some indications that a similar process underlies the phenomenon of enzyme induction. The same phenomenon may be of quite general occurrence and may thus be responsible for the specificity of proteins and other macromolecules.

References

Alexander, J. 1931. Intracellular aspects of life and disease. Protoplasma *14:* 295–306.

Breinl, F. and F. Haurowitz. 1930. Chemical investigation of the precipitate from hemoglobin and antihemoglobin-serum and remarks on the nature of the antibodies. Z. physiol. Chem. *192:* 45–57.

Burnet, F. M. and F. Fenner. 1949. The Production of Antibodies. 2nd Ed. London. Macmillan and Co. 142 pp.

Cohn, M. and A. M. Pappenheimer. 1949. A quantitative study of the diphtheria toxin-antitoxin reaction in the serums of various species including man. J. Immunol. *63:* 291–311.

Crampton, C. F. and F. Haurowitz. 1950. Intracellular distribution in rabbit liver of injected antigens labeled with iodine^{131}. Science *111:* 300–302.

Crampton, C. F., H. H. Reller and F. Haurowitz. 1952. Persistence of 7-C^{14}-anthranil-azo-ovalbumin in injected rabbits. Proc. Soc. Exp. Biol. Med. *80:* 448–451.

Ehrlich, P. 1906. Studies on Immunity. (Translated by Charles Bolduan, New York).

Felton, L. D. 1949. The significance of antigen in animal tissues. J. Immunol. *61:* 107–117.

Friedberg, W., H. Walter and F. Haurowitz. 1955a. The fate in rats of heterologous protein labeled internally by sulfur-35 and externally by iodine-131. Science *121:* 871.

Friedberg, W., H. Walter and F. Haurowitz. 1955b. The rate in fats of internally and externally labeled heterologous proteins. J. Immunol. *75:* 315–320.

Goebel, W. F., P. B. Beeson and C. L. Hoagland. 1939. Chemo-immunological studies on the soluble specific substance of pneumococcus. IV. The capsular polysaccharide of type XIV pneumococcus and its relationship to the blood group A specific substance.

Haurowitz, F. 1942. Separation and determination of multiple antibodies. J. Immunol. *43:* 331–340.

Haurowitz, F. 1954. Serological Approaches to Studies of Protein Structure. Rutgers Univ. Press. p. 2.

Haurowitz, F. and F. Breinl. 1932. Quantitative investigation and distribution of an arsenic-containing antigen in the organism. Z physiol. Chem. *205:* 259–270.

Haurowitz, F., C. F. Crampton and R. Sowinski. 1951. Immunochemical studies with labeled antigens. Fed. Proc. *10:* 560–561.

Haurowitz, F., L. Ellenbogen and H. Walter. Unpublished experiments.

Haurowitz, F. and H. Walter. 1955. Stability of an azoprotein hapten in the organism. Proc. Soc. Exp. Biol. Med. *88:* 67–69.

Heidelberger, M. and F. E. Kendall. 1929. Quantitative study of the precipitin reaction between type III pneumococcus polysaccharide and purified homologous antibody. J. Exp. Med. *50:* 809–823.

Heidelberger, M., H. P. Treffers, R. Schoenheimer, S. Ratner, and D. Rittenberg. 1942. Behavior of antibody protein toward dietary nitrogen in active and passive immunity. J. Biol. Chem. *144:* 555–562.

Humphrey, J. H. and A. S. McFarlane. 1954. Rate of elimination of homologous globulins (including antibody) from the circulation. Biochem. J. *57:* 186-191.

Karush, F. Personal communication.

Landsteiner, K. 1945. The Specificity of Serological Reactions. Rev. Ed. Cambridge, Mass. Harvard Univ. Press. 310 pp.

McFadden, M. L. and E. L. Smith. 1955. Free amino acid groups and N-terminal sequence of rabbit antibodies. J. Biol. Chem. *214:* 185–196.

McMaster, P. D., J. L. Edwards and E. Sturm. 1955. Active anaphylaxis to a foreign protein induced in mice by the transfer of tissue from animals previously injected with the protein. J. Exp. Med. *102:* 119–131.

Morrison, J. L. 1953. Nonspecific precipitation of proteins by polyhaptenic dyes. Canad. J. Chem. *31:* 216–226.

Mudd, S. 1932. A hypothetical mechanism of antibody production. J. Immunol. *23:* 423–427.

Pauling, L. 1940. Theory of the structure and process of formation of antibodies. J. Am. Chem. Soc. *62:* 2643–2657.

Porter, R. R. 1950. Chemical study of rabbit antiovalbumin. Biochem. J. *46:* 473–478.

Tyler, A. 1948. Fertilization and immunity. Physiol. Rev. *28:* 180–219.

Wu, H., Lan-Hua Cheng and Chen-Pien Li. 1927. Composition of antigen-precipitin precipitate. Proc. Soc. Exp. Biol. Med. *25:* 853–855.

Chairman Pauling: (Repeating question from audience) In Professor Haurowitz's experiments was he ever able to say what the rate of antibody production is relative to the amount of remaining antibody in the animal?

Professor Haurowitz: I took the figures of Cohn and Pappenheimer when I said that for each toxoid molecule injected, one million antibody molecules are formed. We can also take our figures; we don't get such a high ratio, because our antigens are not so efficient as diphtheria toxoid. We get figures of about 10,000 to 100,000 antibody molecules per antigen deposited.

CHAIRMAN PAULING: (Repeating question from audience) Let us suppose that a rat or some such animal has the power of regenerating liver after, perhaps, four-fifths has been removed. Repeating this process, might we investigate to see what its antibody production is after this operation?

PROFESSOR HAUROWITZ: We investigated, in our first experiment, chiefly liver and spleen, but it has been shown by L. L. Miller in Rochester that the liver does not form antibodies essentially. Most of the antibodies are formed in lymph nodes and in the spleen. You cannot remove all the lymph nodes from the organism. You can remove the spleen, but this will not help because all the lymphatic tissue still remains. Hence this problem cannot be decided experimentally.

CHAIRMAN PAULING: (Repeating question from audience) It was suggested that it might be possible to inject an antigen that destroys itself rapidly, for example, a 100 per cent isotopic antigen, one containing carbon 11, say, and that this would be a way of seeing whether destruction of the antigen causes cessation of the antibody formation.

PROFESSOR HAUROWITZ: I do not think we can prepare any molecule containing only C-11 which is at the same time antigenic. I do not know what would happen if such a molecule were injected.

CHAIRMAN PAULING: (Repeating question from audience) What is involved in the binding of complement?

DR. PRESSMAN: This is a complicated situation. One possible explanation to which I do not subscribe is that when antigen and antibodies combine there are exposed new sites which now combine complement. However, we also know that antigen and antibodies dissociate. I don't know whether measurements have been made on dissociated antigen or antibody with respect to ability to bind complement, but I presume that neither one alone binds complement. Then any possible new sites which might arise would have to disappear.

An explanation that appeals to me is the possibility (and it is not original with me) that several antibodies may have a weak intrinsic binding for complement and when several antibody molecules are held closely together by antigen enough complement binding sites would be fixed to hold complement itself very tightly.

CHAIRMAN PAULING: Do you have anything to say, Professor Haurowitz?

PROFESSOR HAUROWITZ: Complement fixation is rather non-specific and complement is also bound to systems which have nothing to do with antigen-antibody complexes. This complicates matters very much. I think we simply do not know what happens.

CHAIRMAN PAULING: (Repeating question from the audience) The question is: Does this discussion of hapten inhibition and evaluation of combining constants of haptens with antibodies require the assumption of a single antibody species or not?

Shall I answer this? The answer is that antiserum in general is highly heterogeneous. It contains antibodies with a very great spread and the methods that are used involving 50 per cent inhibition refer to the average antibody.

Specificity of the London-Eisenschitz-Wang Force

Jerrold M. Yos,[1] William L. Bade,[2] and Herbert Jehle[3]

Department of Physics, University of Nebraska, Lincoln, Nebraska

In a number of biological phenomena and in some crystallization and polymerization effects, there is evidence of an attractive intermolecular force which is "specific" in that identical or nearly identical molecules interact more strongly than non-identical ones. H. J. Muller (1922, 1937, 1941, 1947) pointed out that biological evidence indicates the existence of such a specific attraction acting over distances at which the interacting molecules are not in contact, and urged physicists to investigate whether any of the known intermolecular forces was capable of accounting for such a phenomenon. The present paper investigates the conditions under which the London-van der Waals dispersion force between particles immersed in a medium will constitute such a specific attraction. (The London force between two molecules is due to the net effect of interaction of the fluctuating electric dipole moments in one molecule with those of the other.) In the final section of the paper some of the biological implications of the work are discussed, but these remarks must be regarded as highly speculative until the magnitude of the specific London-van der Waals attraction has been established for the various molecules involved.

Observed specificity effects may involve a variety of forces. If the interacting molecules can approach one another closely, the most important interactions are bond and bridge formation, in particular those between complementary structures (Watson-Crick helix), electrostatic interaction of complementary charge distributions, and van der Waals stabilization of those complementary structures which permit a closest fit. These interactions account for many biological specificity effects (Pauling, 1940; idem, 1948; Haurowitz, 1950; Breinl and Haurowitz, 1930; Mudd, 1932; Alexander, 1931), and usually play the decisive role in crystal formation. The simple lock and key picture characterizes these interactions.

[1] NSF predoctoral fellow, 1954–56; at present at Harvard University.

[2] At present NSF postdoctoral fellow, Sterling Laboratory of Chemistry, Yale University.

[3] On leave of absence at Gates, Crellin and Church Laboratories, California Institute of Technology. Paper presented by this author.

On the other hand, if the interacting molecules are not in direct contact, but are still fairly close, the London force might constitute an important specific interaction. In this case identical structures, rather than complementary ones would tend to aggregate. The London interaction would be sharply specific in the case of macromolecules whose representative oscillators had sufficiently large polarizabilities and frequencies covering a wide range.

One can form a model for use in discussing biological London interactions by considering somewhat globular, compact, rigid macromolecules or molecule complexes endowed with an electric charge and imbedded in an ionic medium. Such macromolecules are surrounded by ionic atmospheres. Their electrostatic interaction is highly dependent on the ionic composition of the medium (Debye and Hueckel, 1923; Onsager, 1933; Kallmann and Willstaetter, 1932; Vinograd, 1935; De Boer, 1936; Hamaker, 1937; idem, 1938; idem, 1948; idem, 1952; Verwey and Overbeek, 1946; Overbeek, 1952; idem, 1948; idem, 1954; Levine, 1946; idem, 1948; Derjaguin, 1939; idem, 1940a; idem, 1940b; idem, 1940c; idem, 1954; Derjaguin and Landau, 1941; Harned and Owen, 1950; Klotz, 1953; Prigogine and Bellemans, 1953). The interplay between this Debye-Hueckel-Onsager force and the London-Eisenschitz-Wang force determines whether or not the macromolecules associate. At smaller separations between the macromolecules a similar compensation of their charges is effected by ions inserted between the macromolecules.

Free Energy of Rearrangement

Let E_n denote the energies of the levels of a pair of molecules, and let their partition function and Helmholtz free energy be

$$Z = \sum_n \exp(-E_n/kT)$$

$$A = -kT \ln Z$$

If a temperature bath permits the molecule-pair to occupy its levels according to a Boltzmann distribution, the attractive force between the pair becomes

$$\mathfrak{F} = \sum_n (\partial E_n/\partial R) \exp(-E_n/kT)/Z = (\partial A/\partial R)_T$$

Instead of the force one may simply calculate the difference between the Helmholtz free energies at finite separation and at infinite separation,

$$\Delta A = -kT(\ln Z - \ln Z_\infty)$$

The problem of specificity might be approached by asking the question: How does the interaction free energy A of an identical pair I, I differ from that of a pair I, II where II differs in a variety of minor ways from I? Calling I, II a detuned pair I, I, this procedure may be termed a "detuning approach".

One can also consider a molecule II arbitrarily different from I. (Bade, 1954). In either case one evaluates

$$(\Delta A_{\mathrm{I\,I}} - \Delta A_{\mathrm{I\,II}})/\Delta A_{\mathrm{I\,I}}$$

The answer to this question covers one part of the problem of specificity. Next, one has to realize that the specifically interacting molecules are always suspended in a medium which is also subject to London forces. One needs therefore to evaluate differential effects in the attraction, i.e., one has to consider "buoyancy".

One might illustrate this with a slightly oversimplified scheme, which takes account of buoyancy effects, by considering only two globular macromolecules suspended in an otherwise homogeneous isotropic medium made up from smaller molecules. One compares an arrangement in which the two macromolecules I, I are closest neighbors (left side of Fig. 1) with one in which they are not (right side). A short consideration, well-known from the theory of mixtures, shows that one can take care of the buoyancy effect by grouping part of the medium molecules into globular regions each occupying the same volume as does a molecule I. Those aggregates are then named II (open circles in Fig. 1) and may be called conceptual aggregates. Under certain general assumptions one finds that the difference in free energy of the two arrangements in Fig. 1 is equal to the corresponding difference in Fig. 2 and one calls it the rearrangement free energy for the quadruplet situation represented in Fig. 2.

$$\Delta_4 A_{\mathrm{I\,II}} \equiv \Delta A_{\mathrm{I\,I}} + \Delta A_{\mathrm{II\,II}} - 2\Delta A_{\mathrm{I\,II}}$$

A more complete analysis may be given with the following assumptions which are only made to delimit the present calculations:

(a) For the sake of simplicity consider a mixture of two kinds of molecules, I and II, where the distances of closest intermolecular approach R have the

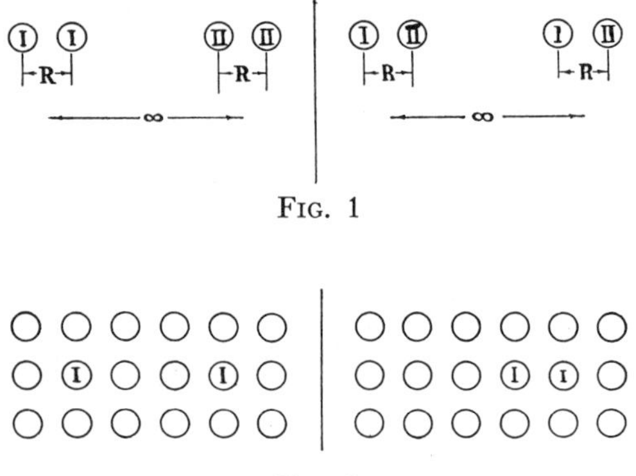

FIG. 1

FIG. 2

same value for any closest pair (I, I), (I, II) or (II, II). This assumption is reasonable for macromolecules I and II which differ only in minor ways in their size, shape, electrical charge etc. This assumption is of course automatically satisfied in the above mentioned set-up where only two identical macromolecules are immersed in a homogeneous isotropic medium.

(b) The interactions are isotropic and additively composed of molecule-pair interactions. The anisotropy is considered later on in this note.

(c) Entropy of mixing is ignored in order to shorten the calculations. Actually this entropy contribution, which takes account of the fact that there are many more arrangements of the right hand type of Fig. 1 than of the left hand type, is not negligible.

The total free energy of a given arrangement is the free energy of the isolated molecules plus the interaction free energy ΔA of each pair. As the interaction free energy has a strong R dependence, one may ignore all but closest neighbor interactions. If $n_{\text{I I}}$ is the number of closest neighbor pairs in which both molecules are of type I, $n_{\text{II II}}$ the number in which both are of type II, and $n_{\text{I II}}$ the number in which one is of type I and the other of type II, then the total interaction free energy of the arrangement is

$$n_{\text{I I}}\Delta A_{\text{I I}} + n_{\text{II II}}\Delta A_{\text{II II}} + n_{\text{I II}}\Delta A_{\text{I II}}$$

The total number of all the closest neighbors of all the molecules I is $2n_{\text{I I}} + n_{\text{I II}}$ and that of the molecules II is $2n_{\text{II II}} + n_{\text{I II}}$. As any closest pair (I, I), (II, II) or (I, II) is assumed to have approximately the same nearest approach R, a rearrangement of the system will (statistically speaking) (d) not change these numbers of closest neighbors. Then, after the system has undergone such a rearrangement, the numbers of closest neighbors will be $n'_{\text{I I}} = n_{\text{I I}} + \delta n$, $n'_{\text{I II}} = n_{\text{I II}} - 2\delta n$, $n'_{\text{II II}} = n_{\text{II II}} + \delta n$. The resulting free energy change is $\delta n(\Delta A_{\text{I I}} + \Delta A_{\text{II II}} - 2\Delta A_{\text{I II}})$. A positive δn would mean that there were more like pairs and fewer unlike pairs of molecules after the rearrangement than before. The sign of the "quadruplet free energy difference" $\Delta_4 A_{\text{I II}}$ thus determines the sign of the free energy change for any particular rearrangement. If this quantity is negative, the interaction tends to bring like molecules together at the expense of separating unlike ones.

These considerations can readily be extended to include situations in which several different types of macromolecules are simultaneously present (Yos, 1956). The assumptions made are: (a) equality of the volumes of these different, somewhat globular, molecules and sole consideration of nearest neighbor interactions, all at the same distance R; (b) isotropy and additivity of interactions; (c) entropy of mixing left aside; (d) number of nearest neighbors per molecule, statistically speaking, the same for every kind of macromolecule. Using a new notation, let n_{ij} denote the total number of molecules of type j which are nearest neighbors to molecules of type i. Then $\text{N}_i = \sum_j n_{ij}$ = total number of all the nearest neighbors to molecules of type i; because of (d), $0 = \delta N_i = \sum_j \delta n_{ij}$ holds for all i. The total rearrangement free energy is

$$\tfrac{1}{2} \sum_i \sum_j \delta n_{ij} \Delta A_{ij} = \text{, subtracting the preceding equation,}$$

$$= \tfrac{1}{2} \sum_i \sum_j \delta n_{ij} \Delta A_{ij} - \tfrac{1}{2} \sum_i \Delta A_{ii} \sum_j \delta n_{ij}$$

$$= \tfrac{1}{2} \sum_i \sum_j \delta n_{ij}(\Delta A_{ij} - \Delta A_{ii}) = \text{, interchanging dummy indices,}$$

$$= \tfrac{1}{2} \sum_j \sum_i \delta n_{ji}(\Delta A_{ji} - \Delta A_{jj})$$

With $\delta n_{ji} = \delta n_{ij}$ and $\Delta A_{ji} = \Delta A_{ij}$, the rearrangement free energy becomes

$$-\tfrac{1}{4} \sum_i \sum_j \delta n_{ij}(\Delta A_{ii} + \Delta A_{jj} - 2\Delta A_{ij})$$

i.e. it can again be expressed in terms of the quadruplet rearrangement free energies.

It is possible to determine the sign of the quantity $\Delta_4 A_{\mathrm{I\,II}}$ under very general circumstances, in which the assumptions (a), (b), (c), (d) above are not necessarily valid (Yos, 1956, and the specificity theorem below). If these assumptions are not made, the free energy change due to the rearrangement cannot be evaluated so simply, and the above discussion can then serve only as a rough guide to the interpretation of inequalities involving $\Delta_4 A_{\mathrm{I\,II}}$.

Some processes of crystallization present a similar situation. A crystal of a globular molecule type I may be surrounded by a mixture of molecules I and II, both of equal size and similar chemical constitution but of different polarizability constitution. An additional molecule I joining the crystal involves an integer multiple of $\Delta_4 A_{\mathrm{I\,II}}$ as free energy change.

The Simplest Rearrangement Inequalities

The London force is due to the interaction of polarizable molecules. In the most elementary case one represents a simple molecule by a single isotropic oscillator whose (circular) frequency may be denoted by $\tilde{\omega}$.

In the classical limit, when the oscillator frequencies are very small,

$$\tilde{\omega} \ll kT/\hbar,$$

the interaction of a pair of isotropic oscillators is

$$\Delta A_{\mathrm{I\,II}} = -3R^{-6} kT \alpha_{\mathrm{I}} \alpha_{\mathrm{II}} \tag{1a}$$

This leads to the inequality

$$\Delta_4 A_{\mathrm{I\,II}} = -3R^{-6} kT(\alpha_{\mathrm{I}} - \alpha_{\mathrm{II}})^2 \leq 0 \tag{1b}$$

Here the free energy change $\Delta_4 A_{\mathrm{I\,II}}$ depends only on one parameter, the polarizability difference.

A more interesting inequality in two variables α and $\tilde{\omega}$ has been pointed out by DeBoer (1936) and Hamaker (1937).[4] In the simple case of the interaction of two isotropic oscillators whose frequencies $\tilde{\omega}$ are large compared with $kT/\hbar$, the interaction free energy is

$$\Delta A_{\mathrm{I\,II}} = -\tfrac{3}{2}R^{-6}\alpha_{\mathrm{I}}\alpha_{\mathrm{II}}\hbar\tilde{\omega}_{\mathrm{I}}\tilde{\omega}_{\mathrm{II}}/(\tilde{\omega}_{\mathrm{I}} + \tilde{\omega}_{\mathrm{II}}), \qquad (1c)$$

as shown by London (1936, 1930, 1942), Eisenschitz and London (1930a, 1930b), and Wang (1927). (The quantities α are the static polarizabilities of the oscillators.) Thus

$$\Delta_4 A_{\mathrm{I\,II}} = -\tfrac{3}{4}R^{-6}\hbar\,\frac{(\alpha_{\mathrm{I}}\tilde{\omega}_{\mathrm{I}} - \alpha_{\mathrm{II}}\tilde{\omega}_{\mathrm{II}})^2 + \tilde{\omega}_{\mathrm{I}}\tilde{\omega}_{\mathrm{II}}(\alpha_{\mathrm{I}} - \alpha_{\mathrm{II}})^2}{\tilde{\omega}_{\mathrm{I}} + \tilde{\omega}_{\mathrm{II}}} \leq 0, \qquad (1d)$$

(Apart from a numerical factor, the expression ($\hbar$ times an average of the frequencies) in equation (1c) replaces the kT in equation (1a); the relations (1c) and (1d) are applicable to simple molecules (e.g. the noble gases) whose optical dispersion formulae contain only one important term.)

If each molecule is adequately represented by a *set* of oscillators, no essential change occurs in (1a), (1b). The sum of the polarizabilities of all the oscillators in molecule I enters instead of the single oscillator polarizability α_{I}, and the same with II; and one obtains again an inequality involving only one independent term

$$-\left(\sum_{l=1}^{N_{\mathrm{I}}} \alpha_{l\mathrm{I}} - \sum_{l=N_{\mathrm{I}}+1}^{N_{\mathrm{I}}+N_{\mathrm{II}}} \alpha_{l\mathrm{II}}\right)^2$$

l numbers the oscillators; the sums contain, strictly speaking, orientation terms.

The same holds for (1c), (1d) if all the oscillators have one and the same frequency (this becomes also evident from equation (10d)). Conversely the equation (1d) and its multioscillator generalization becomes of special interest if the oscillators cover a diversified range of frequencies as well as polarizabilities.

Thus, in the quantum limit case (1c), (1d) one obtains an inequality involving a *set* of negative terms, i.e. a set of inequalities as was first shown by Hamaker (1937). On the basis of such inequalities, he concluded: "The London-van der Waals force between two particles of the same material imbedded in a fluid is always attractive, provided there is no marked orientation of the fluid molecules. If the particles are of different composition, the resultant force may be a repulsion." It seems, however, to have escaped notice at that time that these inequalities might have something to do with the problem of specific interactions, and the question of how many of the inequalities are effectively independent has still to be studied below.

The quadruplet free energy difference $\Delta_4 A_{\mathrm{I\,II}}$ is thus found to be a negative definite quantity both in the classical and in the quantum limit. If one repre-

[4] We are deeply indebted to H. T. Epstein for having drawn our attention to these papers and to T. Y. Wu for a comment on this inequality.

sents actual macromolecules by oscillator sets, these sets will usually show such a wide distribution of frequencies that neither the classical nor the quantum limit results can serve as an adequate basis for the discussion of specificity.

Previous to knowing the work of Hamaker (1937) and de Boer (1936), the present procedure was followed which calculates the many oscillator case and covers the entire range of frequencies. This procedure serves to define and estimate the degree of specificity of the London force.

This method provides a way of discussing the number of independent parameters upon which the rearrangement free energy effectively depends, and the degree of specificity. Specific interactions involve discrimination between a very large number of different molecular partners even though only moderate spreads in the interaction free energy occur. In the present theory this phenomenon is simply a consequence of the multidimensionality of the situation (Jehle, 1950).

The oscillator scheme is very convenient but not necessary. The calculations can also be carried out on the basis of a general level scheme (Yos, 1956). That general calculation readily permits inclusion of anharmonicities, permanent electrical moments and quadrupole interactions.

Free Energy Change for a Pair

Let the molecules I and II have N_{I} and N_{II} oscillators, respectively. The normal modes of the combined system I–II have the frequencies $\omega_l/2\pi$ which depend on the intermolecular distance R. The partition function and the free energy of the pair are

$$Z = \sum_{n_1=0}^{\infty} \cdot\cdot \sum_{n_{N_{\mathrm{I}}+N_{\mathrm{II}}}=0}^{\infty} \exp\left\{- \sum_{l=1}^{N_{\mathrm{I}}+N_{\mathrm{II}}} (n_l + \tfrac{1}{2})\hbar\omega_l/kT\right\}$$

$$= \prod_l \left[\exp\{-\hbar\omega_l/2kT\} \sum_{n_l} \exp\{-n_l\hbar\omega_l/kT\}\right]$$

$$= \prod_{l=1}^{N_{\mathrm{I}}+N_{\mathrm{II}}} \{2 \sinh(\hbar\omega_l/2kT)\}^{-1} \qquad (2)$$

$$A = kT \sum_{l=1}^{N_{\mathrm{I}}+N_{\mathrm{II}}} \ln [2 \sinh(\hbar\omega_l/2kT)]$$

$$= kT \sum_l \left\{\frac{1}{2} \ln\left(\frac{\hbar^2\omega_l^2}{4k^2T^2}\right) + \sum_{s=1}^{\infty} \ln\left(1 + \frac{\hbar^2\omega_l^2}{4k^2T^2}\frac{1}{s^2\pi^2}\right) + \ln 2\right\} \qquad (3)$$

This form is suitable for expansion in powers of the intermolecular interaction. This last expansion is convergent for all positive $\hbar^2\omega_l^2/4k^2T^2$. With properly normalized normal coordinates, the potential energy matrix V has the eigenvalues $\frac{1}{2}\omega_l^2$. Let V be the matrix $(\hbar^2/2k^2T^2)$V with eigenvalues $V_l' = \hbar^2\omega_l^2/4k^2T^2$, and let V' be this diagonalized form of V. The matrix V can be written in the form

$$V = \begin{pmatrix} \mathcal{V}_{I} & 0 \\ 0 & \mathcal{V}_{II} \end{pmatrix} + \begin{pmatrix} 0 & \mathcal{U} \\ \tilde{\mathcal{U}} & 0 \end{pmatrix} = V_{\infty} + U = V_{\infty}(\mathrm{I} + V_{\infty}^{-1}U), \tag{4}$$

where $\sim$ indicates the transposed matrix. Usually V_{∞} and U do not commute. The summation over l in the Helmholtz free energy (3) can be written as the trace of the kT { }, equ. (3), of the diagonal matrix V' and this trace is invariant under the transformation which brings V into diagonal form. Thus

$$A = kT \operatorname{tr} \left\{ \frac{1}{2} \ln V + \sum_{s=1}^{\infty} \ln (\mathrm{I} + V/s^2\pi^2) + \mathrm{I} \ln 2 \right\}$$

$$= kT \operatorname{tr} \left\{ \frac{1}{2} \ln [V_{\infty}(\mathrm{I} + V_{\infty}^{-1}U)] \right.$$

$$\left. + \sum_{s=1}^{\infty} \ln [(\mathrm{I} + V_{\infty}/s^2\pi^2)(\mathrm{I} + (\mathrm{I} + V_{\infty}/s^2\pi^2)^{-1}U/s^2\pi^2)] + \mathrm{I} \ln 2 \right\} \tag{5}$$

Now $\operatorname{tr} \ln x = \operatorname{tr} \ln x' = \sum_l \ln x'_l = \ln \prod_l (x'_l) = \ln \det x$, and also $\det (xy) = \det (x) \det (y)$. Hence $\operatorname{tr} \ln (xy) = \operatorname{tr} \ln x + \operatorname{tr} \ln y$. Using the abbreviations

$$V_{\infty}^{-1}U \equiv U_0\,, \quad (s^2\pi^2\mathrm{I} + V_{\infty})^{-1}U \equiv U_s\,, \tag{6}$$

one can express the change in free energy as

$$\Delta A = A - A_{\infty} = kT \operatorname{tr} \left\{ \frac{1}{2} \ln (\mathrm{I} + U_0) + \sum_{s=1}^{\infty} \ln (\mathrm{I} + U_s) \right\}.$$

Because of the form (4) of U, the trace of odd powers of U_s vanishes, so that, upon expansion in powers of U_s this formula becomes

$$\Delta A = \frac{1}{2} kT \operatorname{tr} \sum_{s=-\infty}^{+\infty} \left\{ -\frac{1}{2} U_s^2 - \cdots \right\}. \tag{7}$$

Actually the oscillators are distributed throughout the volume occupied by each molecule. The assumption of an interaction matrix U (4) implies the neglect of quadrupole and higher multipole terms in the expansion of the interaction in powers of the distance R between the centers of the molecules. This assumption may be an admissible approximation for sufficiently large intermolecular separation R, but it is certainly a very crude assumption in view of the fairly close approaches occurring in specific interactions. "Large" separations R are a necessary assumption insofar as the quadrupole terms would not give simple general results as the dipole terms do. For such large separations R, the terms U_s^2 in the expansion (7) are presumably the only ones of importance, and they make the free energy change vary as R^{-6}.

Specificity Theorem

To proceed further, one must introduce the assumption that the intermolecular interaction $\mathcal{U}$ in equation (4) can be written as a matrix product of two matrices, one depending on molecule I only, the other on molecule II only: $\mathcal{U} = \mathcal{U}_{\mathrm{I}}\mathcal{U}_{\mathrm{II}}^{\sim}$. Dipole interactions clearly satisfy this assumption; $\mathcal{U}_{\mathrm{I}}$ can be written as a matrix with N_{I} rows and three columns, as in (12) below. Introducing the further abbreviations

$$\mathcal{W}_{s\mathrm{I}} \equiv \mathcal{U}_{\mathrm{I}}^{\sim}(s^2\pi^2\mathrm{I} + \mathcal{V}_{\mathrm{I}})^{-1}\mathcal{U}_{\mathrm{I}}\,, \tag{8}$$

which are three by three matrices, one can write

$$\mathrm{tr}\; U_0^2 = \mathrm{tr}\; V_\infty^{-1}UV_\infty^{-1}U = \mathrm{tr}\begin{pmatrix} \mathcal{V}_{\mathrm{I}}^{-1}\mathcal{U}\mathcal{V}_{\mathrm{II}}^{-1}\mathcal{U}^{\sim} & 0 \\ 0 & \mathcal{V}_{\mathrm{II}}^{-1}\mathcal{U}^{\sim}\mathcal{V}_{\mathrm{I}}^{-1}\mathcal{U} \end{pmatrix}$$

$$= 2\;\mathrm{tr}\;(\mathcal{V}_{\mathrm{I}}^{-1}\mathcal{U}_{\mathrm{I}}\mathcal{U}_{\mathrm{II}}^{\sim}\mathcal{V}_{\mathrm{II}}^{-1}\mathcal{U}_{\mathrm{II}}\mathcal{U}_{\mathrm{I}}^{\sim}) \tag{9}$$

$$= 2\;\mathrm{tr}\;(\mathcal{U}_{\mathrm{I}}^{\sim}\mathcal{V}_{\mathrm{I}}^{-1}\mathcal{U}_{\mathrm{I}}\mathcal{U}_{\mathrm{II}}^{\sim}\mathcal{V}_{\mathrm{II}}^{-1}\mathcal{U}_{\mathrm{II}}) = 2\;\mathrm{tr}\;(\mathcal{W}_{0\mathrm{I}}\,\mathcal{W}_{0\mathrm{II}}),$$

$$\mathrm{tr}\; U_s^2 = 2\;\mathrm{tr}\;(\mathcal{W}_{s\,\mathrm{I}}\mathcal{W}_{s\,\mathrm{II}}) = 2\;\mathrm{tr}\;(\mathcal{W}_{s\,\mathrm{II}}\mathcal{W}_{s\,\mathrm{I}}), \tag{9}$$

where s is any integer, positive, negative, or zero. Neglecting higher powers of U_s^2 one can now express the quadruplet free energy difference in the form

$$-\Delta_4 A_{\mathrm{I\,II}} \equiv -(\Delta A_{\mathrm{I\,I}} + \Delta A_{\mathrm{II\,II}} - 2\Delta A_{\mathrm{I\,II}})$$

$$= kT\;\mathrm{tr}\sum_{s=-\infty}^{+\infty}\frac{1}{2}\{\mathcal{W}_{s\mathrm{I}}\mathcal{W}_{s\mathrm{I}} + \mathcal{W}_{s\mathrm{II}}\mathcal{W}_{s\mathrm{II}} - 2\mathcal{W}_{s\mathrm{I}}\mathcal{W}_{s\mathrm{II}}\} \tag{10a}$$

$$= \frac{1}{2}kT\sum_s \mathrm{tr}\;\{(\mathcal{W}_{s\mathrm{I}} - \mathcal{W}_{s\mathrm{II}})^2\}$$

This expression is positive definite if $(\mathcal{W}_{s\,\mathrm{I}} - \mathcal{W}_{s\,\mathrm{II}})$ has real eigenvalues for every s and any pair I-II, that is, if $\mathcal{W}_{s\,\mathrm{I}}$ and $\mathcal{W}_{s\,\mathrm{II}}$ are Hermitean matrices. This provides a sufficient condition for

$$\Delta_4 A_{\mathrm{I\,II}} \leq 0 \tag{10b}$$

to hold in the limit of large distances, R. It can be shown (Ky Fan, 1951) that the inequality holds also for the terms of higher order in the expansion (7).

Since $(s^2\pi^2\mathrm{I} + \mathcal{V}_{\mathrm{I}})$ is a symmetric matrix, $\mathcal{W}_{s\,\mathrm{I}}$ and $\mathcal{W}_{s\,\mathrm{II}}$ are by (8), symmetric matrices. The Hermitecity condition for $\mathcal{W}_{s\,\mathrm{I}}$, $\mathcal{W}_{s\,\mathrm{II}}$ thus implies that all of the elements of $\mathcal{W}_{s\,\mathrm{I}}$ and $\mathcal{W}_{s\,\mathrm{II}}$ are real. As $(s^2\pi^2\mathrm{I} + \mathcal{V}_{\mathrm{I}})^{-1}$ has only real matrix elements, and as $\mathcal{U} = \mathcal{U}_{\mathrm{I}}\mathcal{U}_{\mathrm{II}}^{\sim}$ is real, it follows that $\mathcal{W}_{s\,\mathrm{I}}$ and $\mathcal{W}_{s\,\mathrm{II}}$ will be real if the elements of $\mathcal{U}_{\mathrm{I}}$ and $\mathcal{U}_{\mathrm{II}}$ are either all purely imaginary or all real. One is thus led to two sufficient conditions under either of which the quadruplet inequality (10b) holds.

If both molecules I and II are referred to the same axes (x, y, z), where the z-axis is the line connecting the centers of the molecules, then from (4)

$$\mathcal{U}_{kj} = (\hbar^2/4k^2T^2)\epsilon_k m_k^{-\frac{1}{2}}\epsilon_j m_j^{-\frac{1}{2}} R^{-3}[u_{kx}u_{jx} + u_{ky}u_{jy} - 2u_{kz}u_{jz}] \qquad (11)$$

where the ϵ's are charges, the m's are masses and the u_j's are orientation vectors of the oscillators. The orientation of the oscillators can be described with reference to fixed axes in the molecules, e.g. those determined by the static electric moments. The interaction matrix $\mathcal{U}_{\text{I}}\,\mathcal{U}_{\text{II}}^{\sim}$ has the value (11) if one sets

$$\mathcal{U}_{\text{I}} = \frac{\hbar}{2kT} R^{-\frac{3}{2}} \begin{pmatrix} \cdot\ , & \cdot\ , & \cdot \\ \epsilon_l m_l^{-\frac{1}{2}} u_{lx}\ , & \epsilon_l m_l^{-\frac{1}{2}} u_{ly}\ , & i\sqrt{2}\,\epsilon_l m_l^{-\frac{1}{2}} u_{lz} \\ \cdot\ , & \cdot\ , & \cdot \\ \cdot\ , & \cdot\ , & \cdot \end{pmatrix}$$

$l = 1, 2 \cdots N_{\text{I}}$, and similarly for $\mathcal{U}_{\text{II}}$. This matrix is, however, neither purely real nor purely imaginary.

If the two molecules are referred to coordinate systems $(x_{\text{I}}, y_{\text{I}}, z_{\text{I}})$ and $(x_{\text{II}}, y_{\text{II}}, z_{\text{II}})$ respectively, two right-handed systems whose z-axes are parallel and whose x- and y-axes are antiparallel, then the interaction matrix $\mathcal{U}_{\text{I}}\mathcal{U}_{\text{II}}^{\sim}$ has the value (11) if one sets

$$\mathcal{U}_{\text{I}} = (\hbar/2kT)R^{-\frac{3}{2}} \begin{pmatrix} \cdot\ , & \cdot\ , & \cdot \\ i\epsilon_l m_l^{-\frac{1}{2}} u_{lx}\ , & i\epsilon_l m_l^{-\frac{1}{2}} u_{ly}\ , & i\sqrt{2}\,\epsilon_l m_l^{-\frac{1}{2}} u_{lz} \\ \cdot\ , & \cdot\ , & \cdot \\ \cdot\ , & \cdot\ , & \cdot \end{pmatrix} \qquad (12)$$

and similarly for $\mathcal{U}_{\text{II}}$. In this notation, $\mathcal{U}_{\text{I}}\mathcal{U}_{\text{I}}^{\sim}$ denotes the interaction matrix of a molecule I located at the origin of the coordinate system I with a molecule II at origin II whose dipole distribution relative to $(x_{\text{II}}, y_{\text{II}}, z_{\text{II}})$ is exactly the same as the dipole distribution of I with respect to $(x_{\text{I}}, y_{\text{I}}, z_{\text{I}})$. This molecule II is identical with I except for 180° rotation around the z-axis; this is the mutual orientation of lowest free energy for two identical molecules. With such a definition of pairs of identical molecules I-I and II-II, the matrices $\mathcal{W}_{s\,\text{I}}$ and $\mathcal{W}_{s\,\text{II}}$ are Hermitean and accordingly the quadruplet inequality (10b) holds.

If the two molecules are referred to two mirror image coordinate systems whose z-axes are antiparallel and whose x- and y-axes are parallel, the interaction matrix $\mathcal{U}_{\text{I}}\mathcal{U}_{\text{II}}^{\sim} = \mathcal{U}$ again has the value (11) if $\mathcal{U}_{\text{I}}$ is given by $-i$ times (12), and similarly for $\mathcal{U}_{\text{II}}$. In this case, $\mathcal{U}_{\text{I}}\mathcal{U}_{\text{I}}$ represents the interaction of one molecule with another which is the mirror image of the first one with respect to a plane perpendicular to their line of centers; this is the mutual orientation of lowest free energy for two mirror image molecules. The inequality (10b) holds in this case also. In this case of mirror molecules, however, the specificity of the interaction may be lost if the representative oscillators are anhormonic (Jehle, 1950; Yos, 1956), or for other reasons have permanent dipole moments.

If the term "identical" is used to mean that I-I and II-II, properly oriented, are both pairs of actually identical molecules (or both pairs of mirror image molecules), then the results of the preceding section on the dipole-dipole interaction of systems of coupled harmonic oscillators can be summarized in the *Specificity Theorem*:

If all of the interactions occur at the same separation R, and if the interactions of "identical" pairs of I-I or II-II occur in the mutual orientations of lowest free energy, then, to terms in R^{-6},

$$\Delta_4 A_{\mathrm{I\,II}} \equiv \Delta A_{\mathrm{I\,I}} + \Delta A_{\mathrm{II\,II}} - 2\Delta A_{\mathrm{I\,II}} \leq 0 \tag{10b}$$

Molecular Polarizabilities

In an oscillator model, the static polarizabilities and the dynamic polarizability tensor are defined by

$$\alpha_l = \epsilon_l^2/m_l\tilde{\omega}_l^2, \qquad \boldsymbol{\alpha}(\omega) = \sum_l \alpha_l \mathbf{u}_l \mathbf{u}_l/[1 - (\omega^2/\tilde{\omega}_l^2)] \tag{13}$$

with the dyadic product $\mathbf{u}_l\mathbf{u}_l$. The $\tilde{\omega}_l$ are the normal mode frequencies of the isolated molecules; that is, the eigenvalues of V_∞ are $\hbar^2\tilde{\omega}_l^2/4k^2T^2$. Equations (8), (12), and (13) give

$$\mathcal{W}_{s\mathrm{I}} = -R^{-3} \sum_{l=1}^{N_\mathrm{I}} \frac{\alpha_l}{1 + \dfrac{4\pi^2k^2T^2}{\hbar^2\tilde{\omega}_l^2} s^2} \begin{pmatrix} u_{lx}^2 & u_{lx}u_{ly} & \sqrt{2}\, u_{lx}u_{lz} \\ u_{ly}u_{lx} & u_{ly}^2 & \sqrt{2}\, u_{ly}u_{lz} \\ \sqrt{2}\, u_{lz}u_{lx} & \sqrt{2}\, u_{lz}u_{ly} & 2u_{lz}^2 \end{pmatrix} \tag{14}$$

It is seen that $\mathcal{W}_{s\,\mathrm{I}}$ is, apart from the tensorial factors containing the orientation vectors $\mathbf{u}_l$ the dynamic polarizability analytically continued into the purely imaginary argument $\omega = is2\pi kT/\hbar$. Insofar as the oscillator model corresponds with reality, one can infer from the experimental dispersion curves and absorption spectra α_l, $\tilde{\omega}_l^2$, $\mathbf{u}_l$, because the partial fraction expansion (13) is unique. $\mathcal{W}_{s\mathrm{I}}$ is then determined from these quantities. (1a) and (1c) are readily evaluated from (7), (9) and (14) (cf below).

In studying changes in the rearrangement energy (10a) due to changing the structures of the molecules, a natural idea is to study the effects of small changes in α_l, $\tilde{\omega}_l^2$, and $\mathbf{u}_l$. This approach can be carried out most readily on the basis of (14). Earlier work along this line has been reported by one of us (Bade, 1954) and integrated with the present work (Yos). One may call this the "detuning approach."

The inequality (10b) actually represents six inequalities for every $|s|$, one inequality for each component $\mu\nu$ of the symmetric sum

$$-\Delta_4 A_{\mathrm{I\ II}} = \tfrac{1}{2} kT \sum_s \sum_{\mu\nu} \{(\mathcal{W}_{s\ \mathrm{I}} - \mathcal{W}_{s\ \mathrm{II}})_{\mu\nu}\}^2 \tag{10c}$$

Equation (10c) implies that $\Delta_4 A_{\mathrm{I\ II}} = 0$ rigorously if and only if two molecules have the same set of $(\mathcal{W}_s)_{\mu\nu}$ values, i.e. according to the partial fractions expansion (14), if they have the same dynamic polarizability ellipsoids as function of frequency. This defines what constitutes "identical" molecules in regard to London interactions.

It will turn out that, for the attainment of specificity, strong oscillator polarizabilities with a highly diversified frequency distribution in the quantum region are imperative. The question might therefore be raised why the calculations in this paper deal with the entire partition function rather than with the ground state alone. The answer is that the all-important question is the evaluation of the degree of specificity which depends on the aforementioned distribution of the total set of polarizable oscillators. Only the calculation of the entire partition function will properly delimit the influence of oscillators of low polarizability and of little diversified or low frequencies. Besides, the use of the full partition function turns out to be surprisingly handsome because it yields the rearrangement free energy as the square of a Euclidean distance (10c) in a $\mathcal{W}_s$ space. The s was originally introduced into the calculations only to provide for the series expansion (3). Now one realizes that the expression (10c) for the rearrangement free energy is a very simple one, that it is a sum over s, and not a sum over the normal modes l. This is most simply illustrated for molecules whose oscillators are all oriented parallel to the z-axis, where

$$-\Delta_4 A_{\mathrm{I\ II}} = \frac{1}{2} kT \sum_s 4R^{-6} \left[\sum_{l=1}^{N_{\mathrm{I}}} \frac{\alpha_l}{1 + (2\pi kT/\hbar)^2 (s^2/\bar{\omega}_l^2)} - \sum_{l=N_{\mathrm{I}}+1}^{N_{\mathrm{I}}+N_{\mathrm{II}}} \frac{\alpha_l}{1 + (2\pi kT/\hbar)^2 (s^2/\bar{\omega}_l^2)} \right]^2 \tag{10d}$$

if one has to do with one dimensional oscillators oriented in the z direction. That represents an average situation insofar as one dimensional oscillators in the xy plane would make for a smaller interaction, and three dimensional oscillators would make for a larger interaction.

Degree of Specificity

The preceding sections have discussed particular quadruplet situations arising from a given pair of molecule types I and II. The concept "specific interactions" implies that a given molecule I is able to discriminate between molecules identical with itself and a manifold of other molecules II. One may advantageously generalize this approach by studying the discrimination which an arbitrary molecule in the manifold exhibits in its interactions with the other members of the manifold. In that case one forms averages of the type $\langle(\mathcal{W}_{sI} - \mathcal{W}_{sII})^2\rangle_{Av}$ where I and II are chosen at random from the manifold. Or, equivalently, one can form averages $\langle(\mathcal{W}_s - \langle\mathcal{W}_s\rangle_{Av})^2\rangle_{Av}$ from the distribution of $\mathcal{W}_s$ which are of the same order of magnitude as the preceding averages.

A given manifold of molecular types can be characterized by its $(\mathcal{W}_s)_{\mu\nu}$ distribution. To simplify the discussion, one may forget about the subscripts $\mu\nu$ referring to the fact that $(\mathcal{W}_s)_{\mu\nu}$ are tensors in ordinary three-dimensional space. Then one may simply talk about a distribution in the vector space $\mathcal{W}_s = (\mathcal{W}_0, \mathcal{W}_{-1}, \mathcal{W}_1, \mathcal{W}_{-2}, \mathcal{W}_2 \cdots\cdot)$.

One can illustrate the $\mathcal{W}_s$ as function of $_s$ for two extremely simplified molecules, one of which has appreciable polarizabilities only in a narrow region in the ultraviolet $s_l \approx 78$, the other only in the classical region $s_l \approx 0$.

$$-\mathcal{W}_s = 2R^{-3} \sum_{l=1}^{N} \alpha_l/(1 + s^2/s_l^2), \qquad | s_l | = \hbar\bar{\omega}_l/2\pi kT \tag{14a}$$

If one had a molecule with some polarizabilities in both the indicated spectral regions, its $\mathcal{W}_s$ as function of s, (14a), would be a weighted sum of these ultraviolet and classical $\mathcal{W}_s$, plotted in figure 3. For a special manifold of molecules with polarizabilities distributed only over the two indicated regions (e.g. with ultraviolet polarizabilities = some percentages of that of figure 3, and classical polarizabilities = some percentages of that of figure 3) the $\mathcal{W}_s$ as functions of s would again be weighted superpositions of the two functions illustrated in figure 3. Such a molecular manifold may be said to depend on the two parameters $\sum_l \alpha_l$ in the ultraviolet and $\sum_l \alpha_l$ in the classical region.

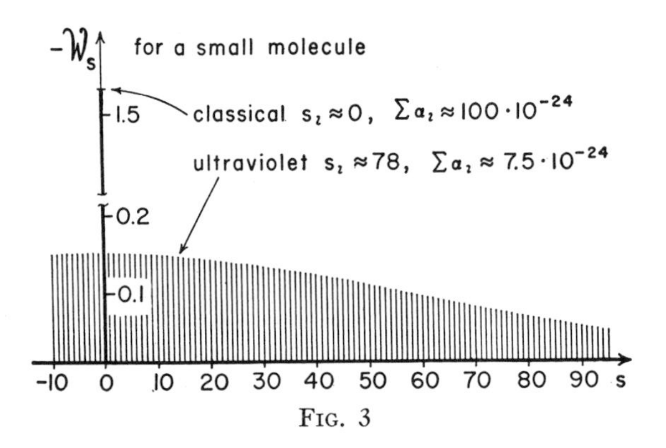

FIG. 3

According to the definition of $\mathcal{W}_s$, one has for a particular molecule always

$$-\mathcal{W}_{|s+1|} \leq -\mathcal{W}_{|s|},$$

and for the manifold of molecules the distribution of adjacent $\mathcal{W}_s$ and $\mathcal{W}_{s+1}$ are correlated. For $s \gg \hbar(\bar{\omega}_l)_{\max}/2\pi kT$ (where $(\bar{\omega}_l)_{\max}$ is the highest oscillator frequency with appreciable polarizability), $\mathcal{W}_s$ drops to negligible values.

A more general molecular manifold than that of Fig. 3, a manifold of macromolecules of a particular size (or number of oscillators N) with specified separation R, can have a many-dimensional $\mathcal{W}_s$ distribution. By definition, the number of parameters on which the manifold of $\mathcal{W}_s$ vectors depends limits the dimensionality of the manifold. The set of all

$$\mathcal{W}_s(-\infty < s < +\infty)$$

is of course not a set of independent quantities. If N denotes the number of oscillators which each molecular type possesses, there are at most $2N$ parameters (the oscillator frequencies and their polarizabilities) on which the $\mathcal{W}_s$ depend. The $\mathcal{W}_s$ distribution can therefore not span out more than $2N$ dimensions (condition 1), but that may be a very large number. But the presence in a molecule, of several oscillators which all have about the same frequency and orientation, does not provide for more independent parameters than a single oscillator.

In order to investigate the *effective* dimensionality of the $\mathcal{W}_s$ distribution of the manifold of macromolecules, one should first of all define a limit of discrimination, i.e. a limit for the magnitude of the rearrangement free energy $\Delta_4 A_{\mathrm{I\,II}}$ (at intermolecular separation R) such that the rearrangement tendency becomes dominant over Brownian motion. One can define it by $(-\Delta_4 A_{\mathrm{I\,II}})_{\mathrm{discr}} = kT$ or

$$\{\sum_s (\mathcal{W}_{s\,\mathrm{I}} - \mathcal{W}_{s\,\mathrm{II}})^2\}_{\mathrm{discr}} = \{-2\Delta_4 A_{\mathrm{I\,II}}/kT\} = 2 \qquad (15)$$

or one can define the discrimination limit between an arbitrary molecule and an average molecule, cf. the circles in Fig. 4.

$$\{\sum_s (\mathcal{W}_s - \langle\mathcal{W}_s\rangle_{\mathrm{Av}})^2\}_{\mathrm{discr}} = 2 \qquad (15a)$$

The right side of Fig. 4 pictures a strongly correlated distribution which one may call "effectively" a one dimensional distribution. The left side of Fig. 4 refers to the special manifold of the type which was discussed along with Fig. 3. Fig. 4 illustrates a distribution of certain practically uncorrelated abscissae and ordinates (representing the $\mathcal{W}_s$ distribution), each of which shows a mean square deviation larger than or even large compared with the discrimination limit 2 (equation 15a). That this be the case one can regard as a necessary prerequisite for calling the manifold "effectively" a two dimensional one. The total mean square deviation $\sum_s \langle(\mathcal{W}_s - \langle\mathcal{W}_s\rangle_{Av})^2\rangle_{Av}$ is the sum of the mean square deviations of the abscissa and of the ordinate and should therefore be $>2 \cdot 2 = 4$ or $\gg 2 \cdot 2 = 4$. As regards more general manifolds, one may call a distribution "effectively" a d dimensional one if the manifold average $\sum_s \langle(\mathcal{W}_s - \langle\mathcal{W}_s\rangle_{Av})^2\rangle_{Av}$ is at least d times the discrimination limit 2 (cf. (15a)), i.e. $2d$, or better, large compared with $2d$ (condition 2).

The caption of Fig. 4 illustrates the procedure of chopping up the interval $0 \leq |s| < \infty$ into a finite number of dimensions ("abscissa", "ordinate", etc.) by forming combinations of mean square deviations $(\mathcal{W}_s - \langle\mathcal{W}_s\rangle_{Av})^2$ so that the distribution over those combinations is not too strongly correlated and that to each combination (dimension) corresponds at least the effective mean square deviation 2. This procedure obviously implies that each dimension comprises at least one unit of the $|s|$ scale (condition 3). In a hypothetical classical oscillator limit case only the term $s = 0$ (cf. (14) or (14a)) would be nonvanishing and one would just get a one dimensional distribution.

As adjacent $\mathcal{W}_s$ and $\mathcal{W}_{s+1}$ are correlated, it is evident that only manifolds whose oscillator frequencies are distributed over wide spectral regions, and whose polarizabilities in these diverse spectral regions are sufficiently large, can be truly many dimensional.

Such limits on the number of effective dimensions which a manifold may be said to have do not provide for an unequivocal definition of the dimensionality of the manifold. Fortunately that is not needed, and one can unambiguously define the "degree of specificity", using Fig. 4 as an illustration.

A many dimensional distribution implies many more or less independent rearrangement inequalities of which (10c) is made up as a sum over regions of the variable s. In order to discuss the implications of such a many parametric distribution one can compare it with a hypothetical one dimensional distribution. In Fig. 4, the two dimensional distribution of Fig. 3 is compared with a one

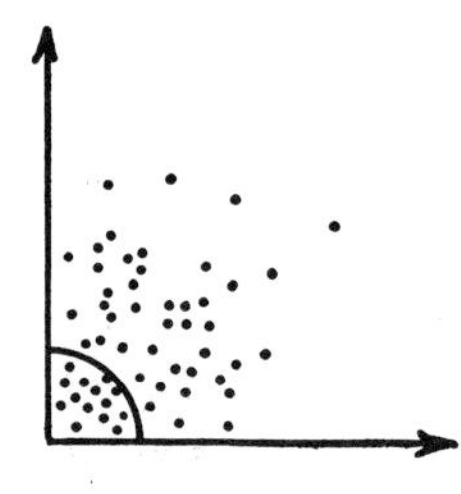

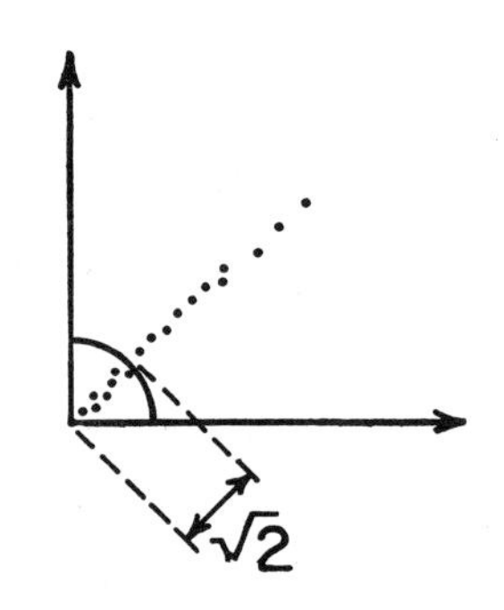

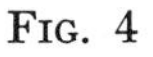
FIG. 4

Abscissae $= |(\mathcal{W}_0 - \langle\mathcal{W}_0\rangle_{Av})|$

Ordinates $= \{2(\mathcal{W}_1 - \langle\mathcal{W}_1\rangle_{Av})^2 + 2(\mathcal{W}_2 - \langle\mathcal{W}_2\rangle_{Av})^2 + \cdots\}^{\frac{1}{2}}$

dimensional one. It is assumed that the distributions of molecule types are reasonably uniform in the $\mathcal{W}_s$ intervals, and for the purpose of comparison it is assumed that the mean square deviations $\langle \sum_s (\mathcal{W}_s - \langle \mathcal{W}_s \rangle_{Av})^2 \rangle_{Av}$ of the two distributions in Fig. 4 have the same value, i.e. that the two distributions have rearrangement energies of the same size.

The notion "*degree of specificity at separation R*" refers to the degree of discrimination of some particular molecular type I when confronted, each time in a quadruplet fashion, with a manifold of types of molecules II. Degree of specificity can be defined as the measure of the subset of types II discriminated against when confronted with type I, divided by the measure of the total set of all types II in the manifold. Generalizing this definition, one can form an average over different molecules I by taking I as well as II from a given manifold of molecular types, all of a similar category and size. Alternatively, one confronts an average molecular type (I) of the manifold with all other types (II) of molecules chosen at random from this same manifold (cf. Fig. 4). On the left in that figure, in the many (two) dimensional case, the relative measure of the non-discriminated subset (i.e. one minus the degree of specificity) is the ratio of the number of points inside the hypersphere "d-tant" (15a) (indicated by a circle quadrant), to the total number of points. On the right, in the one dimensional case, it is the ratio of the number of points inside the linear interval (15a) to the total number of points. The latter ratio is of the order of magnitude of the ratio of the non-discriminated interval length $\sqrt{2}$ to the length occupied by the total set of points. The former ratio (left side of Fig. 4) is a product of several (two) such fractions and may readily become much smaller. If the polarizabilities are sufficiently strong, and of diversified frequency, and if the separation R is small, the relative measure of the non-discriminated subset becomes very small, and that means a high degree of specificity, close to unity. As the actual case (10c) involves oscillators oriented in three dimensions even the situation of Fig. 3 involves an effectively many dimensional manifold $\mathcal{W}_{s\mu\nu}$.

In simple words one can summarize the essential point: The question was: why does a many (two) dimensional distribution show so much higher a degree of specificity than a one dimensional distribution (cf. Fig. 4), even though in both cases there may be, in the average, the same amounts of rearrangement free energies $\Delta_4 A_{I\ II}$ involved? The answer is this: In the one dimensional distribution (right side of Fig. 4) one might perhaps pick out five (about equidistant) dots, $\sqrt{2}$ apart from each other, so that no two out of these five dots are closer together than the discrimination limit $\sqrt{2}$. In the many (two) dimensional distribution (left side of Fig. 4) one can pick out a good many more dots such that no two of them are closer together than $\sqrt{2}$. This is so simply because it is a many dimensional distribution, even though the average distances between pairs of dots is the same in both distributions illustrated in Fig. 4.

It is evident that the degree of specificity is highly sensitive to the values of polarizabilities and to the intermolecular separation R which in turn depends on the ionic constitution of the medium.

The "range" of the interaction may be defined as that distance R_0 at which the rearrangement free energy $\Delta_4 A_{\mathrm{I\,II}} = -kT$. If the oscillator frequencies would only reach from the ultraviolet to the infrared and not all the way down to the classical region, one could simply write

$$R_0 = (3/2)^{\frac{1}{6}}(\hbar\tilde{\omega}/2kT)^{\frac{1}{6}}(N\alpha)^{\frac{1}{6}}(\Delta_4 A_{\mathrm{I\,II}}/\Delta A_{\mathrm{I\,I}})^{\frac{1}{6}} \tag{16}$$

where α is the polarizability per oscillator, and $\tilde{\omega}$ is an average value of the oscillator frequencies of I. R_0 is proportional to $N^{\frac{1}{3}}$ and therefore proportional to the radius of a spherical macromolecule. The range is thus to be judged in relation to the radii of the molecules involved.

There is a relevant connection between the concept of "range R_0" and the concept of "degree of specificity at separation R": If I, II happens to be an "average pair" of molecules types whose squared distance in the $\mathfrak{W}_s$ space (at a particular separation R) is about equal to the average squared distance for all molecule pairs (at the same separation R) taken from that manifold of molecules, then R_0 could also be characterized by remarking that the degree of specificity for this manifold would start to fall well below unity when the separation R is raised to the value R_0.

In the actual biologically interesting cases the most important polarizabilities are in the ultraviolet and in the classical regions. The formula (16) which uses an 'average' oscillator frequency cannot be properly applied to that case and it will therefore be advisable to give a crude estimate of the magnitude of the rearrangement free energy $\Delta_4 A_{\mathrm{I\,II}}$ on the basis of equation (10d).

The ultraviolet contributions to the polarizabilities are evidently contributions from electrons in the valence shells, and the classical contributions are due to fluctuations of the proton distribution over the surfaces of the molecules, of the type investigated by Kirkwood and Shumaker (1952). If one lumps all the ultraviolet polarizabilities together and assigns to them an average frequency which might correspond to $s_l \approx 78$ (14a) and if, on the other hand, one lumps all the classical polarizabilities together, corresponding to an $s_l \approx 0$ (14a), one has a situation like that illustrated in Fig. 3. In such a procedure which disregards all further details of the distribution of polarizabilities over the frequency spectrum, (10d) can approximately be split into an ultraviolet contribution (denoted by $l =$ UV), and a classical one ($l =$ Cl) which only contributes to the term $s = 0$.

$$\begin{aligned} -\Delta_4 A_{\mathrm{I\,II}} &\approx \tfrac{1}{2}\, kT\, 4R^{-6}\, \{[\sum_{\mathrm{I}} \alpha_{\mathrm{UV}} - \sum_{\mathrm{II}} \alpha_{\mathrm{UV}}]^2 \int_{-\infty}^{+\infty} [1 + (s/s_{\mathrm{UV}})^2]^{-2}\, ds \\ &\qquad + [\sum_{\mathrm{I}} \alpha_{\mathrm{Cl}} - \sum_{\mathrm{II}} \alpha_{\mathrm{Cl}}]^2\} \\ &= 2kT\, R^{-6}\, \{(\pi/2)\, s_{\mathrm{UV}}\, [\sum_{\mathrm{I}} \alpha_{\mathrm{UV}} - \sum_{\mathrm{II}} \alpha_{\mathrm{UV}}]^2 + [\sum_{\mathrm{I}} \alpha_{\mathrm{Cl}} - \sum_{\mathrm{II}} \alpha_{\mathrm{Cl}}]^2\} \end{aligned} \tag{17}$$

If one considers the closest approach of neighboring molecules with an R equal to twice the 'radius' of the molecule,

$$R^{-6} = (\pi/6 \text{ volume})^2 \tag{18}$$

$$-\ \Delta_4 A_{\mathrm{I\,II}} \approx kT\ 2\ (\pi/6 \text{ volume})^2.$$

$$\{(\hbar\bar{\omega}_{\mathrm{UV}}/4kT)[\sum_{\mathrm{I}} \alpha_{\mathrm{UV}} - \sum_{\mathrm{II}} \alpha_{\mathrm{UV}}]^2 + [\sum_{\mathrm{I}} \alpha_{\mathrm{Cl}} - \sum_{\mathrm{II}} \alpha_{\mathrm{Cl}}]^2\} \tag{17a}$$

If one considers, as above, I as an average type molecule of a manifold of molecule types, the average rearrangement free energy (of quadruplets of molecule types) is

$\langle -\Delta_4 A_{\mathrm{I\,II}} \rangle_{\mathrm{AV}} \approx$ mean square deviation of

$$[2kT\ (\hbar\bar{\omega}_{\mathrm{UV}}/4kT)]^{\frac{1}{2}}\ (\pi/6 \text{ volume}) \sum \alpha_{\mathrm{UV}}$$

plus that of

$$[2kT]^{\frac{1}{2}}\ (\pi/6 \text{ volume}) \sum \alpha_{\mathrm{Cl}} \tag{17b}$$

In order to get an idea of the magnitudes of these quantities, without going into detailed assumptions about the *manifold* of molecule types under consideration, one can estimate the squares of the quantities listed in (17b) for typical molecules instead of their mean square deviations for a manifold of molecules.

As a first step in estimating the size of the *ultraviolet* terms, one can add up the atomic static polarizabilities of the atoms occurring in a glycine residue and gets, (taking as effective oscillator strength $\sum f$ one half of the number of electrons in the valence shells, i.e. 11) $\sum_{\text{residue}} \alpha_{\mathrm{UV}} \approx 7.5 \cdot 10^{-24}$ cm^3. The frequency is estimated from the ionization energy as $\bar{\omega}_{\mathrm{UV}} \approx 2 \cdot 10^{16}$ sec^{-1}, and the volume per residue $\approx 60 \cdot 10^{-24}$ cm^3. This brings the square of the UV term listed in (17b) up to 1.1 kT.

Actually one has to study molecular electronic states and their polarizabilities rather than atomic polarizabilities. Of particular interest are electronic transitions in molecules which correspond to high electron mobility. There are several possibllities which might greatly enhance the importance of UV terms and make them stronger than 1.1 kT, in particular the occurrence of low frequency electronic transitions, or the presence of excited electronic states which are in reach of thermal excitation. The quantity $\bar{\omega}(\sum \alpha)^2$ which characterizes the square of the ultraviolet term listed in (17b), this quantity is proportional to $\bar{\omega}^{-3}(\sum f)^2$. The total $\sum f$ is, by Thomas Reiche Kuhn (Kramers Kronig 1928) limited by the number of electrons. A shift of the oscillator strengths towards lower frequencies therefore intensifies the interaction. It also provides for a diversification of the distribution of polarizabilities over several ultraviolet regions.

For large macromolecules, each of which presents a large number of repetitions of monomer units, other effects might still come into play which will again substantially raise the UV term for which 1.1 kT was estimated as a minimum in the case of a glycine residue.

In comparing large with small molecules, the values of R equation (18), are used which are large and small, respectively.

In the *classical* region the Kirkwood-Shumaker (1952a and b) proton fluctuations play a decisive role. Even though these are not oscillations but simply fluctuations with relaxation times of the order of 10^{-8} sec, their influence is like that of classical polarizable oscillators. The Kirkwood-Shumaker dipolemoment fluctuations may give cause to an addition to the polarizability, equal to the mean square deviation of the dipole moment divided by 3 kT. Using Kirkwood's data, one may get for the square of the Cl term listed in (17b) a value of 65 kT, in the case of a human serum albumin molecule. In the case of smaller molecules the effect is again smaller, perhaps kT for a molecule of the size of an aminoacid residue.

These Kirkwood-Shumaker forces depend on the right kind of ionic concentrations in the medium. Even if one is not near the isoelectric point, their influence, though not quite as strong, is still important.

It is to be kept in mind that *static* electric charge distributions on the interacting molecules (often causing repulsion between identical molecules) are readily compensated by small ions from the medium; fluctuations of proton distributions are, on the other hand, difficult to compensate when the interacting molecules are close together. Forces due to charge fluctuations are simply there.

The classical terms of the formulae (17) refer to oscillators of low frequency. The Kirkwood-Shumaker interaction includes not only fluctuations of electric dipolemoments (and higher moments) due to mobile protons but also fluctuations of electric charge due to the same protons. The Kirkwood-Shumaker interaction energy, if one disregards the shielding effect of the Debye-Hueckel atmospheres, has thus an R dependence which for large R (where the fluctuating charges give the predominant influence) approaches R^{-2}. This is different from the R^{-6} dependence of the classical oscillator interaction. A little closer inspection (cf. Kirkwood-Shumaker, 1952b, p. 869, formula (13)) shows that nevertheless the interaction of pairs of *adjacent* molecules can be estimated by simply taking as their oscillator polarizabilities the mean square deviation of their dipolemoments of mobile protons divided by $3kT$, and using the oscillator formulae.

London Formulae Derived from the Matrix Formulae

The formulae (1a) and (1c) are limit cases of the general matrix results (7), (9), i.e.

$$\Delta A_{\mathrm{I\,II}} = -\tfrac{1}{2}\, kT \sum_{s=-\infty}^{+\infty} \operatorname{tr}\,(\mathcal{W}_{s\,\mathrm{I}} \cdot \mathcal{W}_{s\,\mathrm{II}}), \tag{19}$$

and of (14), i.e.

$$(\mathcal{W}_{o\,\mathrm{I}})_{zz} = -2R^{-3}\sum_{l=1}^{N_{\mathrm{I}}} u_{lz}^2\alpha_l = -2R^{-3}\sum_{l=1}^{N_{\mathrm{I}}} u_{lz}^2\epsilon_l^2/\overline{K}_l \tag{19a}$$

$$(\mathcal{W}_{s\,\mathrm{I}})_{zz} = -2R^{-3}\sum_{l=1}^{N_{\mathrm{I}}} (\hbar^2\tilde{\omega}_l^2/4k^2T^2)u_{lz}^2\alpha_l/[s^2\pi^2 + (\hbar^2\tilde{\omega}_l^2/4k^2T^2)] \tag{19b}$$

where the force constants $\overline{K}_l \equiv \tilde{\omega}_l^2 m_l$ have been introduced; the polarizabilities (13) are $\alpha_l = \epsilon_l^2/\overline{K}_l$. This shows that 2 tr $(\mathcal{W}_{0\mathrm{I}}\mathcal{W}_{0\mathrm{II}})$ is independent of $\hbar$ (and of the masses, given the force constants). This part $s = 0$ of the series (7), i.e (for one-dimensional single oscillator molecules $u_{lz} = 1$)

$$\Delta A_{\mathrm{I\,II}} = -\tfrac{1}{2}kT\,\mathrm{tr}\,(\mathcal{W}_{0\mathrm{I}}\mathcal{W}_{0\mathrm{II}}) = -2kTR^{-6}\alpha_{\mathrm{I}}\alpha_{\mathrm{II}} \tag{20}$$

represents the classical part of the interaction free energy and is the one-dimensional equivalent of (1a). In the quantum limit case of the same type of simplified molecule model one can replace the sum over s by an integral. s_{I}, s_{II} are used as in (14a).

$$\begin{aligned}\Delta A_{\mathrm{I\,II}} &= -\tfrac{1}{2}kT\int_{-\infty}^{+\infty}\mathrm{tr}\,(\mathcal{W}_{s\mathrm{I}}\mathcal{W}_{s\mathrm{II}})\,ds \\ &= -\tfrac{1}{2}kT\,\mathrm{tr}\,(\mathcal{W}_{0\mathrm{I}}\mathcal{W}_{0\mathrm{II}})\int_{-\infty}^{+\infty}[1+(s/s_{\mathrm{I}})^2]^{-1}[1+(s/s_{\mathrm{II}})^2]^{-1}\,ds \\ &= -\tfrac{1}{2}kT(\mathcal{W}_{0\mathrm{I}})_{zz}(\mathcal{W}_{0\mathrm{II}})_{zz}\pi s_{\mathrm{I}}s_{\mathrm{II}}/(s_{\mathrm{I}}+s_{\mathrm{II}}) \\ &= -R^{-6}\alpha_{\mathrm{I}}\alpha_{\mathrm{II}}\,\hbar\,\tilde{\omega}_{\mathrm{I}}\tilde{\omega}_{\mathrm{II}}/(\tilde{\omega}_{\mathrm{I}}+\tilde{\omega}_{\mathrm{II}}),\end{aligned} \tag{21}$$

the one-dimensional equivalent of (1c).

Summary of the Scope and Results of the Calculations

The London-Eisenschitz-Wang (van der Waals) force between two molecules is due to the net effect of the electrical interaction of the fluctuating electric dipole moments in one molecule with those of the other. The simplest model of a molecule as regards its London-van der Waals interaction is to represent it by a set of harmonic oscillators. Would only their lowest quantum state come into the picture, one would not need to calculate the free energy and the interaction force could be completely characterized by the dependence of the energy (of interaction of these fluctuating dipoles) as a function of the distance R between the two molecules. Actually there are, however, many excited quantum states (energy levels) which are in thermal reach, and the proper assessment of their influence on the present problem is necessary, and it is handled by statistical mechanics, i.e. by calculating partition function Z and free energy A as a function of the separation R. The kinds of macromolecules considered here are of the roughly globular type. If those molecules can actually come into contact with each other, bond formation and steric complementarity will be dominating; and the calculation of London forces between the two macromolecules will be very complicated. At larger separation when the centers of the macromolecules might be more than a macromolecular diameter apart, the London force can be better evaluated and in this case the London force is of great importance. Such separations are usually maintained by the balance between the attractive London force with the repulsive electrostatic force of the two macromolecules. If they are identical, they have equal electrical charges which, however, are somewhat compensated by gegen ions furnished from the surrounding medium. Depending on the circumstances, slow charge fluctuations may be compensated too, but oscillator moments change too rapidly to be compensated.

When one asks for preferences in association of identical versus non-identical molecules imbedded in a liquid medium, one has to consider a differential effect of interaction free energy described in Fig. 1 and designated by "rearrangement free energy $\Delta_4 A_{\mathrm{I\,II}}$". This quantity turns out to be negative under pretty general conditions. The inequality (1b) and Hamaker's inequality (1d) clearly show this fact. In order to handle the general case and in order to be able to define degree of specificity and assess its value, the partition function and free energy are calculated. Provided the polarizability distribution in the macromolecules is strong and diversified enough (both as regards the frequency and spatial distribution), specificity may result due to the multi-dimensionality of the macromolecular oscillators. (The finer details of the polarizability distribution are irrelevant, that is evident from Fig. 3.)

Orientation effects play a significant role too. Specific London interaction implies (as was outlined before equation (12)), that identical macromolecules which are nearest neighbors orient themselves in parallel in the z direction (the z axes are chosen to be directed along the line connecting the nearest neighbors under consideration), anti-parallel in the x and y directions (x and y axes are in the planes perpendicular to that line).

Biological Implications

The object of this paper is not to present a solution to a biophysical problem or to some problems of crystallization, but only to define the simplest kind of model in which London forces play a central role and to work out, by straightforward quantum and statistical mechanics, the conditions under which it shows specificity. Further research will be required to determine the kinds of macromolecules which are capable of exhibiting highly specific London interactions and the conditions, as regards ionic atmospheres and polarizabilities under which this capability can manifest itself. At the present time these physicochemical data necessary for a correct evaluation of the role of the London force in the most interesting macromolecules are not yet available (cf. the discussion period). Before proceeding to suggest some possible biological implications it may be good to recall part of the history of the ideas presented here.

Jordan (1938, 1939, 1941, 1947) attempted an attack on this problem of specific interaction of identical molecules on the basis of quantum-mechanical resonance, and his resonance arguments received a critical analysis by Pauling and Delbrueck (1940). The long range R^{-3} resonance attraction or repulsion, depending on the symmetry of the wave function, is also mentioned in Dr. Hirschfelder's paper; the present note of ours deals, however, with the dispersion force interaction (completed with contribution of excited states) which is proportional to R^{-6}.

The investigation of the present paper had its origin in a fundamental biophysical problem (Muller, 1922, 1937, 1941, 1947). This is the problem of explaining why organic macromolecules or molecule complexes which represent the genes "specifically" attract like molecules or complexes, discriminating with great accuracy between their homologous partners and all others as exhibited in inverted synapsis during meiosis. (The word 'gene' is used in this note both, to refer to the genetic fine structure, i.e. to a particular nucleotide pair, and also, especially in connection with this paragraph, to refer to a much larger structure, i.e. a particularly folded macromolecular complex). The genes have an enormous stability in their natural surroundings. Their stability can be understood if one assumes them to be three dimensional compact structures with many stabilizing internal cross links which guarantee the restitution of their structures if some bond happens to get broken. A well-defined intermolecular structure would then be expected to correspond (in the oscillator model) to a very definite set of oscillator frequencies, as regards the electrical oscillations. Not only these frequencies but also the directions in space of the anisotropic oscillator moments are expected to be determined by the structure. This line of thought suggested the investigation of possible specificity effects of the London-van der Waals interaction.

The present investigation was based on a model which represented the molecules or complexes as compact well-defined structures equivalent to a set of electrical oscillators, and assumed the molecules or complexes to carry appreciable electric charges and to be imbedded in an ionic medium. Electrostatic forces between identical macromolecules (which, as concerns the effect of their identical net charges, repel each other) can be regulated by concentration changes of the ionic composition of the medium in which they are suspended. The interplay between these controllable repulsive forces and highly specific London-Eisenschitz-Wang attractive forces could provide a mechanism for various biochemical processes. The motion of chromosomes in meiosis might perhaps illustrate such an interplay. It might be that changes in the medium's ionic composition allow the chromosomes to come together or to be forced apart.

It might perhaps be permissible to make now a minor observation regarding orientation effects in synapsis. If one considers the London force between two long rods lying parallel, side by side, one runs into the problem that corresponding sections of the rods which lie side by side do not at all have the advantageous mutual orientation required by the London interaction (in the general case of anisotropic polarizabilities). The proper mutual orientation of identical or homologous genes in synapsing chromosomes can, however, be facilitated by the flexibility, or by coiling of the chromosomes; in this regard, it may be interesting to remark that two identical big low-pitch helical coils, lying along side each other with their axes parallel, permit the directly adjacent parts of the neighbor coils to form identical and properly oriented pairs (if the threads out of which the big-low-pitch helical coils are wound, permit some $\pm 90°$ torsion). The big coils might be turned together like a two stranded rope. In a similar fashion four identical low-pitch helical coils can be assembled into a twined four-stranded rope with all directly adjacent parts specifically interacting. Formation of three (or other than two or four) stranded ropes do not permit all adjacent parts to be identical and properly oriented.

As to the problem of self-duplication, Muller wrote, "That this ability to duplicate itself is based in unique properties of some relatively stable genetic material, rather than in the multitude of diverse substances and processes that engage in cycles, may, curiously enough, be inferred more especially from the behavior of the real exceptions to the principle of inner stability. These all important exceptions are the comparatively rare cases in which, even in a "pure line", sudden permanent deviations of type or "mutations", take place. Although of most varied kinds, as judged by their unlike effects on the organism, it is characteristic of the great majority of these changes that in succeeding multiplication they may become regularly incorporated, that is, they now take their place as part of the again stable, self-multiplying pattern. It is scarcely conceivable that, if the reproduction of every part of the organism were due primarily to the marvelous concatenation of a host of individual processes of the cycle, these could have been so arranged that, when disturbed in any one of the innumerable ways, they would still be able to work effectively in reproduction, yet in a manner so correspondingly adjusted as now to effect a repetition of just the given alteration. Rather must it be inferred that the essential process of reproduction consists in the autosynthesis of a controlling genetic material, and that this occurs through some sort of laying down of the raw material after the model of the genetic material already present, no matter what—within certain very wide limits—the pattern of that genetic material happens to begin with. . . ."

"In this as in previous proposals for explaining gene duplication, the "raw" materials in the medium are supposed to become attached to like parts of the pre-existing gene and so to arrive at the same arrangements as it has. There is a known parallel for this in the phenomenon of synapsis, . . . and one has only to suppose that this phenomenon may extend even to the parts of the gene as they are put together during the process of its duplication, to get an explanation of duplication in terms of this remarkable synaptic force."

"There is the apparently insuperable difficulty in attraction at a distance . . . , for the lines of force from different parts would become too dispersed and mixed with one another. It would therefore seem necessary, for explaining a self-specific pattern capable of operating at a distance, to postulate that it is expressed in the form of a temporal fluctuation, that is, a vibrational effect of some sort, varying with each gene."

In other words: A macromolecule or complex which is carrier of genetic properties—let us call it a "gene" for the present—is assumed to be assembled by the original gene itself from smaller "constituent molecules of the gene", that is the process is described as "selfduplication". Constituent molecules are defined on the one hand as small enough so that they can be assumed to be readily available in the surrounding cell medium, and on the other hand large enough so that the specificity of the London force is the determining factor in the interaction. Brownian motion brings, with great rapidity, all kinds of molecules into the neighborhood of the original gene. Those molecules which happen to be identical with the gene's respective constituent molecules will be retained in their neighborhood, with compensating gegenions from the medium interspersed between the identical partners.

The assembly process might actually involve several steps, the formation of chain segments or of chains, and of helixes like the DNA or protein helix, or of sheets, and the folding up or arraying of these basic structures into more complex units.

It is important to consider two universal properties of the gene duplication process:

(1) The stability of the gene which permits it to go unharmed through millions of duplication processes. In view of this extraordinary stability it seems that the structure which guarantees the stability of the gene (whether it is simply a part of a DNA helix, or whether it is a more complex folded structure, the type of folding of which is essential to the specificity of the gene), should never be ripped apart during the duplication process. In that way the stability of the gene is not put in jeopardy.

(2) The accuracy of the replica formation. If one uses only the principles of affinity and steric compatibility between the parts of the replica, i.e. intramolecular bond and steric requirements inside the daughter structure itself, that will not be enough to guarantee correct replication. (If a Watson Crick helix is ripped into halves, it loses its formerly well determined structure at the growth region where it is being ripped apart; the free nucleotide is flexible too, thus it is difficult to see how complementarity can effectively become operative

and prevent wrong molecules from messing up the correct replication.—When the accuracy of replication of a particular mode of folding is under discussion, it is conceivable that in the case of protein folding, the particular amino acid sequence by itself safeguards a unique way of folding characteristic for that sequence (Pauling); it seems, however, that the London force greatly helps to achieve correct folding in the manner discussed along Fig. 5 below). In short it seems that in addition to intramolecular bond and steric requirements, another ordering principle is necessary and the present approach suggests that London force specificity is to be considered to provide for the essential first step, i.e. for the selective collection and adequate orientation of the constituent molecules which are going to form the replica. How the replica formation is to be achieved in detail is certainly an unsolved problem (as is the formation of proteins from the information laid down into nucleic acid genes). A few speculative suggestions which may indicate the broad outlines of the assembly process may be sketched in the following; the scheme may be quite different (a) in the problem of the building of a replica of a helix or of a sheet, and (b) in the problem of folding of a chain or helix, or several chain or helix segments in to a still larger compact unit.

(b) This assembly process may be considered first. In particular the replication of a globular shaped large compact unit which is made up (top part of Fig. 5) from several constituent molecules which might be held together by bonds. Constituent molecules for the daughter unit are selected from the surrounding medium and will be oriented with respect to their counterparts in the original unit as indicated in Fig. 5. But that also makes the relative orientation of the constituent molecules of the daughter unit identical with the relative orientations of their counterparts in the original unit. Thus there is a good chance for the molecules of the daughter unit to assemble correctly. Mistakes made in

FIG. 5

the assembly process might either be broken up or will simply stop growing because they will correspond to a structure which cannot be fitted together any further. A set of a few constituent molecules properly fitted and bonded together will again be specifically attracted and oriented by its counterpart in the original unit.

(a) In the case of a long DNA helix, self-duplication might perhaps come about as follows. The surrounding medium supplies polynucleotides. Brownian motion and specific London attraction provide for a mantle of nucleotide pairs, selected to correspond to the nucleotide pairs of the parent helix, to be laid around this original helix. The London force causes a particular orientation of each daughter nucleotide pair in the mantle with reference to its corresponding parent nucleotide pair. This mutual orientation can be described as follows. Draw a radial line from the parent helix axis through the center of that parent nucleotide pair; the daughter nucleotide pair can be generated by performing a 180° screw translation outwards along this line which puts the parent pair over into the daughter pair, located in the mantle. As the circumference of the mantle is larger than that of the parent DNA double helix, the regularly arranged daughter pentose-phosphate groups are separated by some gaps from neighbor groups along the helixes. The formation of the DNA replica may then occur by the closure of some gaps, and finally all of them, accompanied by ionic concentration changes in the medium, permitting the daughter helix sections to peel off from the parent helix. Such a daughter helix then has the same pentose-phosphate helices and the same sequence of base pairs as the parent helix; however, each base pair is flipped 180° around its radial line, compared with the orientation of the parent helix pair. This replica is therefore a 'flip conjugate' of the parent DNA; the next generation is expected to be again like the original.

Biological specificities occur in many other connections (Rabinowitch, 1941) where it is not always the case that the participating molecules possess as outstanding a stability as the genes do, and where the specific interactions involve non-identical molecules. It would be premature to speculate as to the significance of the above calculations in regard to the wider field of biological specificities. It is clear that complementarity, favored because of electrostatic or because of general van der Waals stabilization, plays a most important role not only in deciding molecular structure, but also in determining intermolecular interaction (Pauling, 1940, 1948, 1957; Pauling, Campbell and Pressman, 1943; Campbell, 1957).

An interesting effect of high specificity may, however, come up in the following fashion. For simplicity of explanation, this effect will be illustrated in terms of two identical protein helixes which possess occasional big side groups. Let the helixes be alongside each other, with their axes vertical, one helix being a little displaced (in the direction of the helix axes, i.e. elevated) with respect to the other, and let the helixes be turned around their axes such that some of their corresponding side groups come to lie just between the helixes in such a way that pairs of identical sidegroups belonging to the two identical protein helixes, respectively, come to lie essentially on top of each other, so that the two proteins interlock with corresponding sidegroups clinging together. The mutual orientations of these pairs of identical sidegroups is the advantageous one according to equation (12). Even if the polarizabilities are not extra strong, the specificity may become very high due to the matching pattern of pairwise identical sidegroups. Intervening spaces are expected to be filled, in a statistical fashion, by small molecules and ions from the medium.

As the association (and proper orientation) between mirror molecules fails in the general case because of permanent dipole contributions, a laevo structure will duplicate a laevo, not a dextro structure in accordance with the behavior of macromolecules in living organisms (Haldane, 1937; Oparin, 1938).

The problem of differentiation, in particular in the early development and growth of a fertilized egg, might also be related to the rearrangement free energies of the type considered here (Weiss, 1949, 1951, 1953, 1955).

With regard to the properties of the London force, molecules are identical if they have the same distribution of polarizabilities. Structural identity is a sufficient but not a necessary condition for the "identity" on which London force specificity depends. Correspondingly London specificity may play a role in a wider group of biological specificity phenomena such as enzyme specificity or antigen antibody specificity.

Before studying the biological implications of the London force it would be appropriate to pursue the question whether the specificity theorem sheds light on the problems of crystal formation, particularly that of van der Waals crystals. One may consider the case of a van der Waals crystal surrounded by a medium composed not only of that particular molecule but of others too, molecules which differ from the one of the crystal only by their polarizability distribution. Attachment of one more molecule to a crystal of its likes implies one of several quadruplet terms $\Delta_4 A_{\mathrm{I\ II}}$ as a free energy change. In most crystallization processes, however, the molecules (or atoms) about to crystallize are not prevented from approaching each other closely; therefore all kinds of bonds come into play which were disregarded in the cases discussed in this note. Nevertheless (and particularly in certain molecular crystals and virus crystals, (Wyckoff, 1949, 1951; Wyckoff and Labaw, 1955)) the quadruplet expressions of London forces may come into the picture. The quadruplet formulation may be used for any sort of additive forces.

In order to give an idea about the kinds of orientation problems which come up in the formation of macromolecular arrays, the problem of orientation preferences is singled out in the following by discussion of a particular case: crystallization of perfectly globular molecules, all identical molecules whose polarizability distributions for the various frequency ranges are highly aniso-

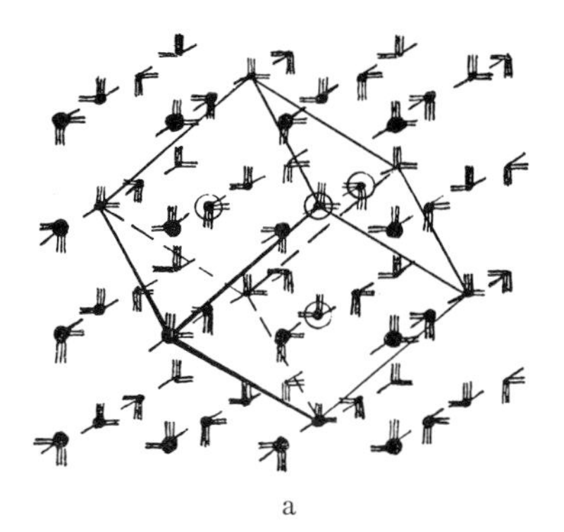

a

b

FIG. 6

tropic and not just confined to one direction or a plane. Considering London van der Waals force anisotropy, closest pair interactions only taken into consideration, the molecules can be placed into the simple cubic arrangement with orientation indicated by the 64 trirectangular trihedrals (repères mobiles, pointers) of Fig. 6. This may be the most advantageous arrangement as regards nearest neighbor orientation effects (provided that one has additivity of the various pair interactions in the lattice and provided one can neglect second nearest neighbor interactions). Fig. 6 also shows the generating parallelepiped (rhombohedron) of one of the four interlocking lattices, each characterized by a particular orientation of its trihedrals. The four differently oriented molecules per generating parallelepiped are marked by circles. This arrangement is of importance if the molecules fit into a cubic (or into a rectangular parallelepiped) arrangement. If the London force of the molecules is isotropic, the tendency to closest packing will determine the structure and orientations. Orientation effects will also be more difficult to evaluate if the molecules are elongated (De Boer and Heller 1937). If other interactions, besides London van der Waals, are taken into consideration, the issue becomes even more complex—one-, two-, or three-dimensional lattices built of repetitive macromolecular arrangements play an important role in biological structures. Their theory still has to be developed.

It should also be mentioned that the specificity of the London force sheds some light on problems connected with solubility, in particular on the fact that similarity of structure between solvent and solute makes for good solubility (with the exception of solutes whose molecules have interactions among each other of a kind which they cannot have with a solvent molecule).

Acknowledgments

We should like to thank the Research Corporation, the National Science Foundation (grant G627, 1954–56), the National Cancer Institute (grant C-3304 BBC, 1957–58), and the University of Nebraska Research Council for their generous support of this investigation. We have received a great deal of valuable criticism and important help from many colleagues and friends to whom we wish to give thanks, in particular Dr. N. H. Cromwell, Dr. H. T Epstein, Dr. W. G. Leavitt, Dr. A. S. Skapski, and most of all Dr. S. T. Epstein, Dr. H. J. Muller and Dr. Linus Pauling. They have given us encouragement, inspiration and friendship through the years.

References

Alexander, J. 1931. Intracellular aspects of life and disease. Protoplasma *14:* 296–306.

Bade, W. L. 1954. Thesis, Ph.D. University of Nebraska.

Breinl, F. and F. Haurowitz. 1930. Chemical investigation of the precipitate from hemoglobin and antihemoglobin-serum and remarks on the nature of the antibodies. Z. physiol. Chem. *192:* 45–57.

Campbell, D. H. 1957. Principles of Immunology. McGraw Hill Book Company, New York.

de Boer, J. H. 1936. Trans. Farad. Soc. *32:* 21.

de Boer, J. H. and G. Heller. 1937. Physica *4:* 1045.

Debye, P. and E. Hueckel. 1923. Phys. Z. *24:* 185.

Derjaguin, B. 1939. Acta Physicochimica, USSR. *10:* 333.

Derjaguin, B. 1940a. Acta Physicochimica, USSR. *12:* 181.
Derjaguin, B. 1940b. Acta Physicochimica, USSR. *12:* 314.
Derjaguin, B. 1940c. Trans. Farad. Soc. *36:* 203.
Derjaguin, B. 1954. Trans. Farad. Soc. Disc. Coagulation and Flocculation. *18:* 24, 85.
Derjaguin, B. and L. D. Landau. 1941. Acta Physicochimica, USSR. *14:* 663.
Eisenschitz, R. and F. London. 1930a. The relation between the van der Waals forces and the monopolar valence forces. Z. f. Physik. *60:* 491–527.
Eisenschitz, R. and F. London, 1930b. Z. f. Physik. *63:* 245.
Fan, Ky. 1951. Proc. Nat. Acad. Sci. USA. *37:* 762.
Haldane, J. B. S. 1937. Biochemistry and the Individual. Cambridge University Press.
Hamaker, H. C. 1937a. A general theory of lyophobic colloids. II. Rec. tray. chim. Pays. Bas. *56:* 3–25.
Hamaker, H. C. 1937b. The London-van der Waals attraction between spherical particles. Physica *4:* 1058–1072.
Hamaker, H. C. 1938. Chem. Weekblad. *35:* 47.
Hamaker, H. C. 1948. in Verwey & Overbeek, Theory of Lyophobic Colloids. Elsevier Press. pp. 161–162.
Hamaker, H. C. 1952. in Kruyt, Colloid Science I. Elsevier Press. pp. 276–277.
Harned, H. S. and B. B. Owen. 1950. Electrolytic Solutions. Reinhold Publ., New York.
Haurowitz, F. 1950. Chemistry and Biology of Proteins. Academic Press Inc., New York.
Jehle, H. 1950. Specificity of interaction between identical molecules. Proc. Nat. Acad. Sci. *36:* 238–246.
Jehle, H. 1957. Proc. Nat. Acad. Sci. *43*.
Jordan, P. 1938. The specific attraction between gene molecules. Z. f. Physik. *39:* 711–714.
Jordan, P. 1939. Quantum mechanical resonance attraction and the problem of immunity reaction. Z. f. Physik. *113:* 431–438.
Jordan, P. 1941. The specificity of antibodies, enzymes, viruses, and genes. Naturwiss. *29:* 89–100.
Jordan, P. 1947. Eiweissmolekule. Stuttgart.
Klotz, I. M. 1953. in Neurath & Bailey, The Proteins. Academic Press Inc., New York.
Kallmann, H. and M. Willstaetter. 1932. Naturwiss. *20:* 952.
Kirkwood, J. G. and Shumaker, J. B. 1952a. Dipolement fluctuations. Proc. Nat. Ac. Sci. *38:* 855–862.
Kirkwood, J. G. and Shumaker, J. B. 1952b. Forces between protein molecules. Proc. Nat. Ac. Sci. *38:* 863–871.
Kramers, H. A. and Kronig, R. de L. 1928. Absorption und Dispersion. Z. f. Physik. *48:* 174–179. Also in Collected Scientific Papers.
Levine, S. 1946. Trans. Farad. Soc. *42B:* 102.
Levine, S. 1948. Trans. Farad. Soc. *44:* 833.
London, F. 1930. Z. f. physik. Chemie. *B 11:* 222.
London, F. 1937. The general theory of molecular forces. Trans. Farad. Soc. *33:* 8–26.
London, F. 1942. Centers of van der Waals attraction. Jour. Phys. Chem. *46:* 305–316.
Mudd, S. 1932. A hypothetical mechanism of antibody production. J. Immunol. *23:* 423–427.
Muller, H. J. 1922. Variation due to change in the individual gene. Amer. Naturalist. *56:* 32–50.
Muller, H. J. 1937. Physics in the attack on the fundamental problems of genetics. Scientific Monthly *44:* 210–214.

Muller, H. J. 1941. Resume and perspectives of the symposium on genes and chromosomes. Cold Spring Harbor Symposia Quant. Biol. *9:* 290–308.
Muller, H. J. 1947. The gene. Pilgrim Trust Lecture. Proc. Roy. Soc. Ser. B: Biol. Sc. *134:* 1–37.
Muller, H. J. 1950. Development of the gene theory, in 'Genetics in the 20th century'. Macmillan. pp. 77–99.
Onsager, L. 1933. Chem. Revs. *13:* 73.
Overbeek, J. Th. G. 1948. in Verwey & Overbeek. Lyophobic Colloids. Elsevier Press.
Overbeek, J. Th. G. 1952. in Kruyt, Colloids. Elsevier Press.
Overbeek, J. Th. G. and M. J. Sparnaay 1954. in Trans. Farad. Soc. Disc. on Coagulation and Flocculation. *18:* 9–23.
Oparin, A. I. 1938. Origin of Life. Macmillan Co. (Dover, new edition) with comments by S. Morgulis.
Pauling, L. 1940. Theory of the structure and process of formation of antibodies. J. Am. Chem. Soc. *62:* 2643–2657.
Pauling, L. and M. Delbruck. 1940. Nature of the intermolecular forces operative in biological processes. Science *92:* 77–79.
Pauling, L., Campbell, D. H., and Pressman, D. 1943. Physiol. Rev. *23:* 203.
Pauling, L. 1948. Nature *161:* 707.
Pauling, L. 1957. Probability of errors in the process of synthesis of protein molecules, Stoll Festschrift. Birkhaeuser, 597–602.
Rabinowitch, E. and Epstein, Leo F. 1941. Polymerization of dyestuffs in solution. J. Am. Chem. Soc. *63:* 69.
Verwey, E. J. W. and J. Th. G. Overbeek. 1946. Trans. Farad. Soc. *42 B:* 117.
Verwey, E. J. W. and J. Th. G. Overbeek. 1948. Theory of the Stability of Lyophobic Colloids. Elsevier Press.
Vinograd, J. R. 1935. in Freundlich, Thixotropy, Paris.
Wang, S. C. 1927. Phys. Z. *28:* 663.
Weiss, Paul. 1949. in Parpart (Ed), Chemistry and Physiology of Growth, Princeton Univ. Press.
Weiss, Paul. 1951. in Jeffress (Ed), Hixon Symposium. Wiley.
Weiss, Paul. 1953. Morphol. *1:* (part 3), 181.
Weiss, Paul. 1955. in Butler (Ed.), Biological Specificity and Growth. Princeton Univ. Press.
Wyckoff, R. W. G. 1949. Electron Microscopy. Interscience.
Wyckoff, R. W. G. 1951. Amer. Scientist *39:* 561.
Wyckoff, R. W. G. Science in Progress, 7th series, p. 203.
Wyckoff, R. W. G. and L. W. Labaw. 1955. Exp. Cell Research. Suppl. *3:* 395.
Yos, J. M. 1956. Ph.D. Thesis, University of Nebraska.
Yos, J. M., Bade, W. L. and Jehle, H. 1957. Proc. Nat. Acad. Sci. *43:* 341–346.

PROFESSOR PITZER (University of California): I was not entirely clear as to just the sort of low frequency terms that you had in mind. Are these molecular vibrations, that is, ordinary molecular vibration terms?

PROFESSOR JEHLE: Low frequency oscillators, i.e. oscillators whose frequencies lie in the infrared, and charge fluctuations whose relaxation times correspond to very low frequencies, play a role in specific London interactions provided their polarizabilities are strong enough according to the criteria laid down in the paper. Let me come back to your question in a few moments.

PROFESSOR PITZER: But surely we know the visible and most of the other important regions of the spectrum for these substances, so this is essentially an answerable question, is it not?

PROFESSOR KIRKWOOD (Yale University): I was just going to ask the same question as Professor Pitzer. You are definitely excluding structural vibrations; you admit that the magnitudes of the effects are too small in those instances.

PROFESSOR JEHLE: As concerns the usual structural vibrations effects, their polarizabilities are very small indeed, so we can ignore them. There are, however, some very strong absorption bands in the 3 μ region in liquid H_2O (Earl K. Plyler and N. Acquista, J. Opt. Soc. Am. 1954. *44:* 505–506) and correspondingly proteins and nucleic acids in their natural aqueous surrounding are expected to have some interesting absorption in that region. Before the intensity of this band is actually established and before the cause for the unexpected strength of this band is understood, I hesitate to state that its significance for London interactions is negligible, even though on a first inspection this band makes but a small contribution. As concerns the charge fluctuations which Kirkwood and Shumaker have investigated, they contribute very strongly to our $\mathcal{W}_0$ terms, if one uses the magnitudes of the terms proposed by these authors, so that even if their estimated values would have to be reduced, there still would be a most significant contribution to our $\mathcal{W}_0$ values. Anisotropy will lend itself to providing for several $\mathcal{W}_0$ components.

PROFESSOR KIRKWOOD: In regard to the second remark of Professor Pitzer, there is some argument about the positions of the electronic states in macromolecules such as protein which is connected with proposals, which I do not think are accepted, that one may have, due to conjugation or hyperconjugation of some sort, a band structure analogous to that in metals. If one has that, then your considerations might apply. However, it is probably true that the ground electronic state of macromolecules, such as proteins and probably nucleic acids, are nondegenerate and that the first energy of excitation is too high to be excited under ordinary conditions of experimentation and ordinary temperatures.

There is another point I want to bring up. It is also true that in the case of macromolecules (and this was pointed out by London and elaborated upon by Overbeek), quite apart from the Casimir corrections, it is not a very good approximation to expand the interaction into multipole terms when the separation between the centers is comparable with the dimensions of the molecules. London, himself, pointed out something which has not been exploited to any great extent. That is, probably it is only important in conjugated systems where one does have resonance extending over a fairly large distance that one can get some very special effects in ordinary van der Waals forces, if the matrix elements of the dipole moment correspond to charge separations which are comparable with the distance of separation of the macromolecules.

PROFESSOR JEHLE: With respect to the first part of your remarks I should like to say that ultraviolet electronic transitions naturally play a very important role in the specificity of London forces. If, in addition, there should be low frequency electronic transitions, this would be interesting, presumably they would have strong polarizabilities. And it will be important to know whether or not there are excited electronic states (which usually have strong polarizabilities) which are in thermal reach.

With regard to the second part of your remarks, referring to the Casimir corrections, it is to be expected that these are negligible in the case of compact macromolecules of about 50 Angstrom diameter—because the range of their specific interaction might be of the order of at most a few times that diameter, which is small compared with the vacuum wavelength of the highest frequency electronic transitions.

I agree with Dr. Kirkwood's last remark. As we have pointed out, the procedure of taking only dipole terms in the expansion is just a very handy, useful approximation which greatly simplifies the problem.

As to the preceding questions relative to the magnitude of the polarizabilities, we felt that the reasonable approach to this problem of the relevance of the specificity of the London force is to answer first of all the question, "For what kinds of oscillator polarizabilities and for which molecular structures and for what kinds of detunings, is the discriminating effect of the London interaction strong enough, at a given separation R, to understand biological specificities on the basis of London force."

The Forces Between Protein Molecules in Solution[1]

John G. Kirkwood

Yale University, New Haven, Conn.

UNTIL THERE IS CONVINCING EVIDENCE to the contrary, it is reasonable to accept the hypothesis that the forces between protein molecules are of the same nature as those acting between simple molecules of low molecular weight. At small intermolecular distances quantum mechanical exchange produces a repulsion which determines the size and shape of the molecules. At larger distances the London dispersion forces act to produce a general van der Waals attraction. Moreover, since proteins are amphoteric polymers of the highly polar amino acids, many of which possess acidic or basic side chains, the molecules undoubtedly possess characteristic distributions of electric charge which give rise to strong electrostatic interactions. Evidence for the dominant role of electrostatic forces is provided by the sensitivity of the thermodynamic interaction of protein molecules to ionic strength. The reduction in interaction with increasing ionic strength, frequently observed, is produced by the screening action of the statistical space charge of the electrolytic environment. It is easy to demonstrate that such screening could be effective only on that part of the interaction which is electrostatic in origin and not on the high frequency exchange forces and van der Waals forces.

Although of the same basic origin as those between simple molecules, the forces between protein molecules possess special features arising from their complex sturctural organization. These special features relate to the pattern of arrangement of the structural elements responsible for the specificity of interaction and to the mobility of the charges responsible for electrostatic interaction. The special forces arising from the mobility of the charge distributions have received theoretical treatment by Kirkwood and Shumaker (1952). They will be the principal subject of this discussion. Proteins, considered as ampholites, contain a large number of neutral and negatively charged basic groups, for example, NH_2 and COO—, to which protons are bound to a degree determined by the pH. Except in highly acid solutions, the number of basic sites generally exceeds the number of protons bound to the molecule so that

[1] Summary of a lecture presented at the symposium, "Molecular Structure and Biological Specificity" in Washington, D. C., March 1955 and at the symposium on Biocolloids in Gatlinburg, Tennessee in April 1955.

there exist many possible configurations of the protons, differing little in free energy among which fluctuations induced by thermal motion, may occur. Fluctuations in the number and configuration of the mobile protons impart to the molecules fluctuating charges and fluctuating electric multipole moments. Let us consider two protein molecules in fixed orientation separated by a distance R. As the result of fluctuations in charge distribution, associated with the Brownian motion of the mobile protons, each molecule produces an alternating electric field at the point of location of its neighbor. These alternating electric fields produce in turn a mutual electrical polarization of the average proton distributions on the two molecules. When averaged over a time long relative to the periods of Brownian motion, this polarization gives rise to the supplementary attractive force between the two molecules with a potential diminishing asymptotically as $1/R^2$. In the presence of an electrolytic environment, the long range of this force is substantially diminished by Debye-Hückel screening. Fluctuations in charge and charge configuration associated with bound ions other than protons also make a contribution to this special type of intermolecular force.

Although it is not in general possible to distinguish between the fluctuating and static electrical interaction between protein molecules by thermodynamic measurements, that part of the fluctuating force arising from total charge fluctuation is a salt-free isoionic solution may be isolated from effects due to all other intermolecular forces, since it gives rise to a term in the excess chemical potential proportional to the square root of the protein concentration, while all other intermolecular forces, both van der Waals forces and electrostatic forces associated with permanent and fluctuating multipoles, contribute only terms proportional to the first and higher powers of the concentration. Timasheff, Dintzis, Kirkwood and Coleman (1955) have carried out measurements of the excess chemical potential and activity coefficient of isoionic bovine serum albumin by the well known technique of light-scattering. Their results verify the prediction of the theory of Kirkwood and Shumaker that the excess chemical potential should decrease asymptotically with the square root of protein concentration at high dilutions, as a consequence of the long range interaction produced by fluctuations in total charge. They determine the value of 3.5 protonic units for the root-mean-square charge fluctuation of a molecule of BSA in isoionic solutions. This value is in excellent agreement with value 3.4 which has been calculated from the titration date of Tanford. Similar measurements, to be reported later, have been carried out on human serum mercaptalbumin and bovine serum mercaptalbumin. The results may be quantitatively interpreted by means of the charge fluctuation theory.

Kirkwood (1955) has recently used the concept of interaction through charge fluctuations to provide an interesting explanation for the participation of the protein moiety of an enzyme molecule in the mechanism of hydrolytic enzymatic reactions. If it is supposed that the catalytic site of the enzyme is situated at the center of a constellation of vicinal basic groups, and if there is a substantial increase in dipole moment in the activation of the catalytic site-substrate complex to its transition state, interaction by the fluctuation mechanism between the basic groups and their attached protons with the dipole moment of the activated complex, can substantially diminish the free energy of activation, in a predictable manner dependent upon pH. One of the interesting features of this interaction is that it passes through a maximum at a pH equal to the pK of the conjugate acids of the participating basic groups. A consistent analysis of the pH dependence of the rates of hydrolysis of esters and amides by a group of representative enzymes has been achieved by the theory.

It seems reasonable to predict that the role of the fluctuation force will turn out to be important and, in certain instances, decisive in many other examples of interaction between protein molecules in solution. It is clear that highly specific interactions might well arise from the fluctuation mechanism if the concept of complementary patterns is invoked. In favorable orientations, steric matching of a constellation on the other could well produce a redistribution of protons leading to a strong specific interaction depending upon the local structural details of the complementary constellations. Considerations relating to the specificity of the fluctuation force, as in the case of other types of interaction, must necessarily remain speculative until more detailed knowledge of the fine structure of proteins is available.

References

Kirkwood, J. G. 1955. The Physical Chemistry of Enzymes. General Discussion of the Faraday Society, No. 20, p. 78. Aberdeen University Press, Ltd.

Kirkwood, J. G. and J. B. Shumaker. 1952. Proc. Nat. Acad. Sci. *38:* 863.

Timasheff, S. N., H. M. Dintzis, J. G. Kirkwood and B. D. Coleman. 1955. Proc. Nat. Acad. Sci. *41:* 710.

Hydrogen Bonding

Jerry Donohue

University of Southern California, Los Angeles, Calif.

MUCH OF THE DISCUSSION so far has been concerned with macromolecules, but we shall now bring the scale down a bit and discuss smaller molecules that have only a dozen or so atoms, because I think that unless we can understand what goes on in these simple substances there isn't much point in trying to worry about the much more complicated systems.

Before discussing the properties of hydrogen bonds in various kinds of crystals and molecules, it will be useful to set forth certain general principles which govern the formation of such bonds. In most biological systems, hydrogen bond donors are the groupings $—\overset{+}{N}—H$ (with two further bonds on N), $>N—H$, or $—O—H$, while hydrogen bond acceptors are generally oxygen or nitrogen atoms, although chloride ion acceptors occur also. One sort of evidence which was formerly invoked to demonstrate the existence of a hydrogen bond was the occurrence of an abnormally short intermolecular distance, such as is found in the dimers of carboxylic acids

$$R—C\begin{matrix} // O \cdots H—O \backslash \\ \backslash O—H \cdots O // \end{matrix}C—R.$$

Here the distance between oxygen atoms is several tenths of an Angstrom shorter than for a normal van der Waals contact. Since the hydrogen atoms in a crystal are not in general located directly by X-ray crystallographic methods, their positions can be inferred from the positions found for the heavier atoms in the following way. If the reasonable assumption is made that the geometrical properties of the hydrogen bond donor group are not appreciably altered by hydrogen bond formation, then the resultant groupings, O—H ··· O, N—H ··· O, and the like, are expected to be very nearly linear. Variation of more than about 25° from linearity is rare. It follows that the directly observed angles, such as C—O···O in the carboxylic acid dimers, will be close to those expected for the covalent bond angle, C—O—H. In the case of the donor group $C—\overset{+}{N}H_3$ (C—N with three H) all six angles (three

C—N ··· O and three O ··· N ··· O) should be close to the expected tetrahedral value. Moreover, it has been found that all available donor groups are usually involved in hydrogen bonds—the presence in a crystal of a possible donor hydrogen atom which does not enter into hydrogen bonding is very unusual.

One of the simplest substances in which a hydrogen bond occurs is hydrazine dihydrochloride (Donohue and Lipscomb, 1947), the structure of which is shown in Fig. 1. The chloride ions are arranged about the positive ions so that the angles N—N···Cl are very nearly tetrahedral. The $N_2H_6^{++}$ ions lie on three-fold axes, so each—NH_3^+ group forms hydrogen bonds to three equivalent close Cl^- neighbors. There is a fourth chloride ion at very nearly the same distance from the nitrogen atom, but reference to Fig. 1 shows that it lies on the extension of the N—N axis, so that, if the angle N—N—H is near the expected tetrahedral value, hydrogen bond formation is geometrically impossible, and the criterion of an abnormally short distance obviously cannot be applied in this case to show the presence of a hydrogen bond.

The geometry of the hydrogen bond system in hydrazine hydrochloride is easy to grasp because of the high (cubic) symmetry of the crystals. For more complicated crystals, those in which the picture is not quite so clear, I have

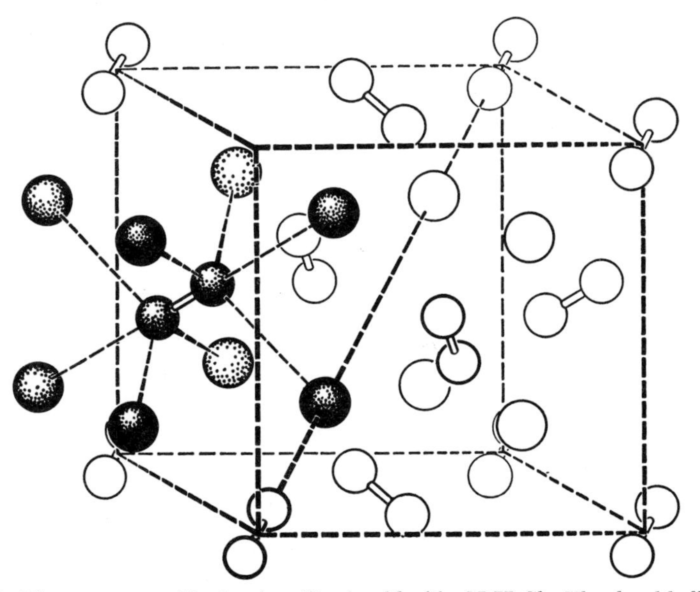

FIG. 1. The structure of hydrazine dihydrochloride, $N_2H_6Cl_2$. The dumbbell shaped groups represent the $N_2H_6^{++}$ groups, the larger spheres represent the chloride ions. Hydrogen atoms are not shown. Note the staggered (ethane-like) configuration of the chloride ions about the hydrazinium ions.

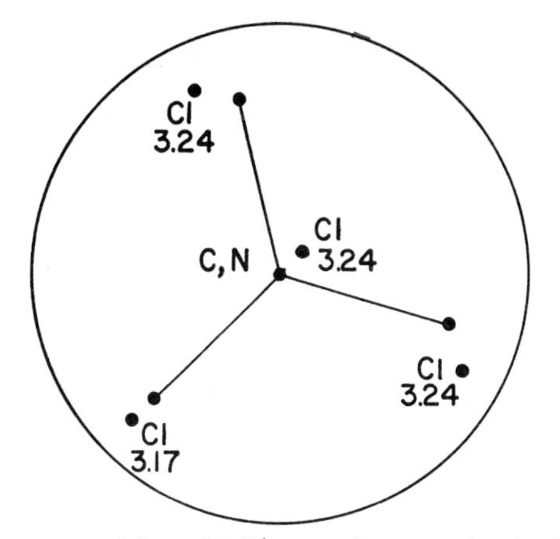

FIG. 2. The environment of the —NH_3^+ group in geranylamine hydrochloride shown in stereographic projection. The numbers give the distances, in Å, of each chloride ion from the nitrogen atom. The assumed configurations of the amino hydrogen atoms are also shown as filled circles connected to the nitrogen atom by solid lines. Note that in projection the angles H—N—H are all 120°. The angles C—N···Cl are all seen to be a little less than tetrahedral, but the —NH_3^+ can be rotated so that each N—H direction very nearly coincides with an N···Cl direction.

used the method of stereographic projection[1] to show the environment of the hydrogen-bond-forming groups.

The close chloride ion neighbors of the —NH_3^+ groups in crystals of geranylamine hydrochloride (Jeffrey, 1945) are shown in stereographic projection in Fig. 2. The directions of the hydrogen atoms, assuming that the angles C—N—H and H—N—H are all tetrahedral, are shown as small filled circles.

[1] The properties and method of construction of stereographic projections may be found in almost any standard work on morphological crystallography. The projection, as used in this discussion on amino acids, is made in the following way: The α-carbon to amino-nitrogen atom covalent bond is chosen as the polar axis of a sphere, with the NH_3^+ group in the center of that sphere. Lines to the bonded hydrogen atoms and near oxygen neighbors of the nitrogen atom are then drawn from the center of the sphere to its surface. This point of intersection is then connected by a straight line with the opposite pole of sphere. The stereographic projection consists of the intersections of these lines with the equatorial plane. The directions, relative to the C—N bond, of the neighbors close enough to form hydrogen bonds to the nitrogen atom, are then shown in the projection. If the angle C—N···O is 90°, the projected oxygen atom lies on the circumference of the projection. Some feeling for angle values can be obtained from some of the following figures by noting that the angles C—N—H were all set equal to 109°28′. Oxygen atoms located so that the angle C—N···O is greater than that value will project closer to the center of the projection. Since the projection shows angular relations only, the distances of close neighbors are indicated.

All three hydrogen atoms of the $—NH_3^+$ group can be brought, by rotation of this group about the C—N bond, into positions such that the angles between N—H and N ··· Cl are agreeably small. There is here, as in the case of hydrazine dihydrochloride, a fourth close Cl^- neighbor for which hydrogen bond formation is not possible because of the unacceptably large value for the angle C—N ··· Cl. This "head-on" sort of contact occurs not infrequently, as we shall see below.

In hydroxylammonium chloride (Jerslev, 1948), $HO—NH_3^+ \cdot Cl^-$, the situation, shown in Fig. 3, is quite similar in that the $—NH_3^+$ group forms three hydrogen bonds to neighboring chloride ions, and that there is a fourth chloride ion contact head-on. It is noteworthy that this last chloride ion is closer to the nitrogen atom than two of the other three, so the distance criterion breaks down here also.

This treatment works well on the amino acids which have been investigated. In Fig. 4, the hydrogen bonding in DL-alanine (Levy and Corey, 1941; Donohue, 1950) is shown, and in Fig. 5, that in L-threonine (Shoemaker, Donohue, Schomaker, and Corey, 1950). Another example of the head-on contact occurs in L-threonine. It is remarkable in these complicated structures, such as L-threonine, where there are four hydrogen atoms available for hydrogen bond formation (three on the $—NH_3^+$ group, and one on the hydroxyl group on the γ-carbon atom) that geometrically acceptable hydrogen bonds are formed by all of them.

A more complex structure, that of the dipeptide β-glycylglycine (Hughes and Moore, 1949), is shown in Fig. 6, where it is seen that the environment of the $—NH_3^+$ group is quite satisfactory. It might be expected that there would be

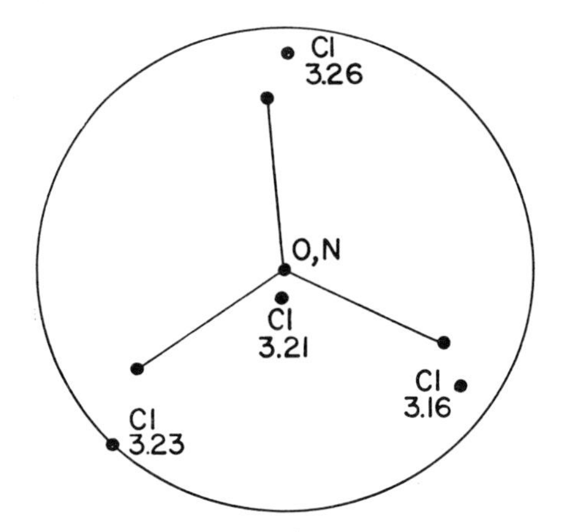

FIG. 3. The environment of the $—NH_3^+$ group in hydroxylammonium chloride shown in stereographic projection. The chloride ion at 3.23Å projects onto the circumference of the projection, indicating that the angle O—N···Cl is 90°.

some correlation between N ··· O distance and the deviation of the angle N—H ··· O from 180°, but the available data appears to indicate that a nice smooth function which relates these two parameters probably does not exist. In the case of β-glycylglycine this fact is obvious, since the shortest hydrogen bond, with N ··· O distance of 2.68 Å, shows a deviation of about 10°, but in the case of a second bond which is very nearly linear, a longer N ··· O distance of 2.80 Å is observed.

The situation in a still more complex structure, histidine hydrochloride monohydrate (Donohue, Lavine, and Rollett, 1956) is shown in Fig. 7. In this crystal

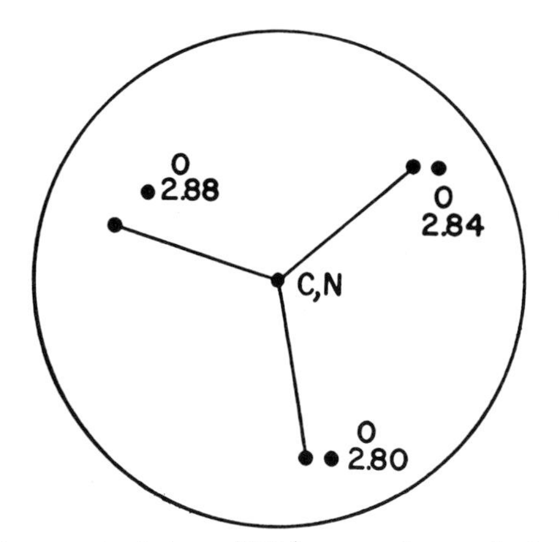

FIG. 4. The environment of the $-NH_3^+$ group in DL-alanine shown in stereographic projection.

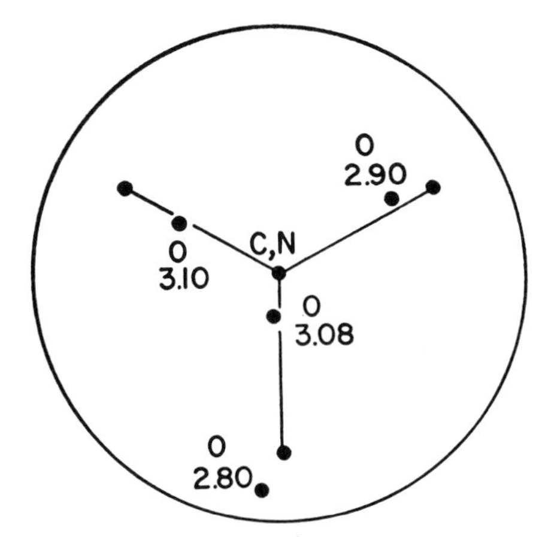

FIG. 5. The environment of the $-NH_3^+$ group in L-threonine shown in stereo graphic projection.

the—NH_3^+ groups have two different sorts of hydrogen bond acceptor neighbors, but everything appears to be quite normal.

The very first amino acid whose structure was determined was glycine (Albrecht and Corey, 1939). In this crystal, the amino group was found to have four close oxygen neighbors, but the angular relations were such that none of these was of the head-on type. The orientation of the—NH_3^+, as postulated by Albrecht and Corey, with its neighbors, is shown in Fig. 8. As can be seen, when the—NH_3^+ group is rotated to minimize the angular deviation in the case of the two bonds of length 2.76 Å and 2.88 Å, the third hydrogen atom

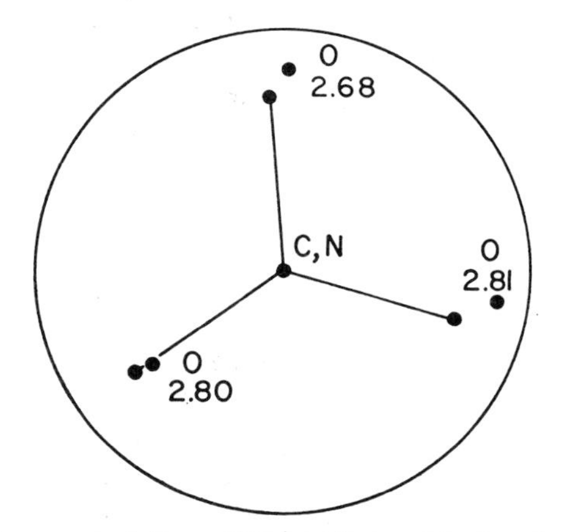

FIG. 6. The environment of the —NH_3^+ in β-glycylglycine shown in stereographic projection.

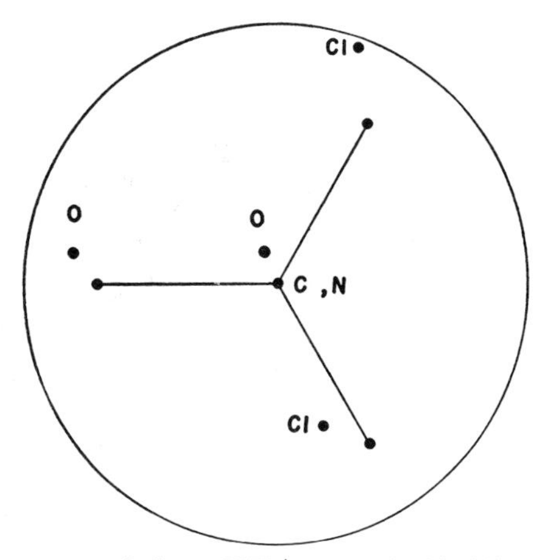

FIG. 7. The environment of the —NH_3^+ group in histidine hydrochloride monohydrate shown in stereographic projection.

lies between the other two close oxygen neighbors, giving a bifurcated hydrogen bond. It was later pointed out that the normal coordination number to be expected for hydrogen is two, and that bifurcated hydrogen bonds should occur rarely (Pauling, 1940). It is possible that a refinement of glycine structure would remove this rather unusual kind of hydrogen bond, since the original study was made many years before the present refinement techniques had been developed.

There have been several other compounds in which bifurcated hydrogen bonds were postulated. Iodic acid (Rogers and Helmholz, 1941) is such an example: an alternate interpretation of the X-ray results was later given by Wells (1949), who showed that the data were consistent with an arrangement without the bifurcated hydrogen bonds. The same is true in the case of dicyandiamide (Hughes, 1940), where the original interpretation included a bifurcated hydrogen bond, but it has since been shown (Donohue, 1952) that this interpretation is probably not correct.

Recently there appeared the results of the determination of the structure of sulfamic acid (Kanda and King, 1951), in which there were said to be *two* bifurcated hydrogen bonds. The results were said to indicate that in the crystals the molecule was in the zwitter ion form, $^{-}O_3S—NH_3^{+}$. The environment of one sulfamic acid molecule with the assumed hydrogen bonds is shown in Fig. 9. Clearly we have here a very complex situation: each molecule has twelve close neighbors; normally we would expect three close hydrogen bond acceptors and three close hydrogen bond donors, leaving the other six neighbors as van der Waals contacts, if there are no bifurcated hydrogen bonds. The environment of the nitrogen atom, projected down the S-N axis, is shown in Fig. 10. In this and the following figures, the notation of the original paper has been re-

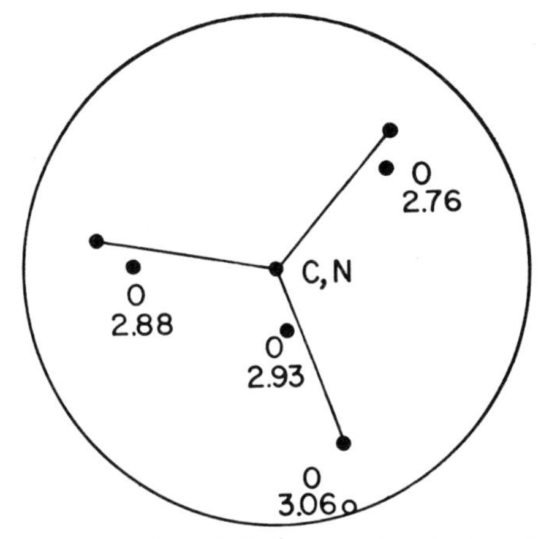

FIG. 8. The environment of the $—NH_3^{+}$ group in glycine shown in stereographic projection. The oxygen atom at 3.06Å is shown as an open circle, indicating that the angle C—N···O is a little less than 90°.

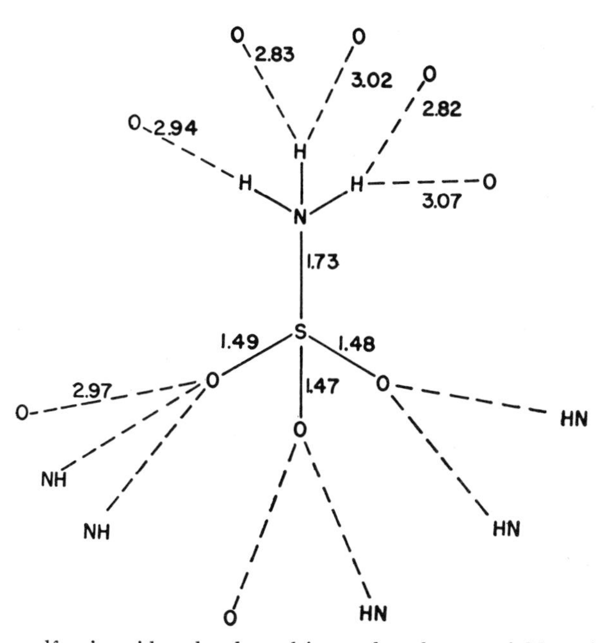

FIG. 9. One sulfamic acid molecule and its twelve closest neighbors in the crystal, showing the hydrogen bond system suggested by Kanda and King. Note the presence of two bifurcated hydrogen bonds.

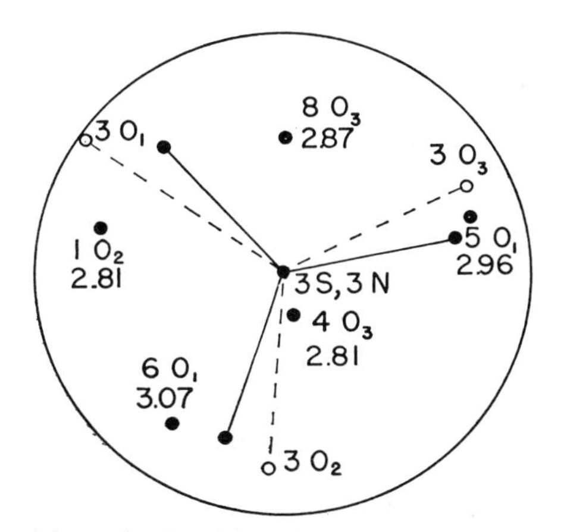

FIG. 10. Stereographic projection down the S—N bond in sulfamic acid. The number prefixes for each atom give which of the eight equivalent molecules in the unit cell that atom belongs to. The numbering of Kanda and King has been retained. The dotted lines and open circles give the orientation of the $—SO_3$ part of the molecule, the solid lines and filled circles give the best orientation for the $-NH_3$ part of the molecule. Note that when the $—NH_3$ group is rotated to bring two of the hydrogen atoms as close as possible to oxygen atoms, the third hydrogen atom (upper left) is in a position unfavorable for hydrogen bond formation.

tained. The numerical prefixes for each atom refer to the several different equivalent sulfamic acid molecules in the unit cell; molecule 3 was the one chosen for examination. Fig. 10 shows, accordingly, the atoms $3O_1$ and $3O_2$ and $3O_3$ (dotted, since they are below the reference plane) and the five close oxygen neighbors from other molecules, of the nitrogen atom, 3N. The $—NH_3^+$ group has been rotated so that the N—H bonds point as nearly as possible toward the oxygen atoms. The contacts $3N \cdots 6O_1$, and $3N \cdots 5O_1$ are possible hydrogen bonds, but this leaves the third hydrogen atom in an unfavorable position; moreover, the contact $3N \cdots 4O_3$ obviously cannot possibly correspond to a hydrogen bond. Note also that the best orientation of the $—NH_3^+$ is eclipsed with respect to the $—SO_3$ group.

Strangely enough, there has not been too much work on whether sulfamic acid is indeed a zwitter ion. The only evidence cited is its high melting point of about 200°C, but this is not really very conclusive, as there are other amides which melt even higher—oxamide, for example, melts at well over 400°C.

Since assumption of the zwitter ion formula does not lead to a very satisfactory hydrogen bonding system, the possibility should be explored that atoms bonded to the central sulfur atom have been incorrectly identified. (The X-ray method is capable of distinguishing between atomic numbers 7 and 8 only if the intensities have been carefully estimated and if the refinement is carried out to a sufficient degree.) We shall then have the formulation

```
 HO
   \
 O—S—NH2 ,
   /
  O
```

and should expect the S—OH bond distance to be quite a bit longer than both the $S—NH_2$ and the two S—O bonds, all of which should all be approximately the same length. The one long bond to the sulfur atom (see Fig. 9) then fixes the atom labelled "N" as the hydroxyl oxygen atom, and the problem is now reduced to deciding which of the atoms labelled "O" is the amide nitrogen. It is found that one of the two close neighbors of atom "O_2", namely, atom $1O_1$, is in a position such that the angle $S—O_2 \cdots O$, is 175°; atom O_2, therefore, cannot be the amide nitrogen. This situation is not found with regard to either atoms O_1 or O_3. The stereographic projection of the environment of atom O_1 is shown in Fig. 11. If atom O_1 is really the amide nitrogen, then we should expect a planar system of bonds about it, and in projection this atom and those with which it is forming hydrogen bonds should be on a straight line. This is almost achieved, and the corresponding hydrogen bonding is shown in Fig. 12.

There is, on the other hand, the possibility that atom "O_3" is the amide nitrogen, since the projection of its environment, shown in Fig. 13, is not unsatisfactory. The corresponding hydrogen bonding is shown in Fig. 14.

Since the accuracy of the original investigation is of the order of ±0.1 Å it is not possible to decide which of the above possibilities is the right one, but

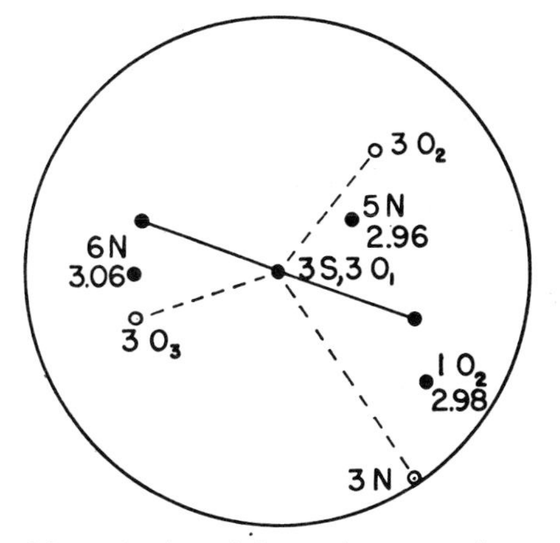

FIG. 11. Stereographic projection of the environment of atom O_1 in sulfamic acid. If this atom is in fact the nitrogen atom, possible positions for its two bonded hydrogen atoms are shown by the solid line and attached filled circles. The orientation of the —S(O)(OH)—O group relative to the $—NH_2$ group is shown, as in Fig. 10, with dotted lines.

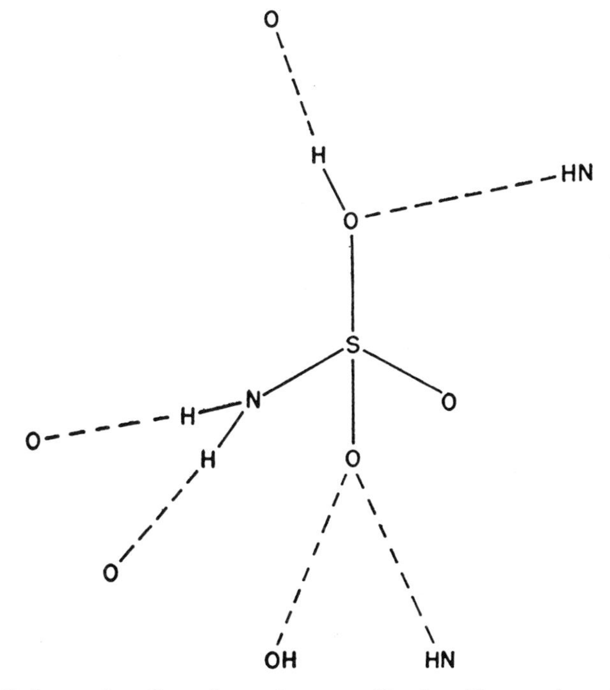

FIG. 12. Hydrogen bonding scheme for one sulfamic acid assuming atom O_1 is the nitrogen atom. The orientation of the molecule is the same as in Fig. 9.

it appears, on the basis of the data presently available, that sulfamic acid may well not be a zwitter ion in the crystals.

In addition to these simple substances, a knowledge of hydrogen bonding is of course important in discussion of the more complicated molecules, such as

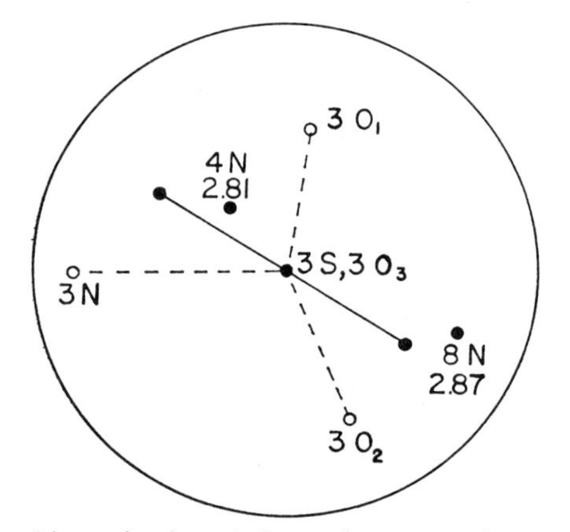

FIG. 13. Stereographic projection of the environment of atom O_3 in sulfamic acid. Remarks in the legend for Fig. 11 apply here also.

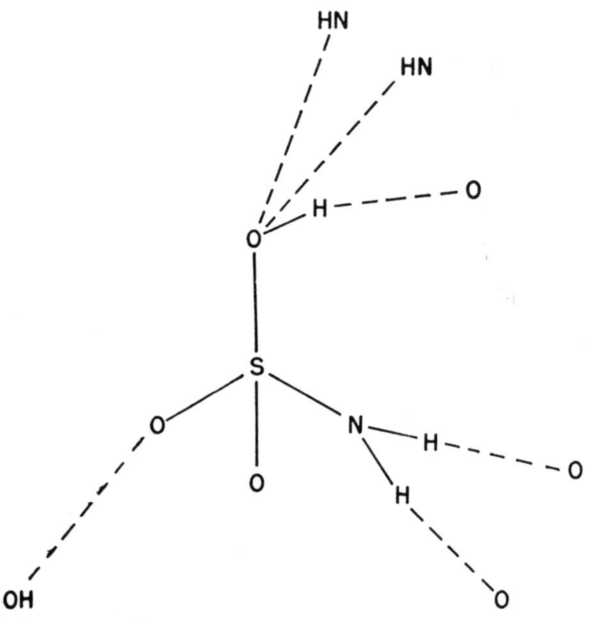

FIG. 14. Hydrogen bonding scheme for one sulfamic acid molecule assuming atom O_3 is the nitrogen atom.

proteins, which are the subject of other papers in this symposium. In this case the models must come first, and these models must be based on the precise geometry as obtained from x-ray results on crystals of the simple substances. As is well-known, that is the way the α and γ helical structures for polypeptides were discovered (Pauling and Corey, 1950)—they were *not* discovered by taking X-ray photographs of hemoglobin or any other protein; they were discovered by first making use of results such as those discussed above, and then looking about in nature to see if one of them could be found somewhere. With regard to a number of proteins of the fibrous variety, undoubtedly they do have the α-helix structure, but in the case of a large number of other ones—and these are the proteins which have had the most work done on them, insulin, hemoglobin, ribonuclease—we must, I think, say that it is a Scottish verdict, of neither innocent nor guilty, but "not proven," as to whether these have a basic α-helix structure.

There are two other polypeptide helices (Low and Baybutt, 1952; Donohue, 1953), discovered some time after the α-helix, which are not too improbable on structural grounds, and which might have some significance in nature. These are shown in Fig. 15. The α-helix lies between them with regard to diameter, pitch, and number of residues per turn. It has not yet been shown whether either one of these, or the γ-helix which was found at the same time as the α-helix, exists in either native proteins or synthetic polypeptides.

Quite recently, knowledge of hydrogen bonding was of great help in postulating a structure for nucleic acid (Watson and Crick, 1953). The basic part of the Watson-Crick structure for deoxyribonucleic acid is shown in Fig. 16. The entire structure consists of two polynucleotide chains joined by hydrogen bonds between their bases, which are adenine, thymine, guanine, and cytosine. Since the bonds in the two chains from the base nitrogen to the carbon atom of each deoxyribose residue are related by a two-fold axis, the sequence of the bases on one chain is immaterial because the position of the base-nitrogen to sugar-carbon bonds relative to the axis of the helix is the same for all four bases. However, for example, whenever adenine occurs on one chain, thymine must occur opposite it on the other, so that the sequence on one chain fixes that on the other. This gives the pairing which made the biologists so happy when this structure was discovered.

I think it is fruitful to attack this nucleic acid problem in much the same way that the polypeptide problem was attacked, that is, to work with models made according to interbond distances and angles from previous work on simpler substances, and see what can be put together without any regard whatever as to what nature is doing. Then, after some acceptable structures have been found, one should look around and see if they exist in the natural substances.

There is a different way of putting together these four bases (Fig. 17) so that they pair in the same way as in the Watson-Crick DNA structure. One pleasing feature of the Watson-Crick structure is that it predicts the observed ana-

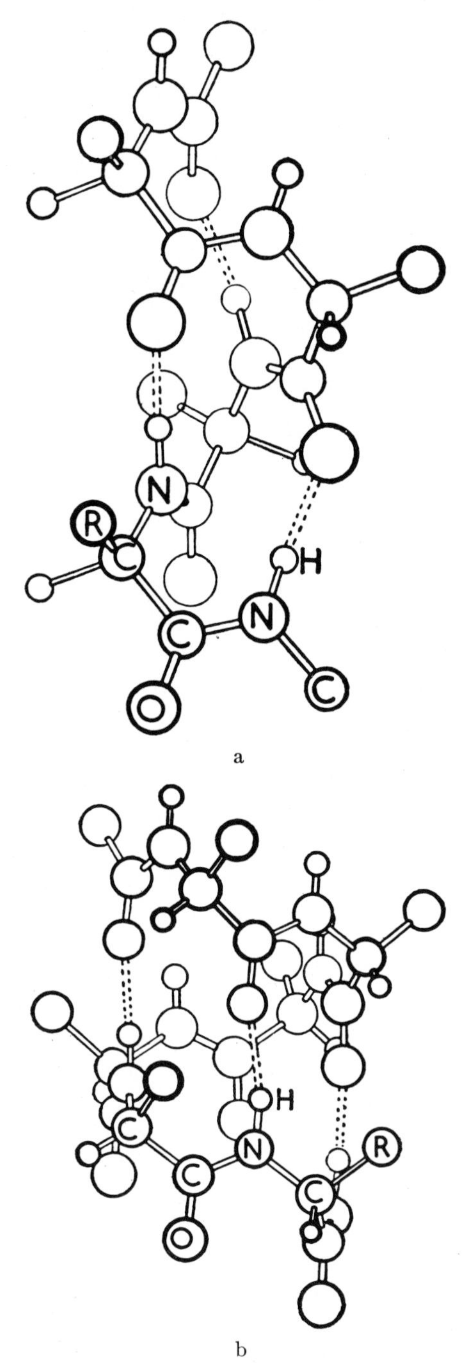

Fig. 15. Two structurally acceptable hydrogen bonded helical configurations of the polypeptide chain. (a) The 3.0_{10} helix. (b) The 4.4_{16} helix. The α-helix of Pauling and Corey (3.6_{13}) lies between these in pitch, diameter, and number of residues per turn.

lytical results that in DNA the adenine content equals the thymine content, and the guanine content equals the cytosine content, even though the ratio of thymine to cytosine may vary widely from one source of DNA to another. The structure shown in Fig. 17 will also lead to this composition. This structure, however, has a two-fold axis coincident with the helical axis, instead of perpendicular to it as in the Watson-Crick structure, and is therefore not in agreement with the X-ray data for DNA.

If we restrict ourselves to two-chain structures involving only pairs of bases, there are a number of other possibilities. Fig. 18 shows the arrangement for chains which contain only the two purines, adenine and guanine. This represents the basis of a molecule containing adenine alone, guanine alone, or both

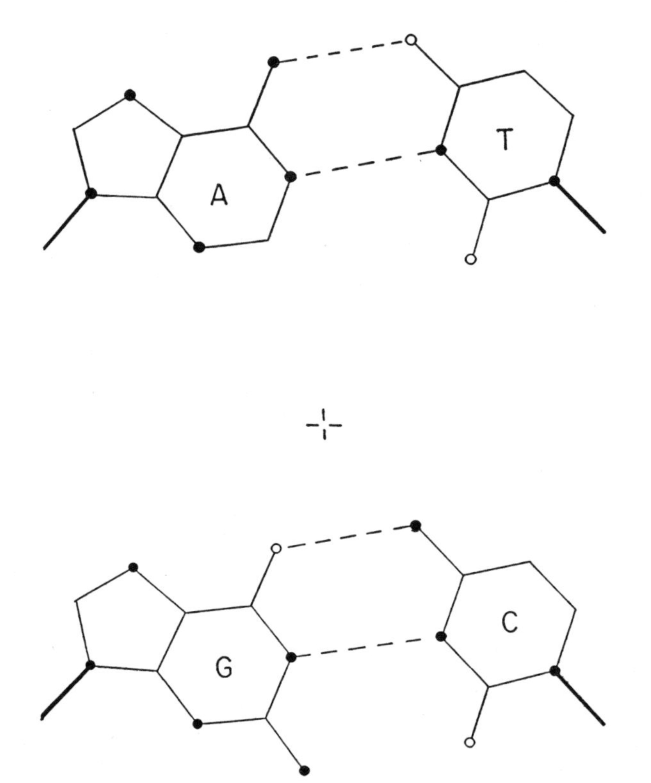

FIG. 16. The pairing of the four bases, adenine (A), thymine (T), guanine (G), and cytosine (C), in the Watson-Circle deoxyribonucleic acid structure. Nitrogen atoms are shown as filled circles, oxygen atoms as open circles, hydrogen bonds as dashed lines. The bonds from the bases to the sugar residues are shown as heavy lines. This structure agrees well with the X-ray data.

together if the two chains are complementary. Fig. 19 shows a corresponding possibility in the case of the pyrimidines, thymine and cytosine.

Systematic attack of this problem has shown (Donohue, 1956) that there are 24 possible pairings, and that of these, there are 5 pairs of pairs which can give rise to complementary two chain structures. One of these is the Watson-Crick DNA structure (Fig. 16), and Figs. 17, 18 and 19 show three of the others. A remaining one allows all four bases, like those of Figs. 16 and 17, but the complementariness is opposite to them, that is, adenine pairs with cytosine and guanine with thymine.

None of these, other than the Watson-Crick structure which is very probably the correct one for DNA, have as yet been shown to have any significance to the nucleic acid problem. In the future, however, samples of another kind of

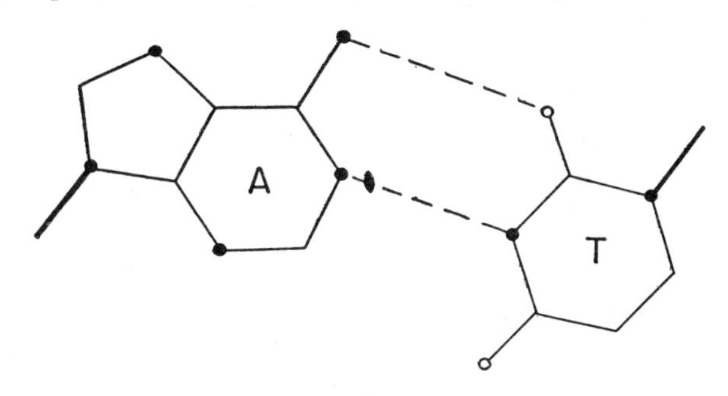

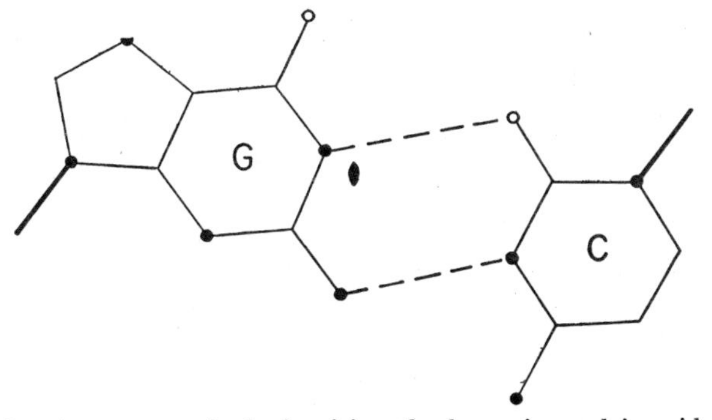

FIG. 17. An alternate method of pairing the bases in nucleic acid which predicts the same analytical composition as the Watson-Circle structure, Fig. 16, but, if the two polynucleotide chains run in the same direction, gives a structure which is not in agreement with the X-ray data for DNA.

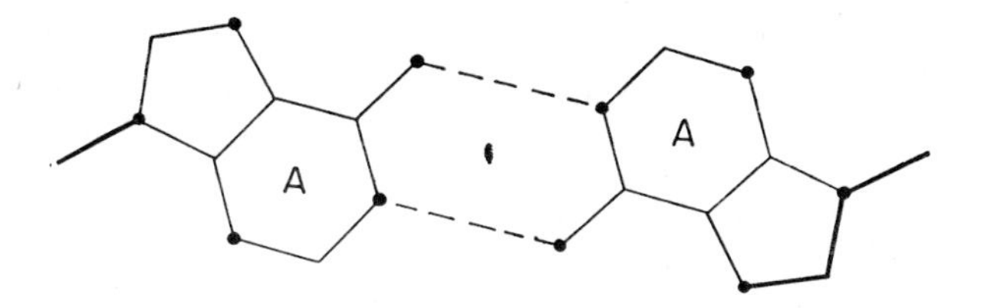

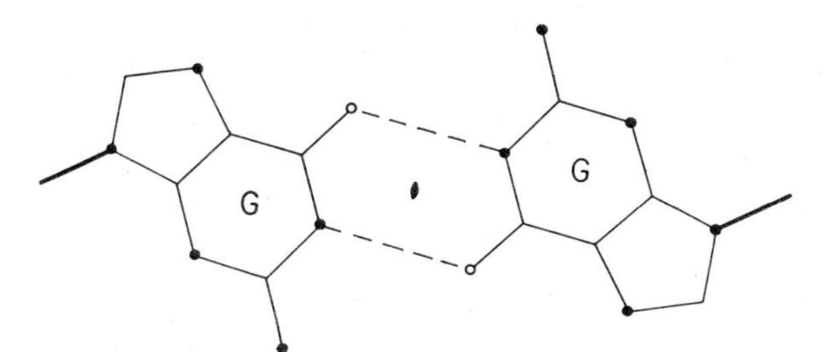

FIG. 18. A possible base pairing for a polynucleotide containing only purines.

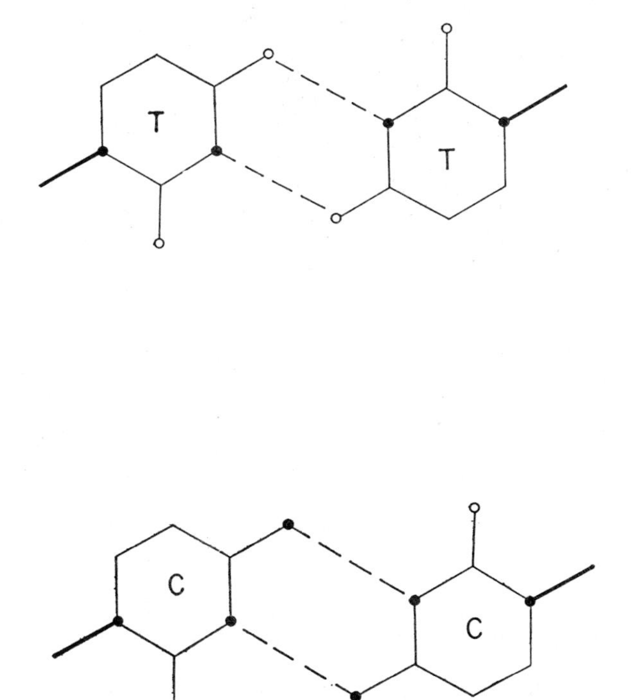

FIG. 19. A possible base pairing for a polynucleotide containing only pyrimidines.

nucleic acid may become available—but whatever structure is then postulated for it, that structure must comply with the dimensions, distances, and angles found in the simpler substances.

References

Albrecht, G. and R. B. Corey. 1939. The crystal structure of glycine. J. Am. Chem. Soc. *61:* 1087–1103.

Bamford, C. H., L. Brown, E. M. Cant, A. Elliott, W. E. Hanby and B. R. Malcolm. 1955. Structure of polyglycine. Nature *176:* 396–397.

Crick, F. H. C. and A. Rich. 1955. The structure of polyglycine. II. Nature *176:* 780–781.

Donohue, J. 1950. The crystal structure of DL-alanine. II. Revision of parameters by three-dimensional Fourier analysis. J. Am. Chem. Soc. *72:* 949–953.

Donohue, J. 1952. The hydrogen bond in organic crystals. J. Phys. Chem. *56:* 502–510.

Donohue, J. 1953. Hydrogen-bonded helical configurations of the polypeptide chain. Proc. Nat. Acad. Sci. *39:* 470–478.

Donohue, J. 1956. Hydrogen-bonded helical configurations of polynucleotides. Proc. Nat. Acad. Sci. *42:* 60–65.

Donohue, J., L. R. Lavine and J. S. Rollett. 1956. The crystal structure of histidine hydrochloride monohydrate. Acta Cryst. *9:* 655–662.

Donohue, J. and W. N. Lipscomb. 1947. The crystal structure of hydrazinium dichloride. J. Chem. Phys. *15:* 115–119.

Hughes, E. W. 1940. The crystal structure of dicyandiamide. J. Am. Chem. Soc. *62:* 1258–1267.

Hughes, E. W. and W. J. Moore. 1949. The crystal structure of beta-glyclglycine. J. Am. Chem. Soc. *71:* 2618–2623.

Jeffrey, G. A. 1945. The structure of polyisoprenes. I. The crystal structure of geranylamine hydrochloride. Proc. Roy. Soc. (London) *A183:* 388–404.

Jerslev, B. 1948. The structure of hydroxylammonium chloride, NH_3OHCl and hydroxylammonium bromide, NH_3OHBr. Acta Cryst. *1:* 21–27.

Kanda, F. A. and A. J. King. 1951. The crystal structure of sulfamic acid. J. Am. Chem. Soc. *73:* 2315–2319.

Levy, H. A. and R. B. Corey. 1941. The crystal structure of DL-alanine. J. Am. Chem. Soc. *63:* 2095–2108.

Low, B. W. and R. B. Baybutt. 1952. The π-helix; hydrogen bonded configuration of the polypeptide chain. J. Am. Chem. Soc. *74:* 5806–5807.

Pauling, L. 1940. The Nature of the Chemical Bond and the Structure of Molecules and Crystals. 2nd ed. Cornell Univ. Press. Ithaca. 450 pp. (p. 286–287).

Pauling, L. and R. B. Corey. 1950. Two hydrogen-bonded spiral configurations of the polypeptide chain. J. Am. Chem. Soc. *72:* 5349.

Rogers, M. T. and L. Helmholz. 1941. The crystal structure of iodic acid. J. Am. Chem. Soc. *63:* 278–284.

Shoemaker, D. P., J. Donohue, V. Schomaker and R. B. Corey. 1950. The crystal structure of L_s-Threonine. J. Am. Chem. Soc. *72:* 2328–2349.

Watson, J. D. and F. H. C. Crick. 1953. The stereochemical structure for deoxypentose nucleic acid. Inst. intern. chim. Solvay, Conseil chim., 9th Conseil, Brussels. *1953:* 110–112.

Wells, A. F. 1949. Bifurcated hydrogen bonds. Acta Cryst. *2:* 128–129.

PROFESSOR SUTHERLAND (University of Michigan): I would like to ask about polyglycines and the letter from Bamford & co-workers (1955) in which they suggest that polyglycine is a 2.2_7 helix.

PROFESSOR DONOHUE: I heard about his letter only last night; *Nature* comes to our library much later than it ought to, so that I have no knowledge of this at all. If it turns out that polyglycine is one of these structures described previously, of course I will be very pleased.

(A different structure for polyglycine has now been proposed by Crick and Rich (1955). They stated that their structure was in "good qualitative agreement" with the X-ray data, but as they chose not to publish the results of the calculations they made on their structure, it is impossible for anyone else to arrive at a conclusion concerning its validity.)

CHAIRMAN PAULING: I would like to comment on Professor Donohue's paper. I think that in the spirit of the true investigator he has concentrated on presenting a number of new ideas and discussing some doubtful points in this talk about the hydrogen bond and has not presented a great mass of crystallographic data on substances in which hydrogen bonds are very well behaved and in which there is no doubt about the interpretation of the crystallographic data. Would you tell me if you agree with this?

PROFESSOR DONOHUE: I would say that *some* of these substances we have talked about this afternoon weren't very well behaved. Glycine is one I still do not like.

CHAIRMAN PAULING: No, and sulfamic acid is questionable. Would you agree that there are a great number of hydrogen bonded crystals in which there is no doubt about the hydrogen bonds? The environment corresponds nicely to that expected.

PROFESSOR DONOHUE: Yes; I agree perfectly. In these many complicated substances, some of which we did not look at, you find everything is just lovely. This is why, when you see something where it is not so lovely, you should be exceedingly suspicious. There are dozens of substances that we could not worry about this afternoon where everything fits your preconceived ideas in a perfect way.

CHAIRMAN PAULING: I think it is astounding that a complex molecule such as that of threonine, which has four hydrogen atoms that are sticking out in various directions, is able to find a way of packing together with its equivalent fellows that corresponds to standard density, that is, no holes, each atom occupying its place, and still it brings an atom that can interact with the OH hydrogen atom in such a way as to correspond to the formation of a hydrogen bond. I think it need not surprise us that sometimes the molecule seems to find it impossible to do this perfectly, that sometimes the hydrogen bond is bent by 10 or 15 or 20 degrees, and that sometimes the distance is not to the 2.80 that one might expect but is 3.06 Å.

This is the point you were making, is it not, that the molecules do an extraordinary job in finding a way to satisfy all structural features?

The results of X-ray analysis of substances such as amino acids and peptides have shown that molecules conform extraordinarily well to structural chemical principles. There is some conjugation in an amide group such as to make a planar molecule more stable than a non-planar one twisted around the C—N bond. You can calculate by simple theory how much strain is involved in twisting this by, say, 6 degrees. The amount of strain is about one tenth of a kilocalorie per mole, much less than kT, much less than the equipartition energy. Yet in general, peptides retain the planar configuration to within 6 degrees, and the other structural features, such as the bending of the hydrogen bond, are, in general, ideal; that is, they do not involve strain to an amount greater than strain energy around a tenth of a kilocalorie per mole for each structural feature.

These structures show a closer approximation to ideal structures than one would anticipate. In the process of crystallization, the forces between molecules are much larger. The heat of sublimation of one of these substances may be 10 kilocalories per mole, or 20, for a molecule as big as threonine, and one would think that the crystallization process might strain the molecule. It is surprising that serious strain occurs so rarely.

DR. PRESSMAN: I would like to ask about the situation in aqueous solution because that is where so many of the biological reactions occur.

How much deviation form a straight line might be tolerated under such conditions? Would you expect bifurcated hydrogen bonds, or is this just something which you fit into the crystal?

PROFESSOR DONOHUE: Obviously a crystallographer shouldn't answer this question, but I will go ahead and try. If, as Dr. Pauling said, a complicated molecule like threonine can set everything up around it so that the situation is satisfactory in a solid where we have symmetry elements to deal with and the molecules are in fixed relationships to each other, then it seems to me that in a solution, where the molecules are moving back and forth all the time, this linearity N—H ··· O or OH ··· O will hold, and also there will not be any bifurcation.

MR. LIPPINCOTT: I would like to ask about the difference between the N ···· O distance in hydrogen bonds involving zwitter-ions and the ones which do not. Is there a significant difference in the N ···· O distance between these two different types?

PROFESSOR DONOHUE: We have not noticed any real correlation here. One would think, of course, that for the NH_3^+ case the distance would be shorter, but this has not turned up. The only thing that comes to mind immediately is the case of urea, where the distances are longer than is observed in the amino acids. But, on the other hand, in the urea molecule there are four hydrogen atoms and only one oxygen atom, so that each oxygen is accepting two hydrogen bonds, and this may be why they are somewhat longer.

In other amides the distances are the same as in these zwitter-ion amino acids.

DR. JACK D. DUNITZ (National Institutes of Health): What is your opinion concerning the structure of oximes? In these structures of binding by oxygen one has to make a choice between, on the one hand, an orthodox chemical structure C═N—OH with an angle of about 70° between the OH and its hydrogen bonded nitrogen, or between an unorthodox chemical structure C≡N⁺H—O⁻ and a normal angle of about 105°. Which do your prefer?

PROFESSOR DONOHUE: A choice between 70° and 105°? Obviously, we will take the 105°. Somebody should get out his Geiger counter and find the hydrogen atom; that would lay this question to rest. I might add that in the case of one of these oximes there is an error in the paper. The angles as quoted by the author are incorrect. Both relevant angles are near to 90°, so that you cannot make the choice. If one of them is 70° and the other is 110° then you could make the choice, but if you recalculate this yourself you will find 85° and 95°, which are about equally acceptable.

Intermolecular Forces

Joseph O. Hirschfelder

University of Wisconsin Naval Research Laboratory, Madison, Wis.

MY KNOWLEDGE OF INTERMOLECULAR FORCES is limited to a study of the properties of small molecules. The problems of intermolecular forces in biological systems are quite different. In this short talk I would like to outline the similarities and the differences from a rather general point of view.

The geometrical structure of two biological molecules is the most important factor in determining their intermolecular forces. It is very helpful to construct molecular models of the sort that Linus Pauling and others have fabricated on the basis of X-ray and electron diffraction studies. With these models one can make preliminary estimates of the separations between each of the atoms in molecule A and each of the atoms in molecule B when the two molecules are held in a particular orientation. Knowing these separations we can turn the theoretical cranks to determine the energy of interaction corresponding to this orientation. Unfortunately the molecular models have one serious defect. Their joints are rigid so that they do not become deformed in the same manner as the real molecules when the attractive or the repulsive forces become large. I understand that some biological molecules can completely change their shape under the influence of even small stresses such as surface tension. This makes the problem of determining intermolecular forces exceedingly difficult because it means that we must take intra-molecular stresses and strains into consideration at the same time that we are estimating the intermolecular interactions.

Then, there is the problem of the additivity of intermolecular forces. In most small molecule problems, it is a good approximation to assume that the forces either between various groups on molecule A and other groups on molecule B or else between various separate molecules are pairwise additive. In calculating the interactions between biological molecules one might also be tempted to assume this pairwise additivity. However, very frequently when two biological molecules approach each other their charge distributions become distorted so as to render such pairwise additivity inapplicable.

Since biological molecules are swimming in a solvent possessing a large dielectric constant, the energy of ionization is much smaller than in the gas and the electrons are much less tightly bound within the molecules. Ions, zwitterions, and structures possessing large dipole moments are common. Thus most of the long range forces between biological molecules are of electrostatic origin rather than being of the London type which is most common in gases.

The short range forces between two biological molecules frequently require the consideration of two or more valence structures corresponding to the possibility of chemical reactions taking place during the collision.

And finally, in biological reactions (such as in photosynthesis) electronically excited intermediates are frequently formed which have unusually large long range forces with other molecules.

Thus the problems of intermolecular forces in biological systems are orders of magnitude more difficult than those for the interaction of two noble gas atoms with which we are reasonably familiar. However, we can examine the qualitative nature of the biological forces.

In the large biological molecules some groups have a large electron affinity and suck electrons away from other groups, which become positively charged. The zwitter-ions provide the classical example. The separations between these positive and negative charge centers often are large compared to the separation between the points of closest approach of two interacting molecules. In such cases the dipole-dipole interactions are quite different than would be supposed on the basis of "ideal dipole" forces. Consider the interaction of two zwitter-ions A and B whose centers are separated by the distance R_{AB}. Let us suppose that the charges on A have the absolute value e_A and those on B have the absolute value e_B. Then the energy of dipole-dipole interaction of these molecules is

$$E = e_A e_B \left[\frac{1}{R_{A+,B+}} + \frac{1}{R_{A-,B-}} - \frac{1}{R_{A+,B-}} - \frac{1}{R_{A-,B+}} \right] \tag{1}$$

Here $R_{A+,B+}$ is the separation between the center of positive charge on A and the center of positive charge on B; $R_{A-,B-}$ is the separation between the center of negative charge on A and the center of negative charge on B; etc.

If as shown in Fig. 1, the positive charge on A comes close to the negative

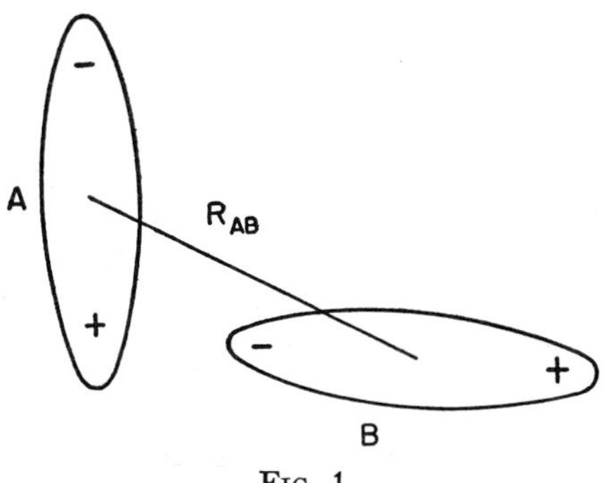

FIG. 1

charge on B so that $R_{A+,B-}$ is smaller than the other three charge-charge distances in Eq. (1), the energy of interaction becomes

$$E = -e_A e_B / R_{A+,B-} \qquad (2)$$

This energy of interaction may be orders of magnitude larger than the ideal dipole-dipole interaction energy which one would calculate on the basis of the dipole moments of A and of B. The usual ideal dipole concept only applies when the distance between the centers of the two molecules is much greater than the distance between the charge centers in both molecules, i.e. $R_{AB} > R_{A+,A-}$ and $R_{AB} > R_{B+,B-}$. Thus in treating biological molecules it is usually wise to forego any considerations of dipole moments but rather think of each of the positive and negative charge centers in the system as interacting in a simple coulombic fashion. Thus the first step in determining the intermolecular forces is to locate the position of each of the electrical charge centers within the molecules and determine how much charge is concentrated at each center.

Hydrogen bonds provide a good example of the strong interactions possible with unshielded dipoles. Consider an interaction, ····O—H O=····, between an OH group in one molecule with an O= on another molecule. Due to electron affinities, the H atom becomes positively charged and the oxygen atoms negative. Thus this interaction resembles the situation shown in Fig. 1 with the H atom serving as the center A+ and the O= serving as the B−. The special feature of the hydrogen bond is that the collision diameter of the hydrogen atom is so very small that the O= can come very close to the center of the H atom making $R_{A+,B-}$ small and hence by Eq. (1) the energy of interaction can be very large.

In addition to the electrostatic interactions of the "permanent" charge distributions which we have just considered we should consider the effects of polarization. The word "permanent" is used to denote the charge distribution of the separated molecules. However, as the molecules come together they polarize each other. That is, the charge distributions on the two molecules become readjusted in such a way as to make the energy of the two molecule system as low as possible. This polarization results in producing much larger energy of interaction than would be possible otherwise. In conjugate double bond systems and many other molecular structures of interest in biology, very little effort is required to make even large changes in the electrical charge distribution. Thus polarization forces are very important. Resonance forces, which we shall discuss subsequently, are special examples of polarization forces.

There is a third type of force which has no classical analogy. It is the London dispersion force. This involves the "transition dipole moment" for the electrons in the interacting molecules jumping to excited states. If $\psi_A(o)$ is the wave function for the initial or ground state of molecule A and $\psi_A(k)$ is the wave function for some excited state k and if $\mathbf{r}_1$ is the instantaneous position of one of the n_A electrons in A, then $\mu_A(ok)$ is the transition dipole moment of A connected with the jump from the ground state to the k-th state:

$$\boldsymbol{\mu}_A(ok) = n_A e \int \psi_A^*(o)\mathbf{r}_1\psi_A(k)\, d\tau_1 d\tau_2 \cdots d\tau_{n_A} \tag{3}$$

The energy required for the molecule to go from the ground state to the k-th state is $E_A(k) - E_A(o)$. Similar transition dipoles can be defined for molecule B. Then if A and B were small molecules, the dispersion energy of interaction between A and B would be

$$E_{dis} = -\frac{2}{3R_{ab}^6} \sum_{k,k'} \frac{\mu_A^2(ok)\mu_B^2(ok')}{(E_A(k) - E_A(o)) + (E_B(k') - E_B(o))} \tag{4}$$

Usually there is only one principal charge transfer transition so that it is only necessary to consider a single excited state k for molecule A and a single excited state k′ for molecule B. Unfortunately, Eq. (4) does not hold for large molecules except at extremely large separations. London (1942) showed that for large molecules the notion of transition dipoles is no longer useful. Instead one must consider the exact spatial configuration of the "transition charge distribution",

$$\rho_A(ok) = n_A e \int \psi_A(o)^*\psi_A(k)\, d\tau_2 \cdots d\tau_{n_A} \tag{5}$$

Here $\rho_A(ok)$ is a function of position within the molecule. There are zones in which $\rho_A(ok)$ is positive and other zones in which it is negative depending on the signs of the wave functions $\psi_A(o)$ and $\psi_A(k)$. These zones are bounded by the nodal surfaces of these two wave functions. Thus the i-th zone has the transition charge

$$\epsilon_A^{(i)}(ok) = \int_{\text{i-th zone}} \rho_A(ok)\, d\tau \tag{6}$$

and its centroid is located at the position

$$\mathbf{R}_A^{(i)}(ok) = \int_{\text{i-th zone}} \mathbf{r}\rho_A(ok)\, d\tau/\epsilon_A^{(i)}(ok) \tag{7}$$

These zones may be called transition monopoles. The energy of dispersion of large molecules is then

$$E_{dis} = -\frac{\left[\sum_{i,i'} \epsilon_A^{(i)}(ok)\epsilon_B^{(i')}(ok')/\left|\mathbf{R}_A^{(i)}(ok) - \mathbf{R}_B^{(i')}(ok')\right|\right]^2}{(E_A(k) - E_A(o)) + (E_B(k') - E_B(o))} \tag{8}$$

Here $|\mathbf{R}_A^{(i)}(ok) - \mathbf{R}_B^{(i')}(ok')|$ is the distance between the i-th monopole in A and the i′-th monopole in B. From Eq. (8), we see that the dispersion energy of two large molecules can become very large when two transition monopoles come close together.

In order to determine the dispersion energy, the first step is to ascertain the principal charge transfer transitions which take place in the molecules. The energy associated with these transitions can be experimentally determined from a study of the index of refraction of light passing through the pure substance as a function of frequency. Crude quantum mechanical arguments can then establish the nature of the transitions and a rough description of the wave-functions in the excited and in the ground states. The free-electron model has been very successful for locating the monopoles in conjugate double bond molecules. Pauling's theory of color should be useful for other kinds of biological molecules. The dispersion energy between large molecules leads to highly directional forces depending on the location of the monopoles. Thus conjugate double bond molecules are found to have a maximum energy of interaction when their axes are neither parallel nor perpendicular.

Finally, we come to the much disputed question as to whether resonance forces play an important role in biological specificities. Let us suppose that molecules A and B are identical but molecule A is in an excited state and molecule B is in the ground state. Then, if the optical selection rules do not forbid, molecule A can emit a virtual photon which is then captured by B. The two molecules can interact at surprisingly long distances. Concurrently the two molecules either are attracted or else repelled by forces which are much stronger than would occur if the two molecules were not identical. Some physicists and biologists have jumped to the conclusion that such forces must be important in explaining specificity. However, a little further consideration would seem to make this explanation seem unlikely. As the two molecules approach each other the usual electrostatic and dispersion forces become much stronger than the resonance forces.

Thus we have outlined the types of problems which will be encountered in a study of the intermolecular forces between biologically important molecules (Haugh and Hirschfelder, 1955; Hirschfelder, Curtiss and Bird, 1954). The problems can be clearly stated but a great deal of work remains to work out the detailed applications to specific examples in order to establish our understanding on a quantitative basis.

References

Haugh, E. F. and J. O. Hirschfelder. 1955. J. Chem. Phys. *23:* 1778.

Hirschfelder, J. O., C. F. Curtiss and R. B. Bird. 1954. Molecular Theory of Gases and Liquids. John Wiley & Sons, Inc. Chapt. 13.

London, F. 1942. J. Chem. Phys. *46:* 305.

Dr. Sidney Bernhard (National Medical Research Institute): In light of the discussion of special roles of resonance, it occurs to me that the vaporization of cyclohexane is not very different from the vaporization of benzene and an additional fact that occurs to me, particularly from work of the type of Dr. Pressman's, is that if one compares the bindings of the molecules which have the benzene ring stuck on one end and then one also measures the binding of a molecule similar in other respects but lacking the benzene rings at one end, then the difference in free energy of bindings turns out to be of the order of the enthalpy of vaporization of benzene and, hence, cyclohexane. In light of such argument how much difference is there in our biological system from the ordinary liquids and the gas phase, and how much does this resonance phenomena really contribute?

PROFESSOR HIRSCHFELDER: I wonder whether the fact that you speak of is due to the cancellation between half of these resonant states being attractive and half being repulsive. This would show up if one studied the viscosity and found that the viscosity differed greatly in the two cases.

CHAIRMAN PAULING: This discussion is about the question of how strong the interaction due to dispersion forces is between conjugated systems. I think, myself, that the people who have made calculations about this probably have been led to overemphasize this importance in some cases.

As has just been pointed out, the van der Waals forces, the polarizability and van der Waals interaction of benzene do not really seem to be abnormally great as compared with cyclohexane. But on the other hand, we know that dyes which have long conjugated systems, such as carotenoids, do interact more strongly with one another than ordinary colorless, unconjugated molecules do.

DR. PRESSMAN: There is evidence that van der Waals forces and polarizability are important in the cases of interaction of haptens with specific antibodies, for example, in those cases where a naphthalene ring is accommodated, such as in the case of β-naphthoate reacting with anti-*para*-azobenzoate antibodies, or the alpha naphthoate ion with anti-*ortho*-azobenzoate antibodies. In these cases, there actually does seem to be an enhanced attraction of the naphthalene over what one would expect for a non-aromatic grouping. We have attributed that to the polarizability.

PROFESSOR PITZER: I would, just as an aside, like to associate myself with those who would regard the conjugation as real but not so important. I think that even when you go to decalins and naphthalene, say, the difference is not very large; it is measurable and significant, but not a major effect. Indeed, we all write on paper with graphite and here you have something of microscopic dimensions conjugated and, even so, the forces between the planes are not so great but that you can tear the crystal apart. Of course, you can tear paraffin crystals apart too, pretty easily, but I do not think this is a major thing.

I do think there is a very interesting question here and I would like enlightenment as much as trying to contribute anything. That is, to what extent do electronically excited states appear in what might be described as the general run of biological interacting systems? There is no doubt that in photosynthesis there are photo-stationary states of the system that absorb the light and very possibly do so in some subsequent steps.

I believe that in a few cases paramagnetic resonance has indicated odd electron spins in systems where they might not have been expected and we do not know whether these are important or not. My general impression was that for most of the biochemical systems, all of the component units of the molecules are in their lowest electronic state and that the explanations are probably to be found in terms of the usual energy potential terms which we recognize in small molecules such as hydrogen bonds, rotational potentials, van der Waals forces of a relatively local type, etc. I think I would be most interested to hear if there are numerous cases where excited electronic states have been identified.

CHAIRMAN PAULING: My feeling has been the same as that of Professor Pitzer, that in biological systems, excited states of molecules are not important except as part of reaction mechanisms.

PROFESSOR JEHLE: Excited states are indeed interesting only in that thermal accessibility of excited states limits the specificity. We have analyzed this in the paper already referred to, where we stated four conditions for the specificity to be effectively a many-parametric one. A manifold of macromolecules may show specific discrimination if the molecules possess sufficiently diversified (with respect to frequency distribution) and strong polarizabilities, provided these frequencies are well above the classical domain.

Interaction of Organic Molecules with Proteins

I. M. Klotz

Northwestern University, Evanston, Ill.

IN CONTRAST TO THE PRECEDING PAPER I should like to revert to the chemical level, instead of the quantum mechanical level, in describing some of the interactions of organic molecules with proteins.

Studies of these interactions with proteins other than the immune globulins have been carried out particularly intensively in the last 10 or so years, and I think one can say without exaggeration that almost every factor which one can possibly think of which might affect the strength of these interactions has been examined to some extent, by somebody. I do not think it would be profitable just to describe the wide variety of factors which are known to be able to affect the strength of these complexes, even though that might be of interest, let us say, to an enzymologist searching about for some possible models, relatively simple models, with which to explain particular effects which he may have observed.

Instead, it seems to me more appropriate in a symposium of this type to pick a few factors which show specificity of varying degrees and to see to what extent we can account for and understand these specificities in terms of the molecular structure of the participants.

It has helped me, at least in picking and trying to interpret these phenomena, to think of the effects of the factors which can affect the stability of the protein complex with the small molecule as either residing in the environment outside of the protein or being an expression of the protein structure itself. So what I am going to do is pick two or three examples of each type: extrinsic factors where even in the outside environment of the protein one can find specificities; and intrinsic factors which will show certain similarities and dissimilarities, as you will see, with the interactions with immune globulins.

Let me proceed, then, first to take one or two examples which demonstrate the effect of the environment on the strength of a protein complex.

In the first figure (Fig. 1), largely for purposes of orientation, I would like just to remind you that, if we represent a protein molecule schematically by a sphere, protein molecules, particularly serum albumin, beta lactoglobulin and to some extent, casein, can form complexes with organic molecules, which I have indicated schematically as a smaller sized molecule (even though, from some of the specific examples which you have seen, these can be fairly large).

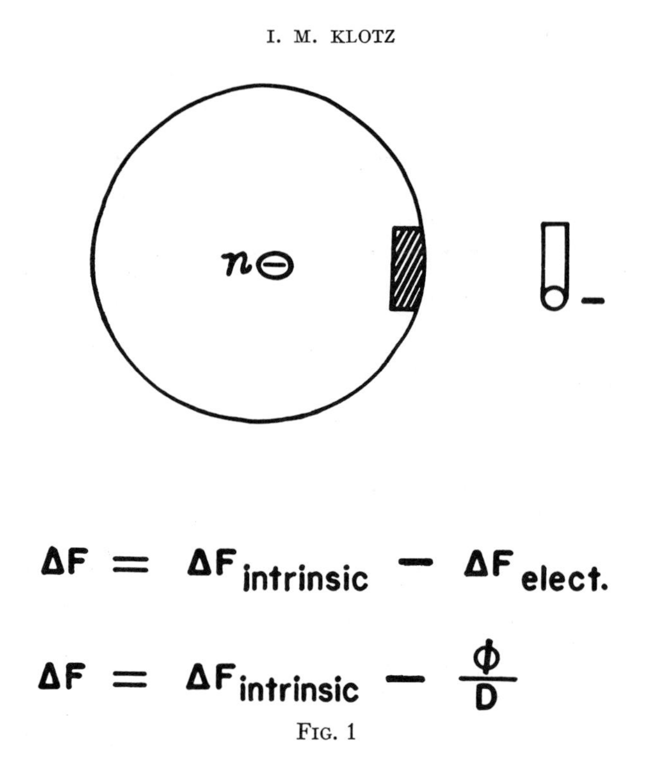

FIG. 1

Now, these complexes can be rather surprisingly strong even if the protein carries a very substantial negative charge and the organic molecule which we are considering also carries a negative charge. In fact, the last example which I shall discuss will point out that despite the fact that the protein carries a negative charge, if we compare the binding of two molecules, organic molecules of roughly equal size, one of which has a minus charge and the other of which has a plus charge, in which case you would expect the plus-charged one to be more strongly bound, quite the contrary happens; the negatively-charged one is more strongly bound.

That is a puzzle we may have to get to if I have time, but, for the moment, let us just examine the more common case of a negative organic molecule. This is perhaps a more interesting case anyway, because so many of the metabolites in biological systems are anions and the enzymes with which they interact are usually at a pH at which they, too, are anions.

There are many ways in which one can affect the strength of this interaction through the environment. For one thing, you can change the ionic environment, as Professor Kirkwood mentioned, and then you will get the Debye-Hückel screening effect, but I shall not go into that. You can change the charge on the protein, too. One effect that I want to mention in detail, because I hope to give something that we have not published yet, is the effect of the dielectric constant of the medium on this interaction. For this purpose I have indicated schematically (Fig. 1) the only one or two theoretical equations which I shall have here.

The free energy of the binding can be thought of as consisting of two terms. One is an intrinsic affinity of the protein for the organic molecule—you can think of that factor as being essentially the affinity present if you just blot out the $n\ominus$ in Fig. 1 from your vision and imagine that there is no charge on the protein. Under these circumstances there is merely the intrinsic affinity of some particular site on the protein surface for the organic molecule.

Then, in addition, there is the repulsive factor. If there is a negative charge, there must be an electrostatic repulsion factor. So I put a minus sign before the term $\Delta F_{\text{elect.}}$ in Fig. 1. I do not mean that this is actually a negative free energy term; that would be an incorrect indication. I just want to indicate that this factor, the electrostatic factor (due to anion and a negative protein), is opposite to the intrinsic factor and tends to decrease the extent of the interaction.

Now, if you examine the nature of this electrostatic factor in more detail, without going into all the quantities involved, you find that it depends, among other things, upon the shape and the charge on the protein, and on the size of the organic ion, but I have lumped all of those terms in one factor ϕ and emphasized the dielectric constant D as the one thing to which we want to pay particular emphasis. It occurs in the denominator of the bottom equation in Fig. 1. This would be the macroscopic dielectric constant of the medium as such. So you can see that if you could, let us say, decrease the dielectric constant, this negative term ϕ/D would become greater and you would expect a greater repulsion factor and a decrease in binding.

This has been tried (Fredericq, 1954) but I think the results cannot be considered unequivocal because the kinds of substance which you might add, let us say dioxane, will decrease the dielectric constant, but simultaneously these molecules can compete with the negative ion for attachment to the protein, so that two factors occur simultaneously to decrease the binding.

Consequently, we thought we ought to try to operate in the other direction, to try to increase the dielectric constant in an aqueous solution. Essentially, I think the only effective way of doing that is to add an amino acid in its isoionic form and to operate at a pH, of course, at which the amino acid would remain in its isoionic form. So, as I will show you in a moment, if you increase the concentration of glycine from zero to two molar in an aqueous solution so that the dielectric constant rises, roughly, from 80 to 120, the denominator in ϕ/D (Fig. 1) will become larger. Consequently this factor is decreased and you would expect less of a contribution of the electrostatic factor and thus an increase in the attraction of protein and organic molecules, since you have decreased the effect of the repulsion force.

The next illustration (Fig. 2) shows these results (Klotz and Ayers) summarized in terms of the free energies. The increase in $-\Delta F_1^\circ$ means increased binding, and the extent of binding is shown here in terms of the free energy, for water alone, for five-tenths molar glycine solution, for one-molar and two-molar solutions. As perhaps a first approximation, you might notice that the graph is linear. Perhaps I should have pointed out in the preceding figure (Fig. 1) that if the factor ϕ does remain constant, then the free energy should have varied reciprocally with the dielectric constant, which to a first approximation it does.

To a certain extent we have specificity even here in that the only molecules which would effectively increase the dielectric constant by an appreciable amount are the amino acids; but that is a very nebulous specificity.

I would like to proceed to another example which illustrates the effect of changes in the environment (Fig. 3) in which we have somewhat greater specificity. Here again I will have to give just a little background information.

We measure the extent of binding in this case and represent it in terms of the following coordinates: the number of molecules of a particular dye (whose structure I shall show you shortly) bound by each protein molecule against concentration of the free dye in the solution, represented here on a logarithmic basis. Then, for the particular protein which is shown here, which is pepsin, if there is no metal present and dye is present, the extent of binding is very small (Fig. 3) and it does not matter whether the pH is anywhere between 4 and about 7. I have indicated just two pH ranges in Fig. 3 (by two different symbols), but over the pH range of 4 to 7 there is essentially no binding or very little binding.

However, if you add to this solution a small amount of zinc, of the order of 10^{-3} or 10^{-4} molar, at pH 4 there is a small but definite effect and at pH 5 you can see there is a very substantial effect. The zinc increases the binding (Klotz and Loh Ming, 1954).

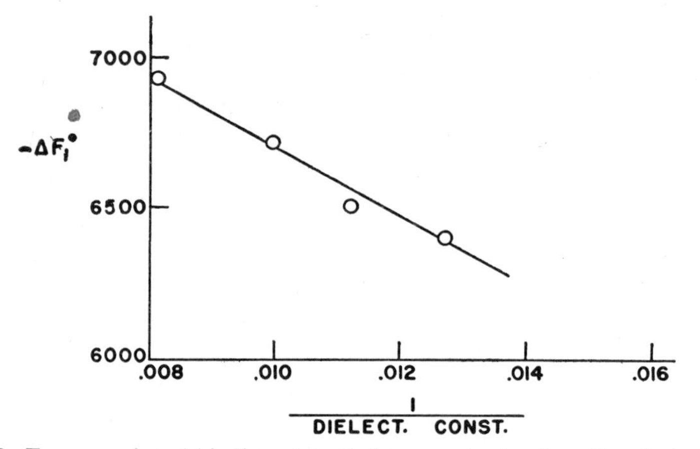

FIG. 2. Free energies of binding of methyl orange by bovine albumin in aqueous glycine solutions of different dielectric constant.

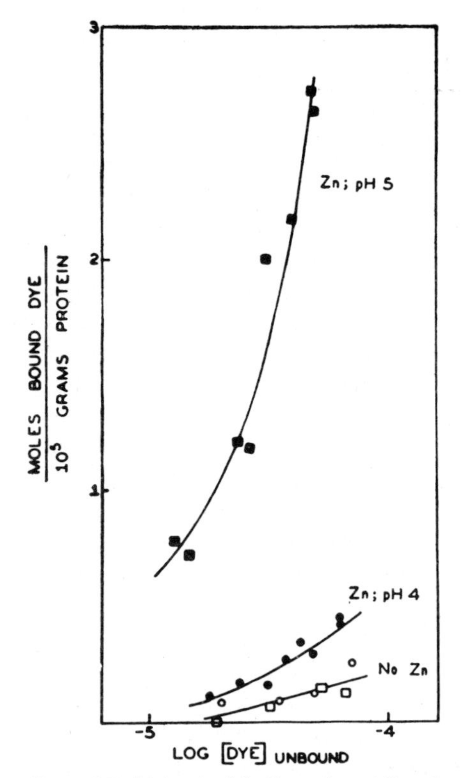

FIG. 3. Mediating effect of Zn^{++} in the binding of pyridine-2-azo-*p*-dimethylaniline by pepsin.

There could be several reasons why this effect might occur. First, in Fig. 4 let me show you the scheme which we are rather certain is true. For the moment ignore the zinc and consider the dye molecule. This specific structure can be bound by the protein, pepsin, or by serum albumin. In the absence of zinc, however, the amount of binding is small and probably due to the hydrogen bond shown (Fig. 4).

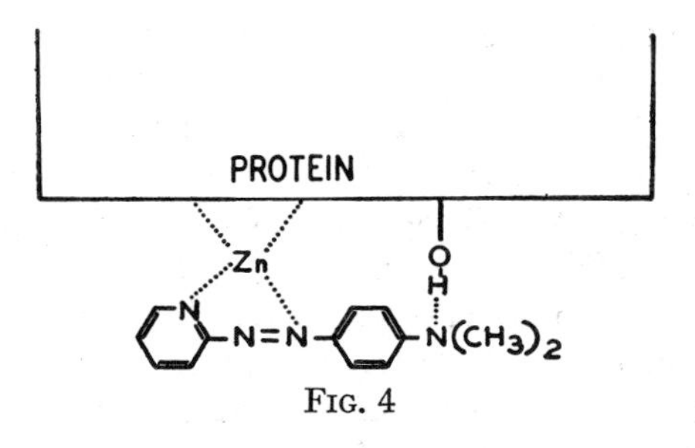

FIG. 4

However, when zinc is put in, it is possible to form a chelate of the type shown. It is also known that the zinc can be bound to the protein so that it seems likely that the zinc actually forms a bridge. However, that is not an absolutely certain interpretation, at least with the information I have given you so far, because it is also known that if you add hydrogen ions to a solution you can increase the extent of binding of a large number of dyes and I do not think anyone would be foolish enough to say that the hydrogen ion acts as a tetrafurcated hydrogen bond. What hydrogen ion does, as is well known, is to cause some change in the protein; change in charge, change in its structure, sometimes change in its degree of folding. So, of course, it is possible that the zinc operates by a similar mechanism; that is, that it too causes some change in the protein rather than acting as a bridge to the organic molecule.

One of the experiments which we think rules this out is essentially the following. If zinc had its effect on the binding of this dye, due to some change in the protein, then if we took a structurally analogous dye in which the pyridine nitrogen is at the extreme left of the structure (Fig. 4) so that the zinc cannot form a chelate, we should still obtain the same effect in the presence of zinc. You have a molecule exactly the same size, and with the same type of basic groups involved. If the effect of the zinc is on the protein, then zinc ought to increase the binding of the parapyridine dye just as much as it increases that of the ortho one shown in Fig. 4. As a matter of fact, the parapyridine dye acts in the presence of zinc just as if zinc were not present. It is bound to the same extent in the absence of zinc as the ortho (Fig. 4) is bound, but if zinc is put in, the ortho is bound much more strongly and the para dye is not bound to any extent above that to which it would be bound if there were no zinc present.

So I think that this experiment indicates quite clearly that it is essential that the zinc be able to form a chelate with the dye. Consequently, since we know by separate experiments that the zinc is bound to the protein—in fact, I shall show you some of those results, too, in passing—it is quite clear that the zinc is acting as a bridge in the ternary complex (Fig. 4).

Let us look at this matter in a little more detail. It takes a relatively large amount of routine manipulation to get the extensive data of binding as a function of concentration of the type shown in Fig. 3. Instead of that, because we use dyes, we can do the following. When the dye is bound to the protein through zinc or otherwise, it changes its absorption so that at least semiquantitatively all we need to do is follow the increase in absorption at a suitably chosen wave length to have a measure of extent of binding of dye in the presence of zinc.

I can summarize the data (Hughes and Klotz, 1956) in terms of an optical density experiment of the type shown in Fig. 5. The greater the optical density, the more the binding, and I have summarized the data for a fairly extensive pH range, out to about 11. You can see that first there is an increase in the extent of binding as we increase the pH from approximately 6 to 7.5, and thereafter there is a drop in the extent of binding.

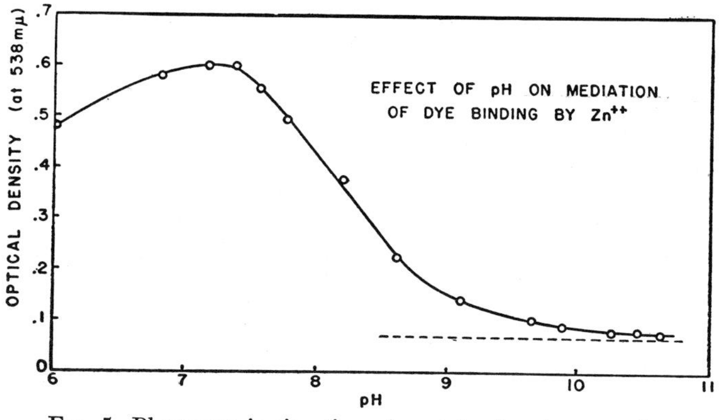

FIG. 5. Photometric titration of protein-zinc-dye complex

I would like to consider each of those regions in more detail and see if we can understand them. The increase at the lower pH end is fully understandable, since we already have data which show that the amount of zinc bound by the protein increases in this region, because the protein itself acquires a more negative charge and so binds these metallic cations more strongly.

The next illustration (Fig. 6) demonstrates that if you do measure the extent of the binding of zinc as a function of pH, where you have a fixed total amount of zinc in the solution, the number of zinc ions bound is found to increase from 5 ions per mole of protein at pH 6 to about 12 or 13 at a pH a little over 7, and then to about 28 at approximately 8. So there is a substantial increase in the zinc binding with increasing pH. There are more sites then at which the dye can be chelated to the protein and that, essentially, is why the binding will go up at first.

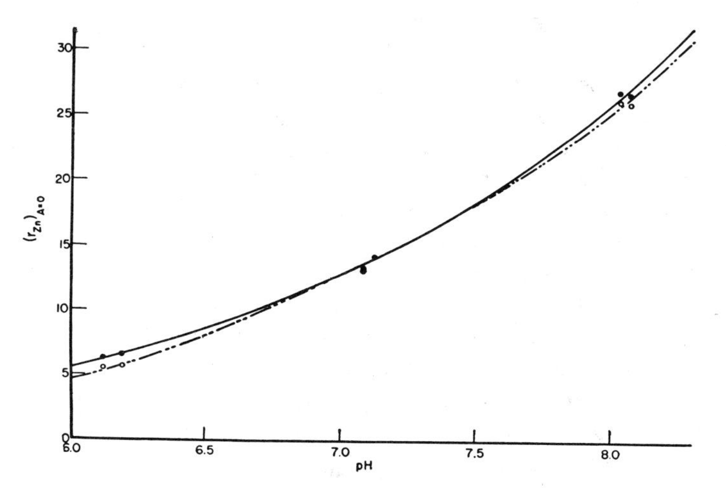

FIG. 6. Effect of pH on binding of zinc

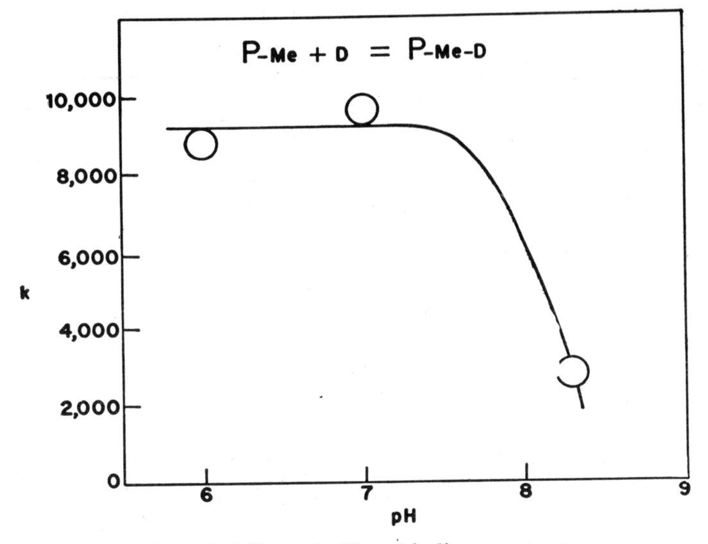

FIG. 7. Effect of pH on binding constant

To prove to ourselves that this could account almost entirely, within experimental accuracy, for the increase, we calculated, as is shown in the next illustration (Fig. 7), the actual binding constant (Hughes and Klotz, 1956) for the process of dye going on to the zinc which is already attached to the protein. In calculating this association constant, which is plotted in Fig. 7, we have already taken into account in our equation the extra zinc which is bound by the protein. With this correction the constant is substantially level over the pH range of 6–7.5. In other words, you can account entirely for the increase in the extent of binding in terms of the extra zinc which is present on the protein.

However, just as before in the photometric curve (Fig. 5), there is a very steep drop-off as soon as you exceed about pH 7.5, either in the constant (Fig. 7) or in the extent of binding measured semi-quantitatively (Fig. 5). This was a puzzle but only for a short time.

The explanation must lie, as is shown in the next figure (Fig. 8), in hydrolytic changes. I would like to point primarily to the first equation; I shall come back to the others in a moment. The explanation must lie in the hydrolytic equilibrium of the zinc. We have to keep in mind that OH ions at increasing pH's become of importance and can displace the dye from the metal protein combination by a displacement or substitution mechanism.

If this is true, then we would expect that not only should this mechanism work for zinc, but since we have studied 8 or 10 other metals, it should work for these other metals also. Since the affinity for hydroxyl ion of other metals

$$\text{P-Me-Dye} + OH^- = \text{P-Me-OH} + \text{Dye} \quad (1)$$

$$\text{P-Me-Dye} + OH^- = \text{P} + \text{HO-Me-Dye} \quad (2a)$$

$$\text{HO-Me-Dye} + OH^- = Me(OH)_2 + \text{Dye} \quad (2b)$$

	$k_{P\text{-}Me}$	$k_{Me\text{-}D}$
Cu (II)	~ 10^4	1×10^5
Zn (II)	4×10^3	0.2×10^3

FIG. 8

is known, then we should at least get a parallelism between that affinity and the onset of the pH effect.

For example, for copper [which also can act as a bridge here (Fig. 4), as we know from independent experiments], which has a much greater affinity for OH ions, you could expect this competition of OH and dye to occur at an earlier pH; and indeed it does, as the next illustration (Fig. 9) shows.

Here (Fig. 9) we have the same type of photometric titration with copper as

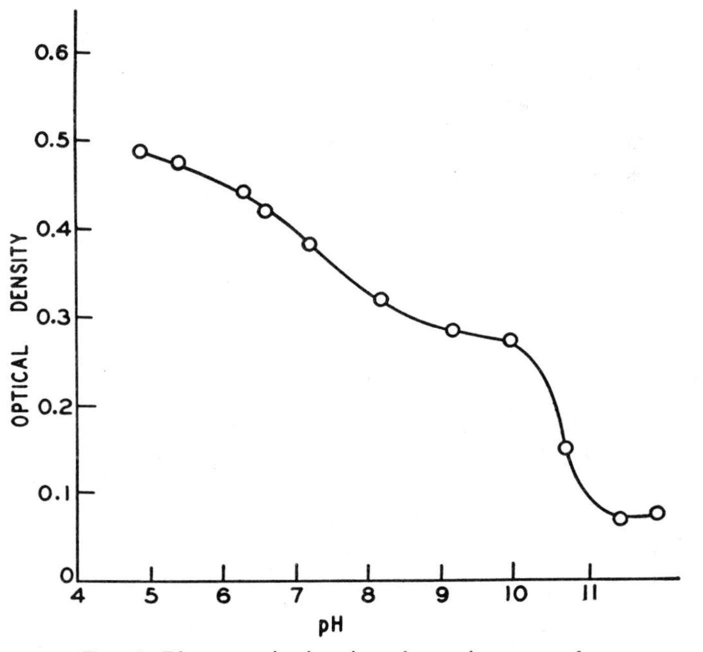

FIG. 9. Photometric titration of protein-copper-dye

was shown before with zinc (Fig. 5), and you will notice that even at pH 5 the extent of binding is decreasing. If we take a metal such as cadmium, which is known to have a lesser affinity for hydroxyl than either zinc or copper, the photometric titration curve continues to go up until pH 9 and then it drops precipitously. So specific effects result when these metals are present. The zinc would act very differently in an experiment, however, with a zinc enzyme at pH 7. The zinc would have unusual properties, compared to the other two metals which I have chosen as examples, which are really due to its hydrolytic equilibria or to its interaction with the solvent. In other words, we have specific effects here which are essentially due to the environment rather than to the protein itself.

There is something else in this curve (Fig. 9), though, which also shows a certain specificity which some of you will surely notice. In the zinc curve (Fig. 5) after the rise, once the drop came in, there was a continuous drop. In contrast in the case of copper we have here (Fig. 9) a plateau near pH 9 and then a subsequent second drop which is somewhat puzzling until you examine the structure of this complex schematically and in more detail. Let us turn to the next illustration (Fig. 10).

I have assumed, because my reference point is so strongly colored toward the dye, that the OH could go in only at the Me—D bond (top, Fig. 10) but, of course, if you look at the full structure you really have to ask the question: Where *will* the OH go in? It can combine with the metal either by displacing the metal-protein bond or by displacing the metal-dye bond. I think it is pretty clear that which place it will go depends upon which bond is the weaker. It will go to the weaker one.

If we look at some of the data which we have for zinc and copper, evidently

P—Me—D
↑ ? ↑
OH^- OH^-

P $\xrightarrow{1 \times 10^4}$ Cu $\xrightarrow{1 \times 10^5}$ D
↓ OH^-
P + Cu—D (OH)
↓ OH^-
$Cu(OH)_2$ + D

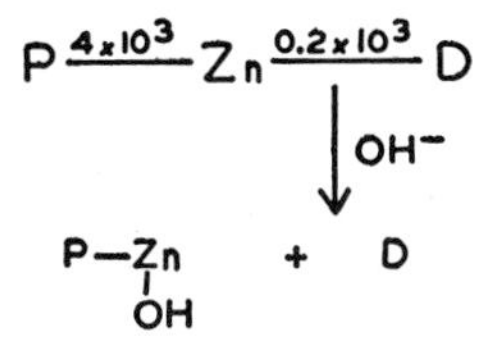

FIG. 10

that difference is responsible for the behavior. In the case of zinc, we know that for the zinc-dye bond the stability constant is about 0.2×10^3. This is an association constant. The zinc-protein bond is some 20 times stronger with a constant of 4×10^3, so it would seem that in this case the OH would displace the dye and, since there is only a single step here, we will get only one change in the spectrum.

Now, in contrast, let us look at the copper situation (Fig. 10). Copper tends to form stronger complexes than does zinc with nitrogen atoms and the stability constant for the copper-dye bond in the chelate is a good deal larger than that of zinc. However, the stability constant of the copper for the protein is not of the same order (Fig. 10) and, consequently, the OH ion should first displace the metal at P—Cu and, afterward, if you still increase the OH ion concentration, then you will get a split at Cu—D also.

Thus, the first drop in absorption is due to the break at P—Cu, because when the dye is no longer in the neighborhood of the protein its aqueous environment is different from the protein environment and so its spectrum changes. A second drop occurs when the dye is separated from the copper; its spectrum changes. So we can, I think, account for these differences in behavior in terms of the properties of the metals which are involved and their behavior with respect to the environment.

Let me turn next to some examples which involve the protein rather than the environment. Again, I would like to give some background information in order to be able to explain some of the new information more clearly.

We have also examined a number of different dyes (you will notice a great similarity to those which have been used in the hapten work) in binding or in complex formation, in this particular case with serum albumin. Now, when the dye is bound to serum albumin, its environment is changed, so the spectrum changes (Fig. 11) and this is indicated in the left-hand section; the solid line is the spectrum of the dye, the spectrum of the dye in its protein complex is given by the broken curve.

For the serum albumins, beta lactoglobulin and casein, which one can complex with these dyes, the spectrum shift is always in the direction shown in the upper left diagram of Fig. 11. The shift is in this direction at any pH for all proteins except one, human serum albumin. Human serum albumin at pH 9 behaves in an anomalous fashion from our reference point. While the spectrum of the dye is not changed, the spectrum of the dye bound to the protein is significantly different, which indicates that the environment of the dye on the protein is different at pH 9 than at 6.

We attempted to localize that change and to interpret it in terms of the specific interaction involved.

One thing that we knew from early work was that if the charge is removed from the sulfonate substituent (Fig. 11), the ability of this compound to be bound to the albumins disappears and the spectrum reverts to that of the unbound form. On the other hand, in contrast to the situation with the immune globulins, on change of the anionic group from sulfonic to carboxylic to phosphonic to arsonic, all the compounds behave in the same way. With any one of these dyes and serum albumin you get the upper-left spectrum at pH 6 and the lower-left spectrum at pH 9. Hence, the nature of the interaction in this case is certainly identical in quality for all three; there are slight differences in the extent of binding and the extent of displacement, but the displacement is always in the same direction. It is quite clear that there is not the same type of steric fitting phenomenon here that is involved in other cases of steric relationships, such as with the gamma-globulins.

We also found that if we changed the sulfonic acid group from the para position to the meta, it made no difference. The meta compound also behaved in the same way, showing the shift with pH; but if we went to the ortho position, then we did get a marked difference. At pH 9 the spectrum was no longer shifted upward but shifted to the left, just as it is in the upper left of Fig. 11. Evidently then, there is some critical steric effect which occurs when the sulfonic acid is at this particular point.

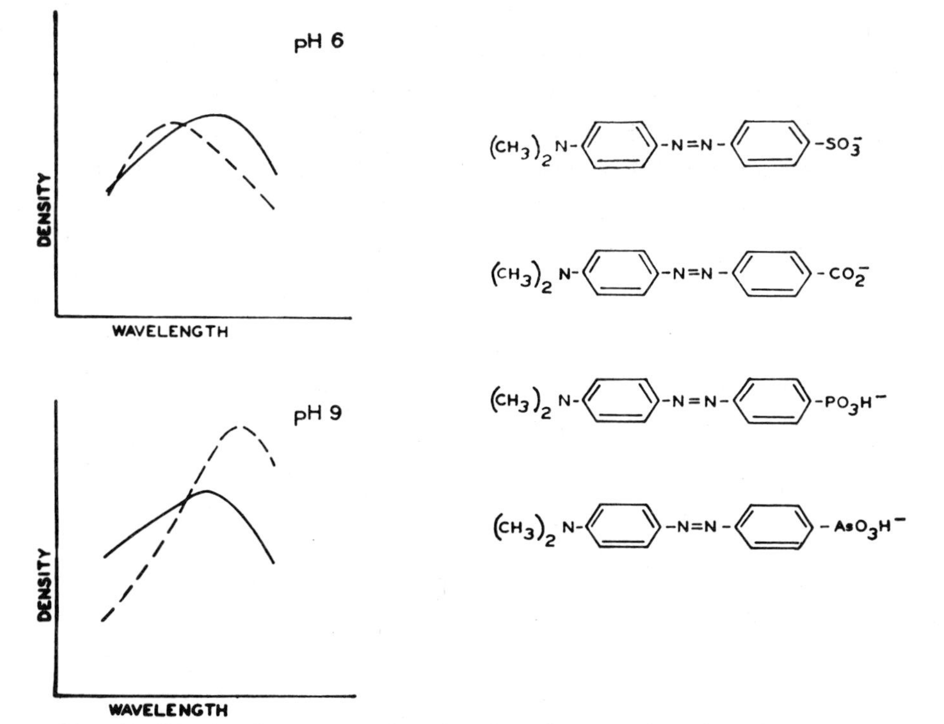

FIG. 11. Spectra of some organic anions bound, or not bound, to human serum albumin.

The first tendency, I think, would be to say that the interaction of the protein must involve the azo group in some way. By having the sulfonic acid in the ortho position we are blocking access to this azo group. Perhaps I should also mention that the same thing happens with the carboxyl group and the same thing happens with the phosphonic acid group. We have not tried the arsonic acids simply because we did not have the ortho one to use. Using the sulfonate or carboxylate as an example, if we put the anionic substituent in the ortho position, we get an effect very different from the para position and it may indicate, then, that access to the azo group is blocked. If that were true, then we can reason from models shown in the next illustrations (Fig. 12). B represents the meta

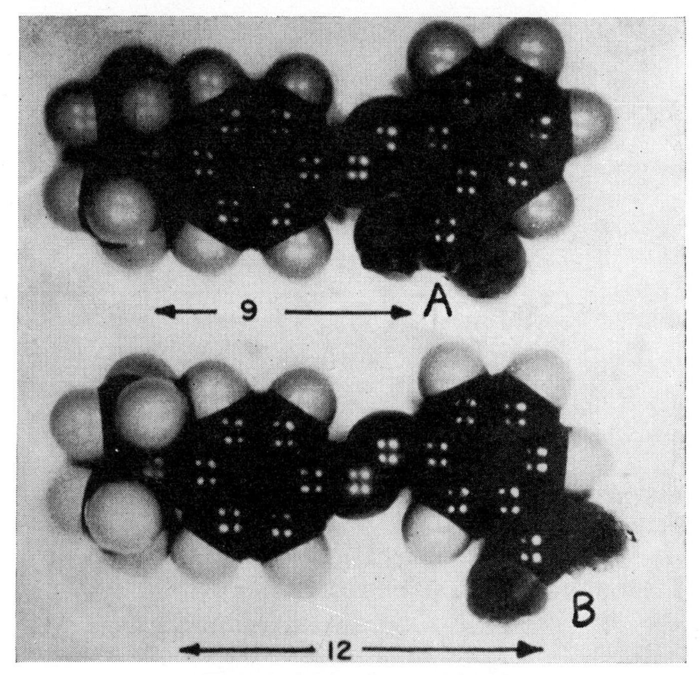

FIG. 12. Molecular model of

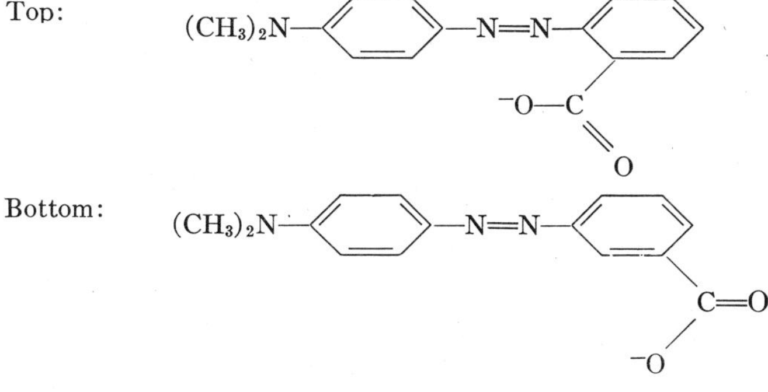

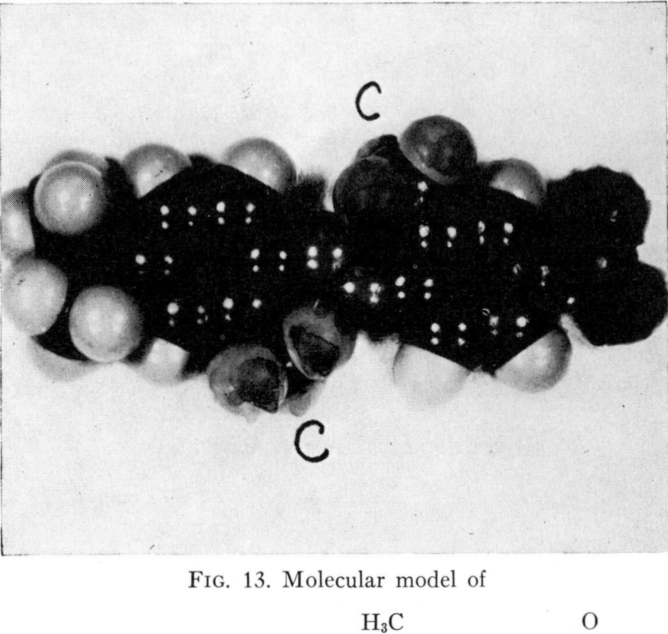

FIG. 13. Molecular model of

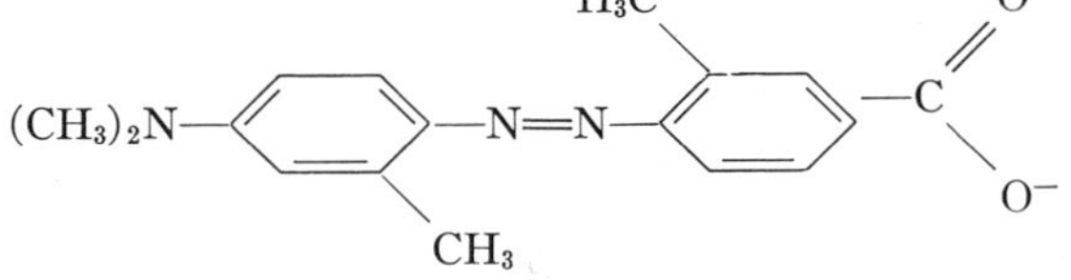

carboxylic arrangement and A the ortho. You can see that there is very definitely a hindrance of access to this azo group in A. We reasoned then, as is shown in the next illustration (Fig. 13), that if we could block access to this azo group by a different method, keeping the carboxylic acid group out in the para position, by putting in some methyl substituents, which I think you can see at C (Fig. 13), these should block the access to the azo group, certainly as much as the carboxyl did (Klotz, Burkhard, and Urquhart, 1952).

Then, if the azo group is the critical point, blocking access to it is what causes the disappearance of the interaction and, therefore, in this particular molecule (Fig. 13) we should also block the interaction. In other words, this should act like an ortho carboxylic acid despite the fact that the $—CO_2^-$ group is available in the para position. On the other hand, if the group involved is not the azo group but, perhaps, is the $(CH_3)_2N—$ nitrogen, then the fact that we have blocked access at the azo should make no difference as long as we have the carboxyl group back in its para position. Actually, this molecule with the methyl groups in the ortho position acts exactly like the molecule which does not have methyl groups in the ortho position. It acts like the para carboxylic acid and

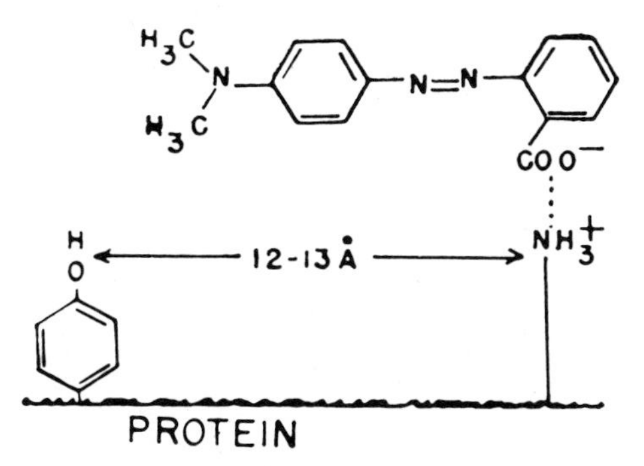

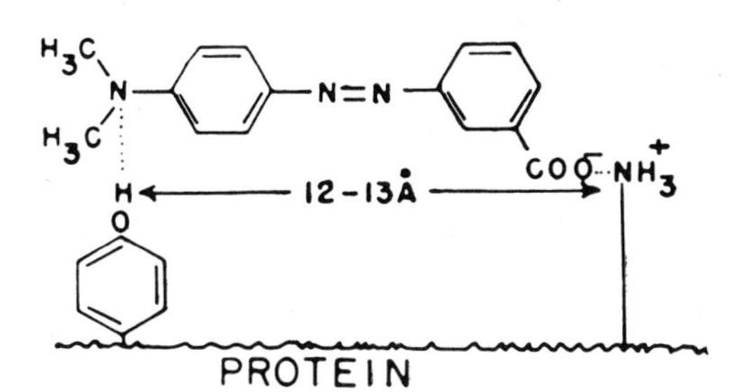

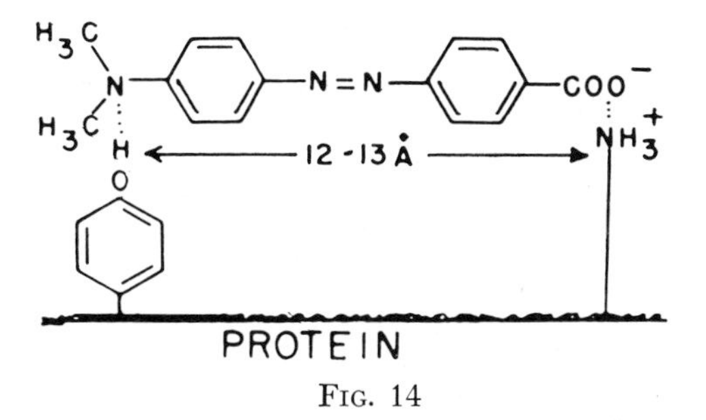

FIG. 14

the para sulfonic acid. So, it seems evident that blocking access to the azo is not really important.

In that case, then, we thought, as is shown in the next illustration (Fig. 14), that perhaps—looking at the bottom part first—the interaction involved the dimethylamino group as well as the carboxyl group. We know the carboxyl must still be involved because, if you remove its charge, ability to be bound by protein disappears. Then, if this group is involved, and if we show, as we have from chemical evidence (Klotz, Burkhard, and Urquhart, 1952), that it is likely that a protein tyrosine chain is involved in the interaction with the $(CH_3)_2N$—, and if we assume that the removal of the anionic charge followed by disappearance of binding indicates that a positively charged group of the protein is involved, then we can make a model of a particular molecule as shown in Fig. 12 and, from a scale model, get the distance between $(CH_3)_2N$— and —COO^- substituents.

In the case of the para dye its maximum extension is 12.8 Å. (Fig. 14). In the meta dye, the distance between $(CH_3)_2N$— and —COO^- depends on the extension but it can vary from about 10.5 to 12.8 Angstroms, so at maximum extension it too can cover a distance of about 12 Å. On the other hand, in the ortho dye, the maximum distance you can reach from $(CH_3)_2N$— to —COO^- is only approximately 8.5 Å. So, as an alternative explanation, it would seem, then, that perhaps the binding to the protein was at two points and that these two exterior substituents were involved. In the para and meta molecules the exterior substituents can span the distance between the two side chains of the protein which are involved, but with the ortho molecule that distance cannot be spanned and, as a result, the electrostatic bond being stronger, there is only a bonding here and the $(CH_3)_2N$— group is too far away to give anomalous spectrophotometric interaction, or to give the bond at this particular point.

If this explanation is true, then we felt we ought to be able to argue in another direction. If the reason the ortho dye molecule does not interact with the human serum albumin to give the particular special spectrum is because it is too short, then it ought to be possible to separate these groups by too long a distance and have the same phenomenon occurring as it occurs here.

We could put in a methylene group between —COO^- and the ring and we did (Peticolas (1954)), and found that the methylene compound acted exactly like the regular para dye. Perhaps that was not quite far enough apart, however. So we put in two methylene groups, but that, too, acted like a regular para dye. That is not too puzzling, though, for if you make the model (Fig. 15) you will find that while, of course, at maximum extension the distance is approximately 14.5 Å, there is a methylene group with free rotation and you can rotate the anionic substituent around and you will get an extension which is only approximately 13 Å (Fig. 15).

That, then, says that what we need is a rigid bond between the ring and the anionic substituent, and as is shown in Fig. 16 and 17, bottom, clearly we should use a cinnamic acid in which case we cannot obtain rotation. So in this case (Fig. 17, bottom) we should have too long a distance between the $(CH_3)_2N$— group and the COO^- group, approximately 14.5 Å and, consequently, this dye too should not be able to span the distance between protein side chains. Thus this molecule should show a spectrum not like the para compound of Fig. 17 (top) but like the ortho substituted one, which, indeed, it does.

I would like to show you, then, Fig. 16 with models indicating the comparison of the regular compound (top) which does span the distance of the side

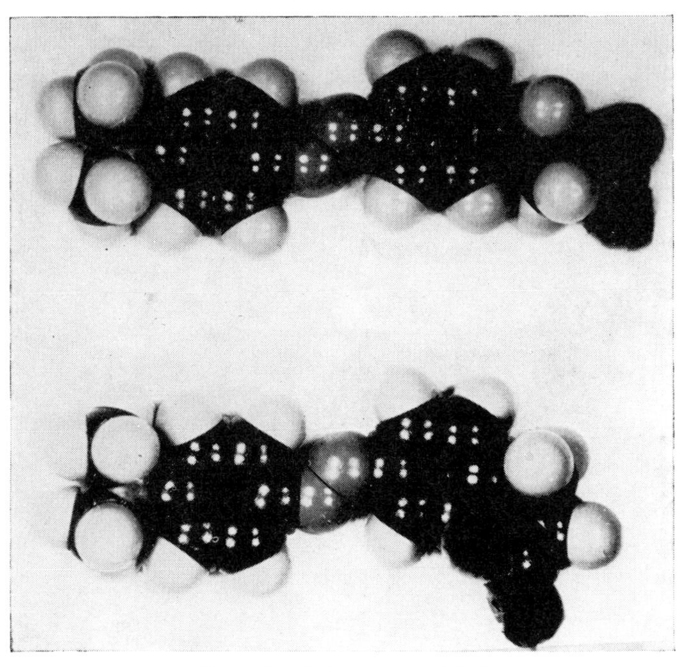

FIG. 15. Molecular model of

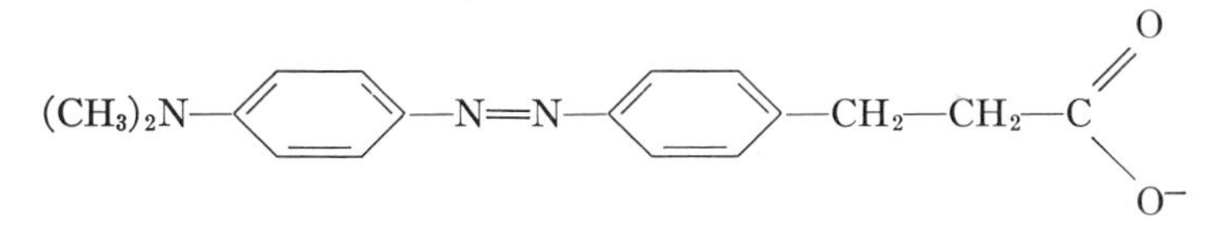

at maximum extension (top) and with —COO^- curled back (bottom).

chains properly, and the cinnamic acid compound (bottom) which has a double bond in the side chain, and consequently cannot be rotated over to one side.

There actually is a much longer span with the latter than with the former. Consequently, too long a molecule, as well as too short a molecule, will not fit between these protein side chains.

These specificities, although I have described them, of course, in terms of the organic molecules, the small ones interacting with the protein, reside, presumably, in the protein itself.

I mentioned at the beginning that if we take a protein molecule such as serum albumin, which carries a negative charge, let us say at pH 7, where the negative charge is approximately 12 units per molecule, and measure the binding of an anionic molecule (Fig. 18), it is bound very substantially despite the fact that the protein has a negative charge which ought to repel it.

Recently we prepared a molecule which, as you can see in Fig. 18 (lower

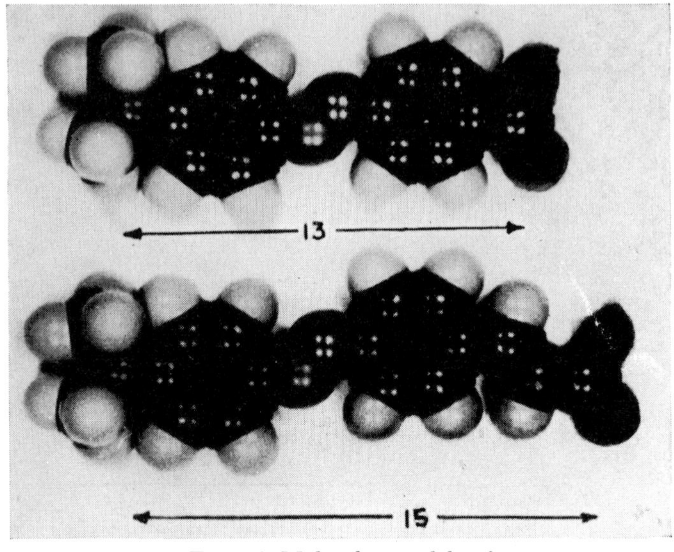

FIG. 16. Molecular models of

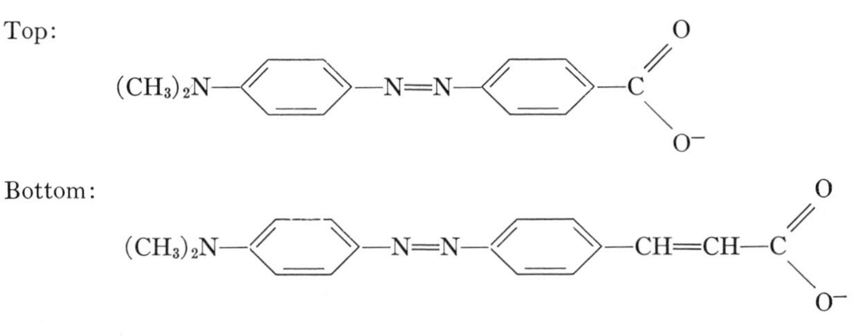

right), has a base structure which is fundamentally identical with the upper one but in which we replace the anionic group by a cationic group. Despite the fact that the protein carries a negative charge, and the organic molecule is plus charged, there is essentially no binding. There are a few points in the lower curve slightly above the zero axis, but when you get to these higher concentrations we can not even be positive that these points are significant, because we are measuring small differences between very large numbers.

Why should this be true? Presumably there is some specificity in the protein configuration. We have an explanation, which initially we thought of in a different connection, which would account for the difference in anionic vs. cationic binding automatically. I am not absolutely sure it is true, but certainly it seems to me at the present time to be convincing, and so I thought I might outline it in the next illustration (Fig. 19).

We indicate, first, again going backward a little, where I think the origin of

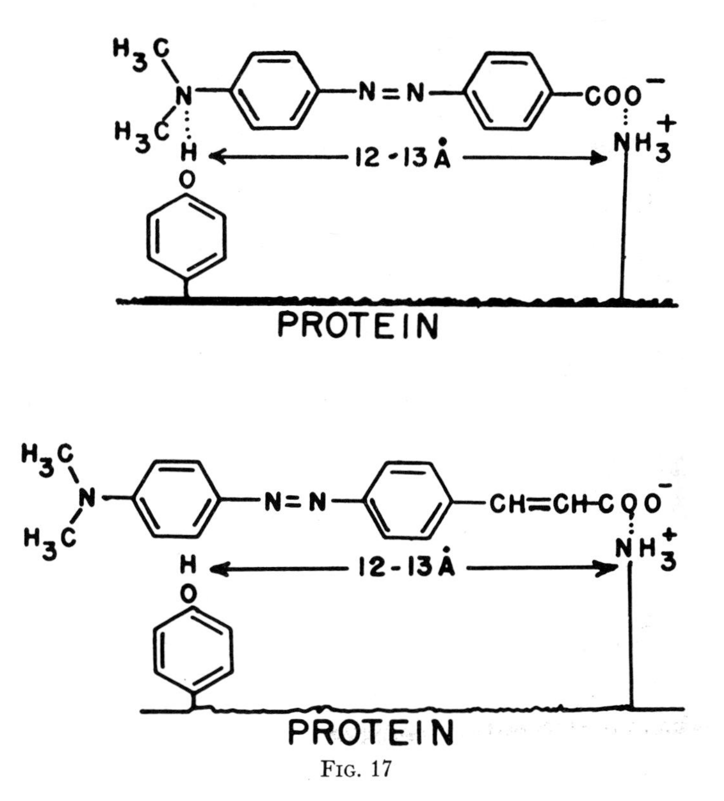

FIG. 17

the specificity may lie. Suppose we compare first, not so much the data of the preceding figure, but, rather, a different question which we were worried about some 6 or 7 years ago. Serum albumin is an outstanding protein in its ability to bind anions in a very general, non-specific way. There are a couple of others, such as beta lactoglobulin, which come somewhere in that neighborhood, but they are not nearly as good, and the great majority of proteins simply will not form complexes non-specifically with the anions which I have shown you. So, let the left side of Fig. 19 represent serum albumin for the moment, and the right side represent, let us say, serum globulin, because that is a good example of a protein which does not bind non-specifically. Gamma globulin will bind the haptens for which it has been built very strongly, but not these other anions.

What we found was that, if you examine the amino acid composition of these proteins, serum albumin was distinct in that the number of its hydroxyl amino acids was relatively small compared to the number of its carboxylic and cationic amino acids; whereas, in serum globulin, the number of hydroxyl amino acids is relatively large compared to the carboxylic and cationic amino acids.

Now, if we assume that an OH—O hydrogen bond is stronger than OH—N, then if you have a limited number of hydroxyl amino acids they would tend to

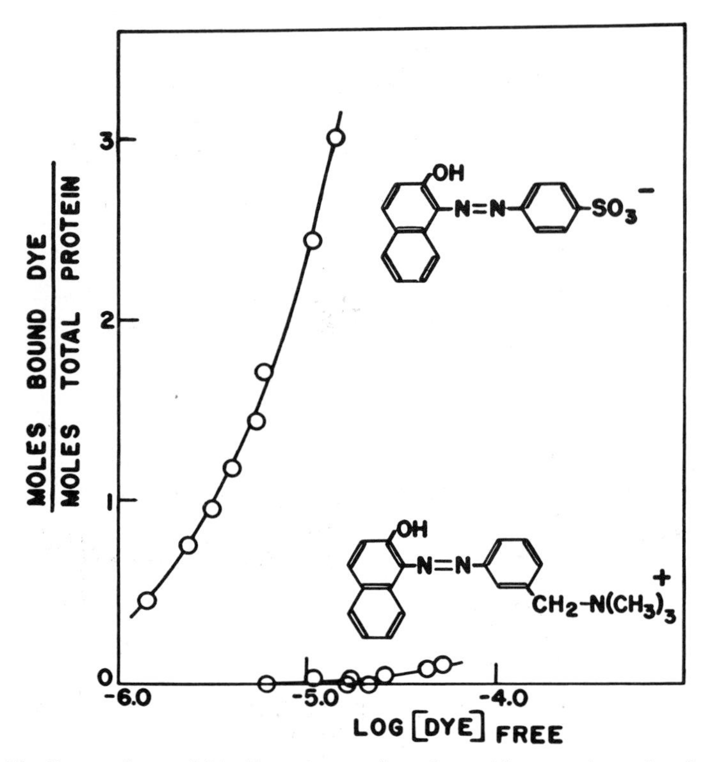

FIG. 18. Comparison of binding of organic anion with organic cation by serum albumin.

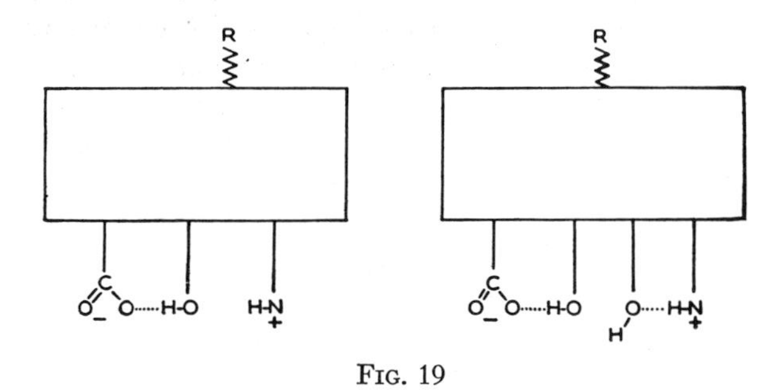

FIG. 19

form cross bonds with —COO^- side chains rather than with $\equiv NH^+$. The result would be that the $\equiv NH^+$ side-chain, let us call it a lysine to visualize it more concretely, would be relatively free. It would not be restricted in its configuration. It would be able to come relatively close to organic-type side chains, say leucines, which I have indicated by R (Fig. 19). The important thing is that you could have in a relatively close geometric position, because of the freedom of motion of the $\equiv NH^+$ side chain, a plus side group and an organic side chain to supply the van der Waals forces, in order to complement the negative charge on the anion and the organic part of the anion, respectively.

However, if you go to serum globulin, which has a very large number of hydroxyl amino acids, there are enough of these side chains to rigidly hold in configuration the carboxylic acid side chains and there are still plenty left over to hold the $\equiv NH^+$ rigidly. On that basis, then, we said the cationic side chain was not free, so that it could not come into the neighborhood of a suitable leucine or phenylalanine group and, consequently, you would not have a stable complex with an organic anion.

As I said, this was initially suggested in order to account for the differences in proteins, but I think you can see that it also accounts for the differences in the interaction of a given protein with the two types of ion, because, according to this picture, if we now take a positively-charged small ion, it would have to interact with the $-COO^-$ group; but this group is blocked—or it is rigid—and so you can not really get the necessary juxtaposition of the R and $-COO^-$ side chains so that you can obtain the additional van der Waals interaction to complement this electrostatic interaction, to hold the plus-charged organic ion.

Consequently, on this basis, you can see that we would have expected that a cation, an organic cation of the same size as an anion which is bound strongly, would not be bound strongly. Furthermore, if we go to gamma globulin, there is no reason why it should behave any differently. It too has its carboxylic acid groups strongly hindered, or rigidly held and, consequently, it too should not bind organic cations. This, indeed, is the fact.

These are some of the examples which I wanted to bring to your attention as illustrations of specificities of various degrees and of the explanations which we can give on a molecular basis.

I hope that I have indicated that dyes are really only incidental to our work, that they are just a convenience because it is easy to make these measurements with dyes. I emphasize this particularly because Professor Hirschfelder brought up the question as to whether the excited states might be involved. With dyes you would immediately think how they absorb light, and consequently we have special interactions here due to the existence of these excited states. In the few cases where we have made similar measurements on the non-colored organic ions, the results are substantially the same, so there is nothing special about the dyes. The specialty arises in the nature of their molecular structure.

These are some of the factors which can be involved. I think, while you can not necessarily go from these systems to enzymatic and other biological systems, you, nevertheless, have certain features which are outlined here and which act, you might say, as boundary conditions in order to give you some idea of the limits within which the biological interactions must operate.

References

Fredericq, E. 1954. Interactions de proteines et d'anions en solution. Arch. Internat. de Physiol. *62:* 150–151.

Hughes, T. R. and I. M. Klotz. 1956. Mediation by metals of the binding of small molecules by proteins: Effect of hydrolytic equilibria of the metal. J. Am. Chem. Soc. *78:* 2109–2116.

Klotz, I. M. and J. Ayers. Unpublished work.

Klotz, I. M., R. K. Burkhard and J. M. Urquhart. 1952. Structural specificities in the interactions of some organic ions with serum albumin. J. Am. Chem. Soc. *74:* 202–208.

Klotz, I. M. and W. C. Loh Ming. 1954. Mediation by metals of the binding of small molecules by proteins. J. Am. Chem. Soc. *76:* 805–814.

Peticolas, W. L. 1954. Ph.D. Dissertation, Northwestern University.

MR. LEOPOLD MAY (Johns Hopkins University): I wonder how you can extend the interaction between the anion and the proteins to explaining why precipitations occur between proteins and substances such as trichloroacetic acid.

PROFESSOR KLOTZ: Essentially you have the same thing with hapten-antibody interactions. You can visualize, I think, mechanisms in which there may be cross-linkages, or there may be merely cancellation of charge. Let us consider trichloracetic acid with protein in an acid solution. The protein carries a plus charge, which would interact with the solvent, but as these groups are covered with negative charges of $Cl_3 CCOO^-$ ions, the polar substituents are neutralized, which decreases the ability of the protein to interact with the solvent. I think that this might cause a precipitation.

MR. MAY: We made an observation with bovine serum albumin and human serum albumin precipitated with trichloracetic acid. The precipitate will dissolve in 95% ethyl alcohol, methyl alcohol or acetone, whereas, the precipitate with phosphomolybdic acid or some other reagents is not soluble in these nonaqueous media. I wonder how these facts could be explained.

PROFESSOR KLOTZ: This is, I think, implicit in what I said. In the case of trichloracetic acid you would have the protein with all its plus groups holding the trichloracetate anions and with the organic groups extending out into the solvent, so that the organic end of the complex would suffice to get the complex in solution in organic solvents. On the other hand, perhaps with the phosphomolybdic acid precipitate there is a cross linkage between protein molecules and the organic solvent cannot break that up (Fig. 1a).

DR. PRESSMAN: I would like to ask one question and then make a comment. First, when you vary the dielectric constant by the use of glycine, how are you sure that the effect you observe is not due to a displacement of the bound substance by the glycine, as you indicated to be the effect of dioxane?

Then there is probably more to the problem of charge than you have indi-

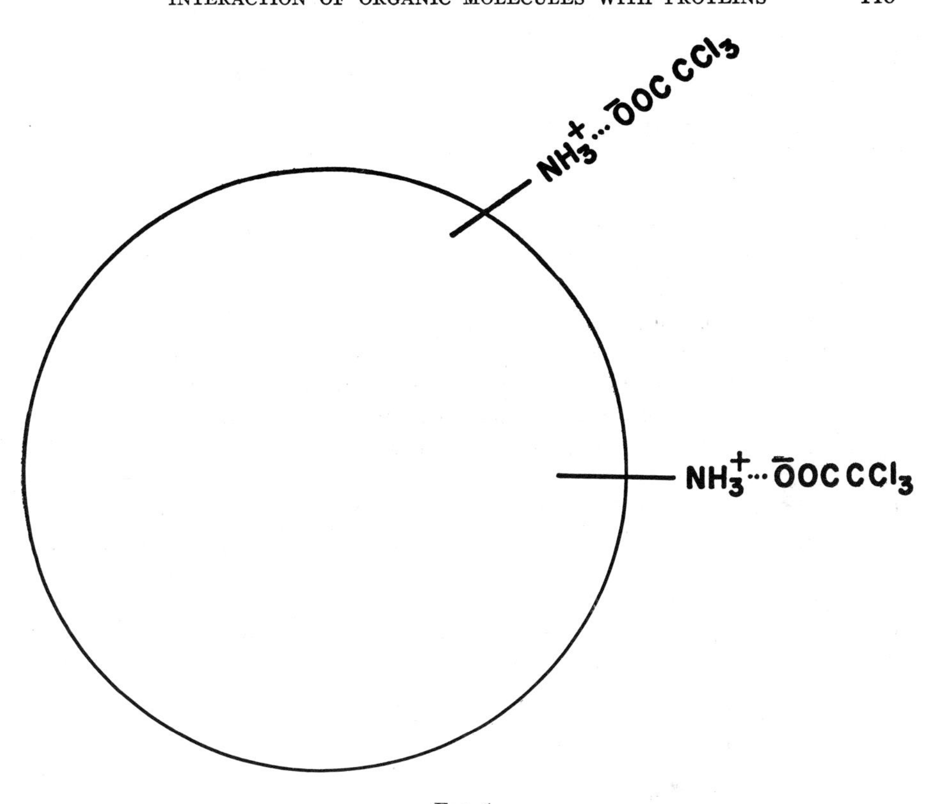

FIG. 1a

cated. The effect of a positive center is quite complex. We had occasion to measure the binding to serum albumin of some substances containing positive groups. Let us take the two haptens which I described previously which were used for determining the charge interaction or the closest approach of the positive charge to the specific region of the antibody. You will recall, they were the following:

(a)

(b)

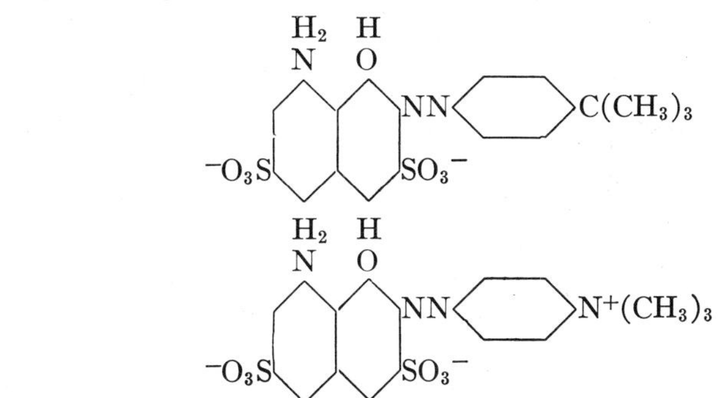

(a) binds very strongly to albumin and it is a negative ion. If the *tertiary Butyl* group is replaced by a carboxylate group, i.e.

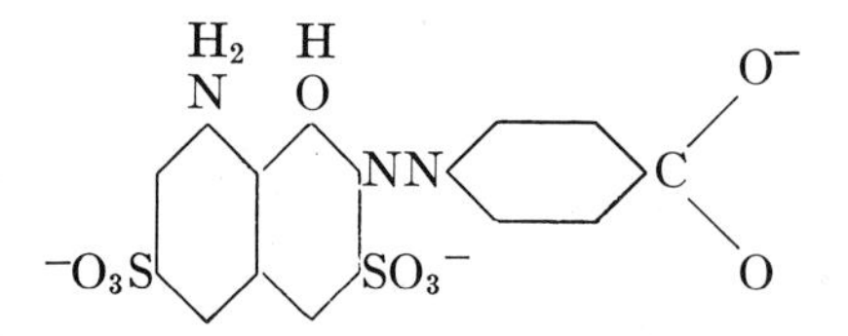

we have a tri-negative ion which still binds strongly to albumin. However, the compound containing a positive group, compound (b), is still a negative ion and if the bindings here are due to the negative containing charge in all cases we would expect a continued binding, even of the substances of the positive ion, since it still has the same configuration about the negative charges as in substance (a). Actually, we find that the presence of a positive ion group in compound (b) decreases its ability to bind to albumin tremendously, although we have the same negative charge configuration as in the case of the tightly bound non-polar substance. Thus, the effect of the positive ion appears to be more complex in certain cases than in the situation you mentioned where the compounds you studied did not bind simply because there was apparently no receptor site for it.

PROFESSOR KLOTZ: Evidently, I should have shown another illustration. Suppose we are measuring the extent of binding against the concentration of

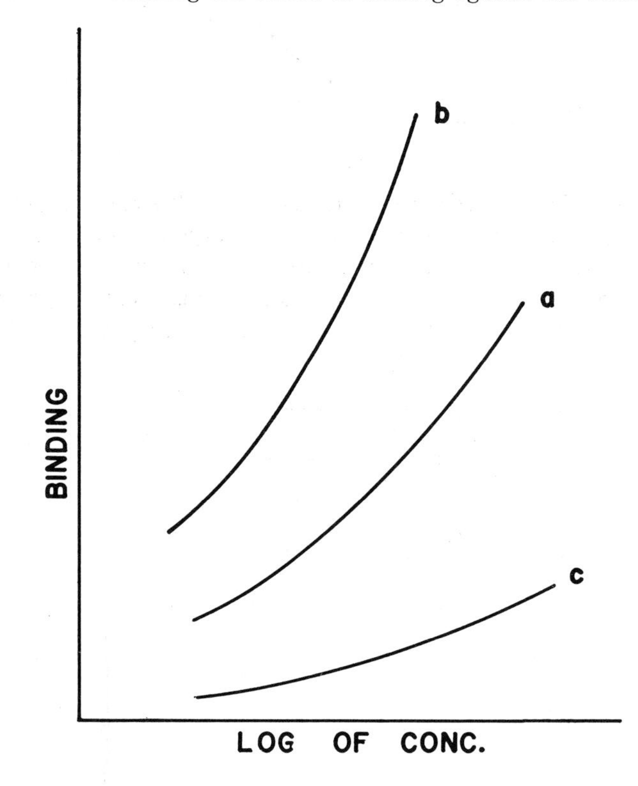

the dyes (Fig. 2a). Let us say curve (a) represents the binding in water. In dioxane, as I said, you decrease the dielectric constant, so there would be a drop in binding due to increased repulsion and there might also be competition. So with dioxane you expect something like curve (c) and that is what you get.

What would we expect with glycine? With glycine we increase the dielectric constant, there is less repulsion, so you would expect an increase in binding, and if there is any competition then binding ought to drop down.

The figure shows that there is an increase in binding, that binding really goes up. However, you could still claim, I think quite rightly, that maybe it would have been way up above curve (b) though, and that it is perhaps down to (b) because there is still some competition bringing it down.

First we and several others have tried to measure the binding of glycine and other amino acids and we can not find any. Secondly, I did bring in the point in my talk that there seemed to be a linear relation in ΔF of binding. If there were competition, I would not have expected that to be because the linear relation was a simple relation for the free energy dependence on dielectric constant only.

The Effect of Dye Structure on Affinity for Fibers

H. E. Schroeder and S. N. Boyd

E. I. duPont de Nemours & Co., Wilmington, Del.

DYEING PROCESSES HAVE BEEN FOUND to involve straightforward physical chemical principles in all of the cases which have been studied carefully. I plan to discuss only the chemistry of systems essentially at equilibrium. Dyeing kinetics are diffusion controlled and too complicated for treatment in a short period of time.

There is a wide variation in the chemical features of specific systems since the characteristics are those of a particular dye structure responding to a particular environment. In general, dyeing may be regarded as a competition between water and fiber for dye. Therefore, as the solubility of dye in water becomes less and the solubility in the fiber more, there is greater absorption of dye by fiber. Conversely, relatively greater solubility of dye in water favors desorption. The physical-chemical question concerns the forces capable of favoring the energy and the entropy changes involved and resulting in a concentration of dye inside the polymer structure.

The problem can be broken down into simple elements: first, the primary processes that attract individual dye molecules into the polymer; next, the more subtle forces that result in marked superiority of one dye structure to another, despite their superficial equivalence. A good deal can be learned about both of these by considering the isolated physical-chemical systems at equilibrium, on the basis of the particular dye structures which show affinity for or react with different polymers.

Fibers vary from essentially hydrophobic types like ethylene terephthalate and nylon to hydrophilic materials like cotton. Also they may be relatively non-polar or may contain a great number of ionizable groups. Since a similar variation is possible in dye structures, practically all the normal chemical forces can be involved, ranging from those occurring in simple intermixing of non-polar molecules through intermolecular association even to formation of ion pairs.

In the simplest case, a fiber devoid of ionizable groups, like cellulose acetate or polyethylene terephthalate, is dyed only by water insoluble molecules *lacking* ionic groups—compounds such as: 1,4-diamino-anthraquinone or aminoazobenzene derivatives—while ionic dyes highly soluble in water will not even stain these fibers. With dyes of the former type the fibers become colored rapidly when heated in the presence of an aqueous dispersion of the dye.

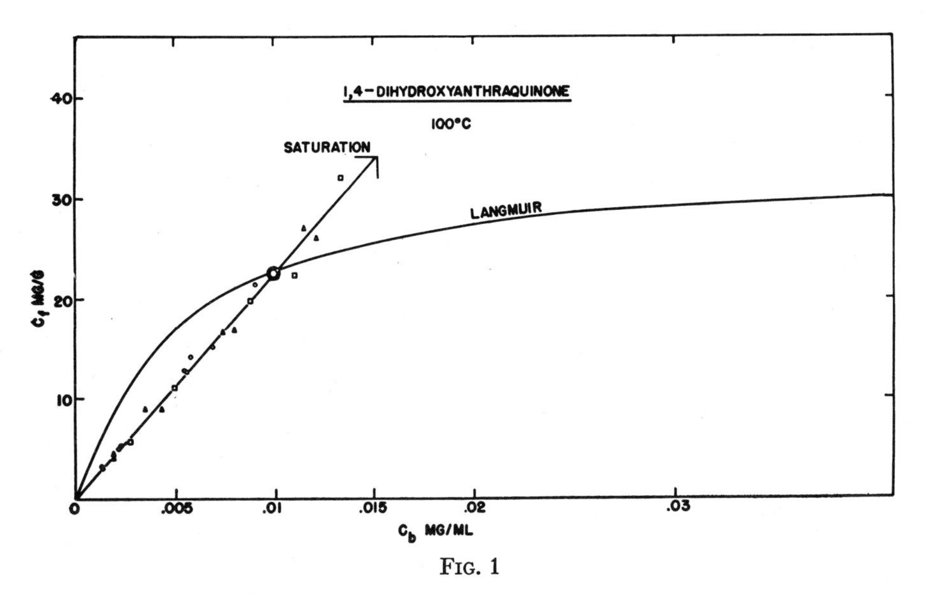

FIG. 1

Careful physical-chemical analysis of the ethylene terephthalate-dye system shows the fiber is being dyed by a solution mechanism. At equilibrium the ratio of dye dissolved in fiber to dye dissolved in water is a constant, equivalent to a partition coefficient. As shown in Fig. 1, an excellent fit of data to a straight line is obtained. The limiting concentrations are those of saturation in both phases. There is no sign in any of the many isotherms we have measured that the dye is associated with specific sites which show a chemical affinity for dye

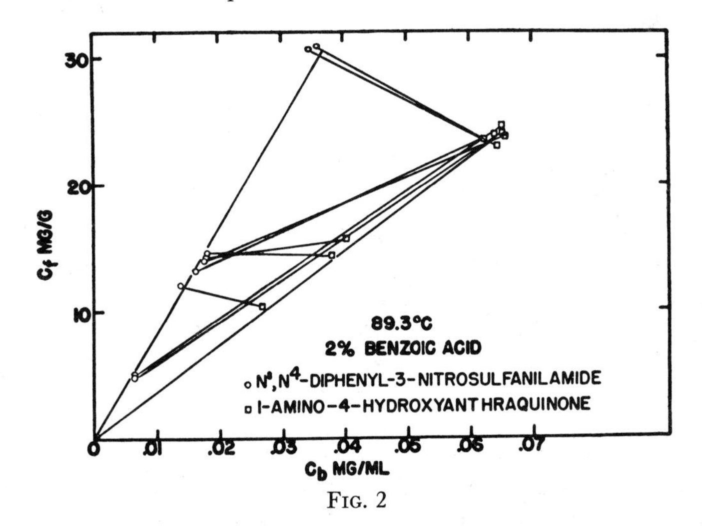

FIG. 2

and are limited in number. If sites were involved a typical Langmuir isotherm would result. The linearity of the experimental isotherms suggests that the dye is monomolecularly dispersed in both phases. Isotherms for two dissimilar dyes dyed together (Fig. 2) show complete independence of solubility in accord with simple solution theory. In the case of a limited number of chemical sites, there would be competition between dyes for the sites. The dyeing mechanism is best described as solution in the fiber, probably only in the non-crystalline regions. As the curves show, ethylene terephthalate is an excellent solvent capable of dissolving substantial amounts of many non-polar dyes. The heat of dyeing of ethylene terephthalate calculated from isotherms at various temperatures is large, −14.7 Kcal, indicating non-ideal solution and interaction between dyes and fiber, possibly by hydrogen bonding. A very similar picture is observed for cellulose acetate (Fig. 3).

For these fibers the equilibrium constant and the rate of dyeing are profoundly influenced by structural variations in size, shape and polarity of the dyes, as shown for polyethylene terephthalate in Fig. 4 and 5. These indicate that practical dyes must be of restricted size and shape and possess very low water solu-

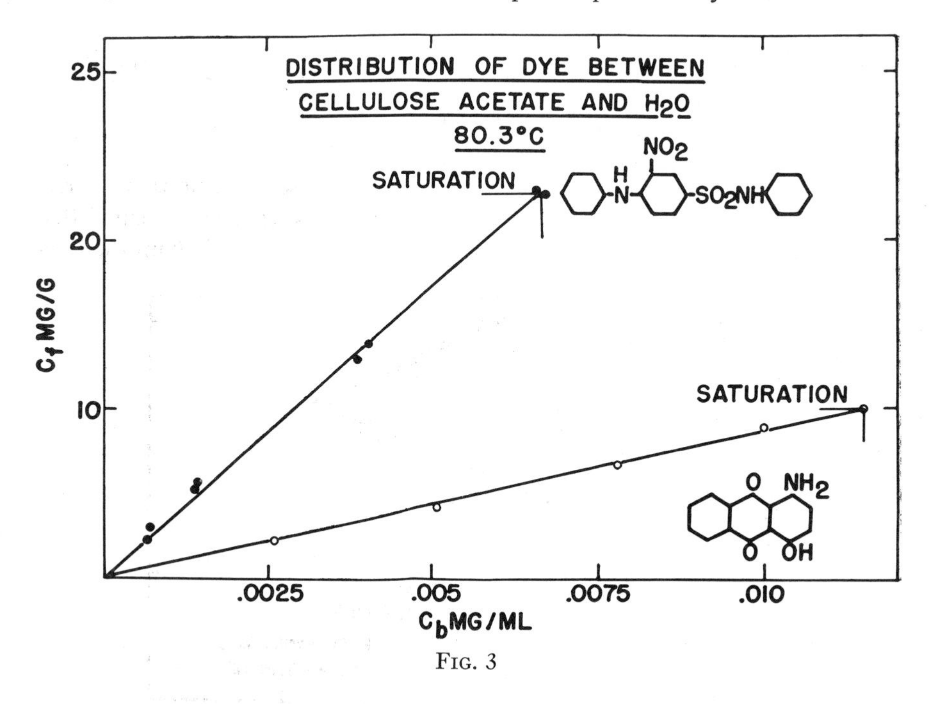

FIG. 3

bility. The amount and rate of dye pick up are a function of structure of both dye and fiber. They are also certainly greatly influenced by the degree of internal order or crystallinity of the fibers. Dyeing is believed to occur in the non-crystalline regions and is promoted by agents which decrease internal order even temporarily, such as heat or soluble carriers like benzoic acid (Fig. 6).

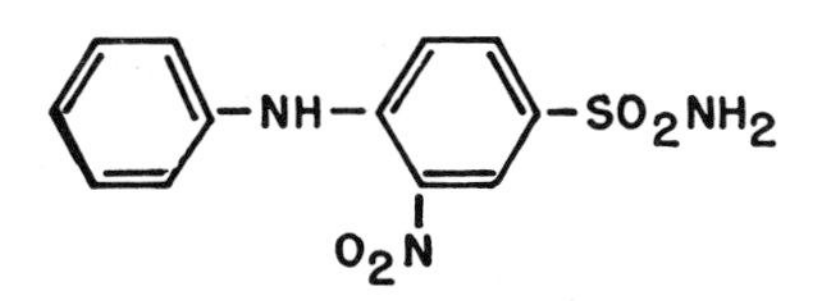

POOR

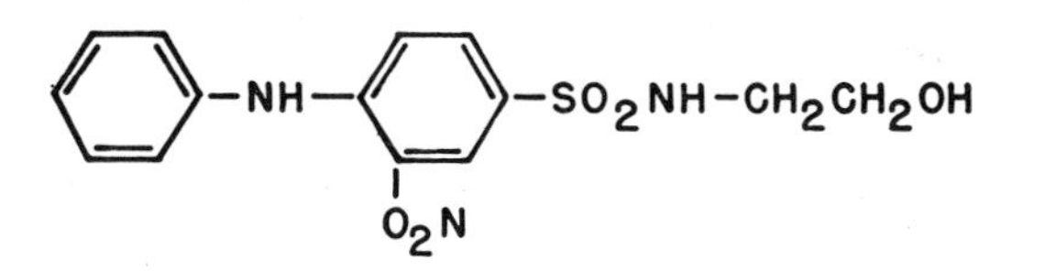

POOR

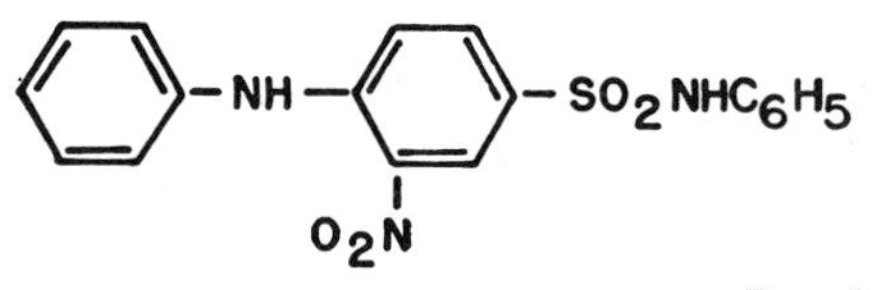

GOOD

Fig. 4

M.W.

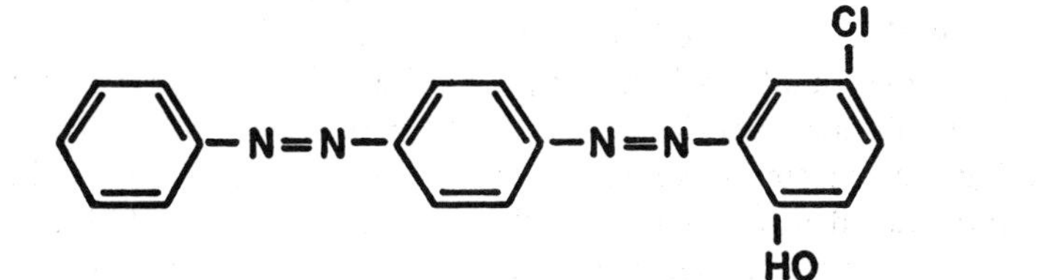

337

DYES RAPIDLY

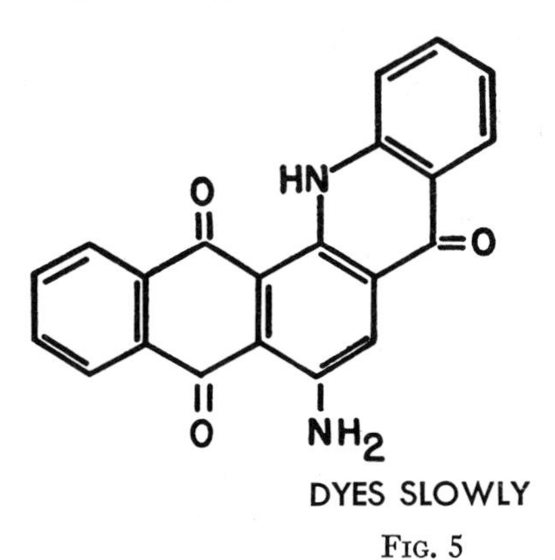

340

DYES SLOWLY

Fig. 5

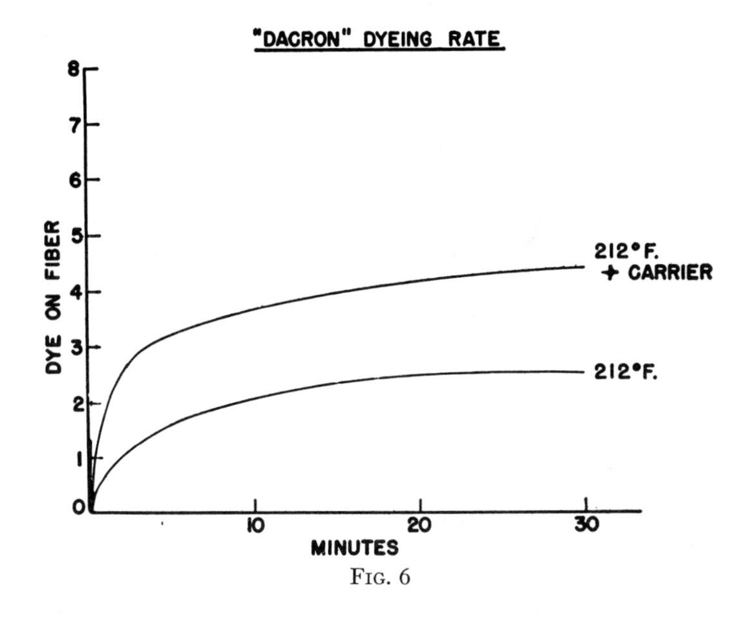

FIG. 6

These considerations of solution mechanism appear to apply in general to polymers of the relatively non-polar type. Coloration occurs by a reversible process involving solution of the dye in the fiber at no specific sites.

In the case of the hydrophilic polymers such as the various forms of cellulose, forces of intermolecular association appear to play a dominant role, although the dyeing mechanisms involved are not clearly defined. The significance of structural coincidence probably reaches its maximum here. Cellulose is a highly ordered hydrophilic molecule which absorbs dyes very rapidly from dilute aqueous solutions of appropriate anions and cations. The dyeing process appears to involve association, probably hydrogen bonding, between polar dye molecules and polar cellulose. The water soluble direct dyes which show affinity for cellulose have groups capable of associating through hydrogen bond formation. In a few cases in which precise measurements have been made the free energy involved approximates that involved in formation of two, three or more hydrogen bonds; i.e., 5–10 Kcal (Fig. 7).

Characteristics that these direct dyes possess in general are relatively great molecular length, a large ratio of mass to charge and great molecular size (surface area). It is particularly important that the direct dye be not too soluble in water if it is to be strongly affinitive, since this displaces equilibrium in favor of the water. These are all features favoring apparent laying down of long flat dye molecules on the long flat cellulose chains. Their effect on affinity is portrayed in Figs. 8, 9, 10 and 11. In Fig. 11 the methoxyl groups of the second molecule force the biphenyl nuclei out of a co-planar situation and destroy affinity of the dye for cellulose.

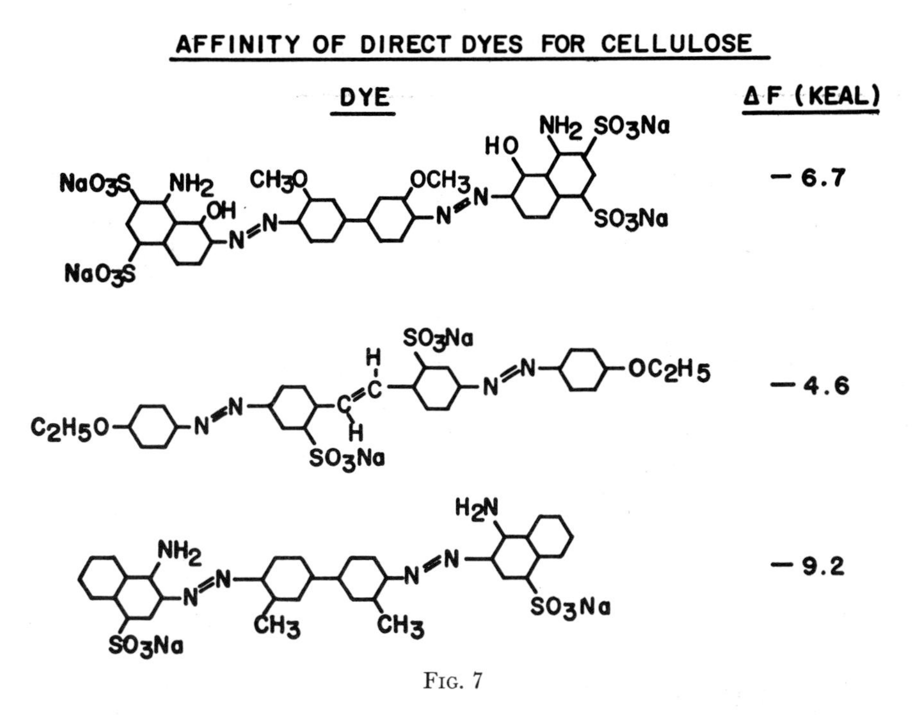

FIG. 7

The best direct dyes contain a number of electron donor or acceptor groups capable of hydrogen bond formation with the many hydroxyl groups present in cellulose. Affinity is greatly promoted by the presence of at least two groups selected from those listed in Fig. 12. There is some evidence that favorable spacing of such groups will lead to exceptionally great affinity as in the case

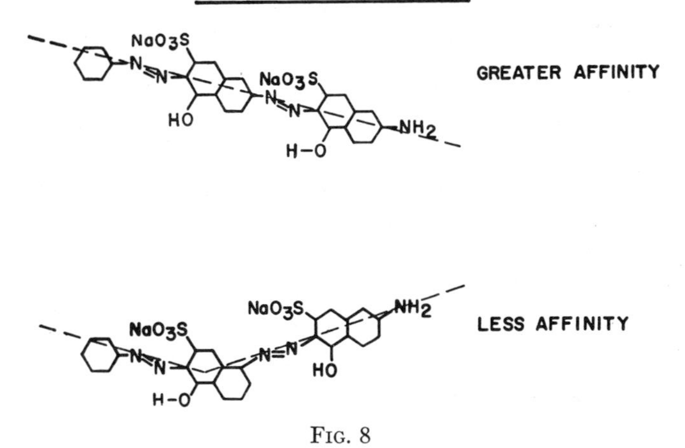

FIG. 8

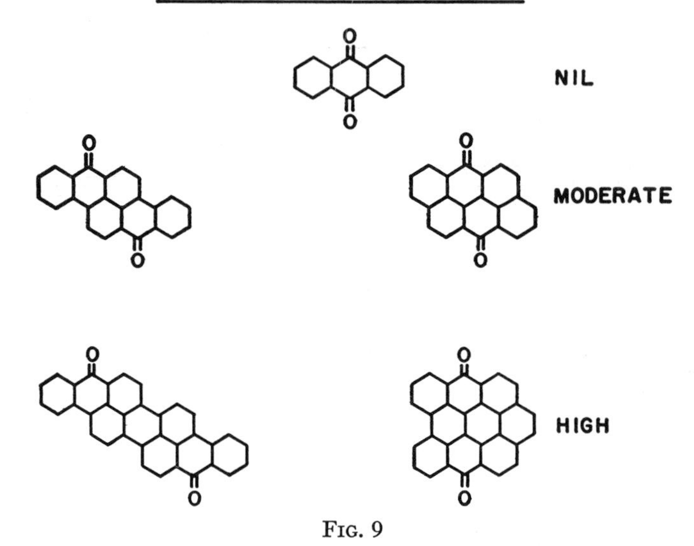

Fig. 9

of benzidine derivatives, where correlations have been made between high affinity and a spacing between azo groups which correspond to the 10.3 Å period between appropriate hydroxyl groups in a cellobiose crystal unit. Specific arrangements such as this may certainly promote affinity, but as has been shown by Robinson, cellulose has so many available hydroxyl groups that explanation of affinity exclusively through such coincidence is not tenable. It is certainly true, however, that dyes for cellulose are unusually sensitive to minor changes

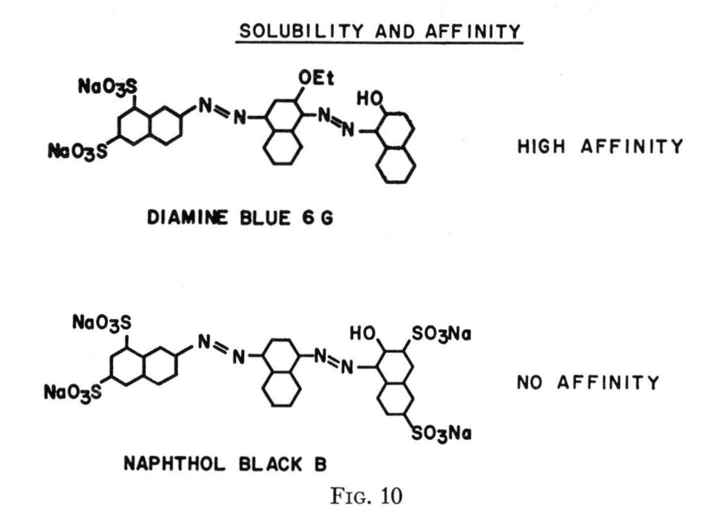

Fig. 10

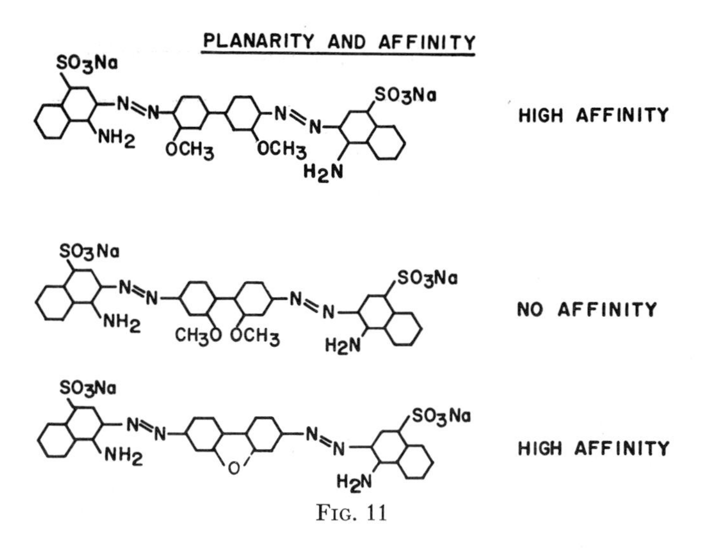

FIG. 11

in geometry. The next figure (Fig. 13) illustrates a case where a change in arrangement of groups appears to prevent the molecule from layering properly on cellulose and thus diminishes its affinity.

Dyeing of cellulose is, therefore, a complex subject—best explained at present by assuming association between polar molecules and a polar substrate with indications that an exact fit rather strongly increases affinity.

Another mechanism comes into play in dyeing fibers containing ionic groups. Both hydrophobic and hydrophilic polymers with ionizable groups are dyed by a reaction which results in the formation of ion pairs and the consequent attachment of the dye ions at specific ionic sites. The physical chemistry has been worked out in detail by Gilbert and Rideal for the absorption of acids by wool, by Remington and Gladding for the absorption of dye anions by nylons, and by Blaker, Katz, and co-workers for the absorption of dye anions by polyacrylonitrile containing cationic sites. In each of these cases the observed isotherms are of the limited site type, and the reaction is one of the ion pair formation. As a matter of fact each of these polymers absorbs colored anions in much the same way that an ion exchange resin absorbs colorless ions. In some cases the dyeing reaction is a simple ion exchange in which the more affinitive dye anion displaces a simple inorganic anion such as bisulfate.

Considering the case of wool and nylon, which are amphoteric materials, dyeing is regarded as attachment of dye anions on the protonated amines. For these cases thermodynamic expressions have been derived expressing the simple ionic reactions. These predict a linear relationship. For the absorption of metanil yellow on nylon the experimental data give a straight line whose intercept with the abscissa is an exact measure of the concentration of amino groups, the sites to which dye and proton become affixed.

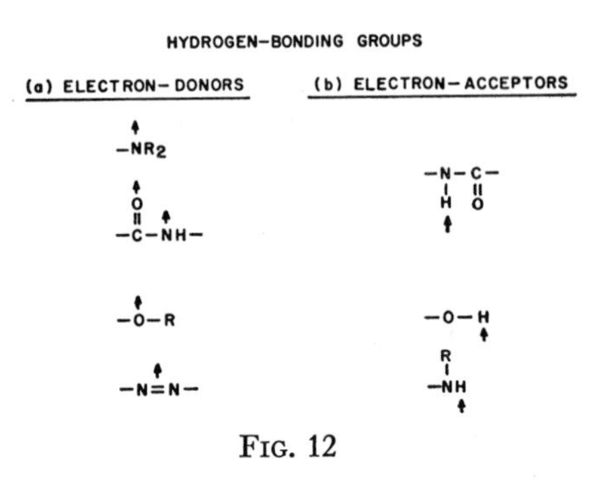

FIG. 12

A similar picture is obtained with polyacrylonitrile which can be basified by copolymerization of acrylonitrile with vinyl pyridine. A cationic site is created by treatment with acid, or by dyeing at low pH. Dye anions are then fixed on the cationic sites. The case of the polyacrylonitrile is interesting in that it has been necessary to assume for absorption of proton the existence of two types of site, differing in basicity. At very low pH where all the basic sites will appear equivalent, an excellent fit with straight line results. At higher pH it has been necessary to calculate a new expression for two types of site. The fit of data with the derived two site expressions is excellent.

The primary attraction of anionic dyes to basic polymers is thus ascribable to ionic forces functioning in the same way as in the absorption of simple acids.

A whole class of dyes, the so-called "*acid* dyes," dye wool or nylon by just this simple process. These colors consist of a very simple organic chromophore with attached negative charge (Fig. 14). Despite considerable variety in their chemistry, they have no particular structural features promoting dyeing other than their anionic nature. Simple coulombic forces result in affixation of dye anion on the protonated fiber cation. Indeed, this process is practical for dyeing

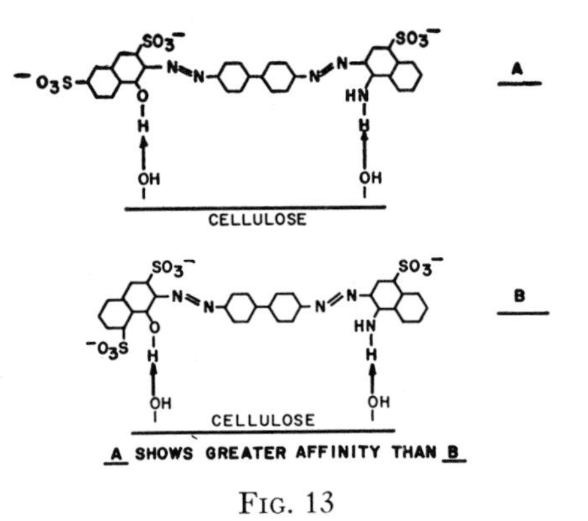

FIG. 13

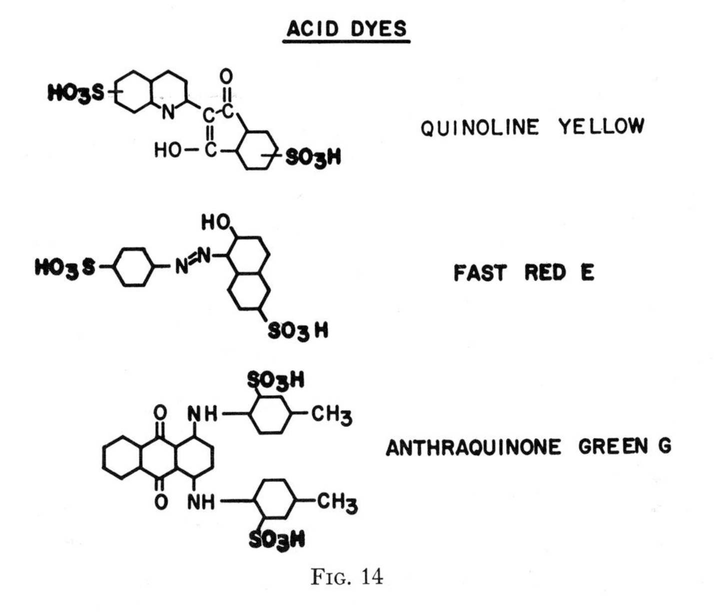

Fig. 14

purposes only under conditions most favorable to absorption of anion; i.e., at low pH where the fiber is completely protonated.

There is an interesting relationship that can be developed for the adsorption of anions on cationic sites in wool or nylon. In general as the mass/charge ratio is increased (for example, the organic portion of the molecule containing a single sulfonic acid is enlarged), the affinity of the dye increases sharply. Equilibrium distribution of color between fiber and bath is changed in favor of fiber. This is

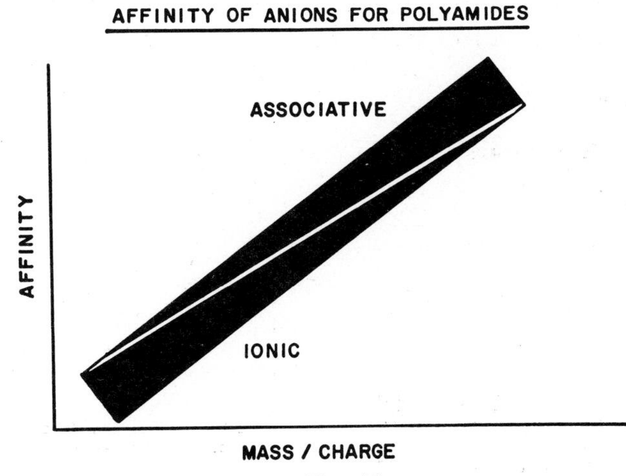

Fig. 15

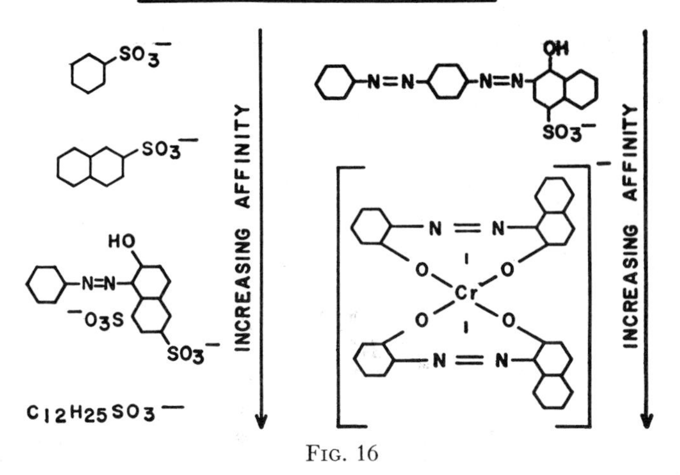

FIG. 16

indicated schematically in the graph (Fig. 15). It may be assumed that this increase in the proportion of organic moiety decreases the water solubility of the dye. As a result under dyebath conditions involving acid and some salts, the thermodynamic activity or effective concentration of the dye may be increased in the aqueous phase, and the equilibrium shifted in the direction of the fiber. There are also indications that as the organic moiety becomes larger, the dye molecule is held increasingly by forces in addition to the simple coulombic ones, quite probably by the simple solution forces observed for ethylene terephthalate or the associative forces so important in the case of cellulose.

As the dye gradually acquires an ability to associate with the wool molecule, its affinity increases to the point where it is not necessary that all the amine groups be protonated. In fact pH can for certain classes of colors be raised to the isoelectric point and for others to neutral conditions. This change with structure is illustrated in Fig. 16.

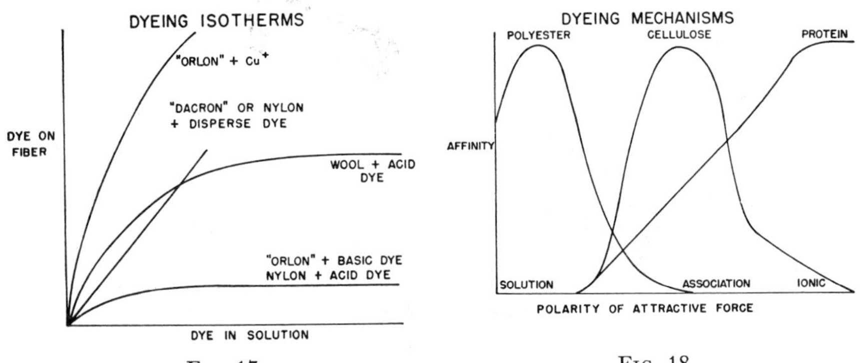

FIG. 17

FIG. 18

You will note the gradual increase in affinity as molecular size increases relative to the charge. Polar donor and acceptor type groups capable of associating with the amide groups in the wool and more hydrophobic groups capable of dissolving in the non-polar portions of the polymer chain are also effective in helping fixation of dye. The ultimate use of this approach is the last example where the molecule is constructed to emphasize the organic portion. This is a prototype of a class of negatively charged metal complexes containing a few simple hydrophilic groups. As a class these colors do not need protonated amino groups to dye either wool or nylon. They are affinitive under neutral conditions, and probably dye either as ions on amino groups or by dissolving in the fiber, depending upon the application conditions and the particular structures. Evidence of this is the ability of these dyes to reach a concentration level in nylon beyond that which could be held on the terminal amino groups present.

In conclusion, the last two illustrations (Fig. 17 and 18) present a summation of the physical processes which appear to be involved in dyeing the various fibers discussed. The picture ranges from a simple story for polyethylene terephthalate to very complex situation for wool and particularly nylon which can be dyed by a variety of mechanisms.

PROFESSOR PITZER: If you have evidence that this is really a solubility in the body of the dyes, that is, in the volume of the material rather than on the surface, then this is an extremely plausible picture in which there is merely a partition equilibrium between the volume of the two phases. This is the sort of thing happening on surfaces where you saturate a single layer and, therefore, run out of the type of site needed. It is not likely to happen because the molar concentration in the interior of the materials is very low and there is no particular reason to believe that the line would be other than linear.

The other question, of course, concerns the interference when you were putting on more than one dye and it seems to me this is subject, again, to pretty simple physical-chemical interpretations if, again, they are going into the volume of the material. If each dye molecule is remote from any other, then they are going to go in quite independently. On the other hand, if the two dyes do in some manner get together in the material and have some direct interaction, then there may be interferences which may be either positive or negative. In other words, one may tend to draw the other one in or it may tend to force it out. It depends upon the type of sites.

On the Structural Basis of Ribonuclease Activity

C. B. Anfinsen and R. R. Redfield

National Heart Institute, National Institutes of Health, Bethesda, Md.

THE PROBLEM OF THE MOLECULAR BASIS of enzyme action has, until very recently, been contemplated by biochemists with understandable awe because of the well-entrenched assumption that enzyme action may involve the organized participation of the entire integrated molecular structure in the transfer and rearrangement of electrons (Szent-Gyorgyi, 1941; Wirtz, 1948; Evans and Gergely, 1949; Geissman, 1949). In addition, knowledge of the details of the covalent structure of enzymes has been so fragmentary that unambiguous assignments of amino acid sequences and areas to the "active centers" of enzymes has been essentially impossible. The elegant investigations of Sanger and his collaborators (Sanger and Tuppy, 1951; Sanger and Thompson, 1953; Ryle, Sanger, Smith and Kitai, 1955) furnished biochemists with the confidence and methodological background for the studies on enzyme structure which are now taking place in many laboratories. As a result of such structural studies and of other investigations dealing with the involvement of the secondary structures of proteins in their catalytic activity, the view has begun to emerge that the activity of many enzymes may, indeed, be associated with only a relatively small part of the protein molecule (Anfinsen, Harrington, Hvidt, Linderstrøm-Lang, Ottesen and Schellman, 1955; Richards, 1955; Hill and Smith, 1955; Anfinsen and Redfield, 1956). It has been known for some time that minor modifications could be made in enzymes without loss of activity. Thus, for example, modification of side chains by introduction of iodine atoms or acetyl groups has been shown to be without detrimental effects in some cases. More recently a number of enzymes have been shown to be unaffected by more drastic procedures such as the removal of C-terminal residues and sequences by the proteolytic enzyme, carboxypeptidase, or of N-terminal sequences by leucine-aminopeptidase. The biologically active proteins thus studied include insulin (Harris and Li, 1952), tobacco mosaic virus (Harris and Knight, 1955). ACTH (Harris and Li, 1955), ribonuclease (Kalnitsky and Rogers, 1956), chymotrypsin (Gladner and Neurath, 1954), and papain (Hill and Smith, 1956). The latter three, ribonuclease, chymotrypsin, and papain, are of particular interest since their activity, after carboxypeptidase or amino-peptidase treatment, could be tested *in vitro*, and the possibilities of resynthesis of the original form during *in vivo* testing could thus be exlcuded.

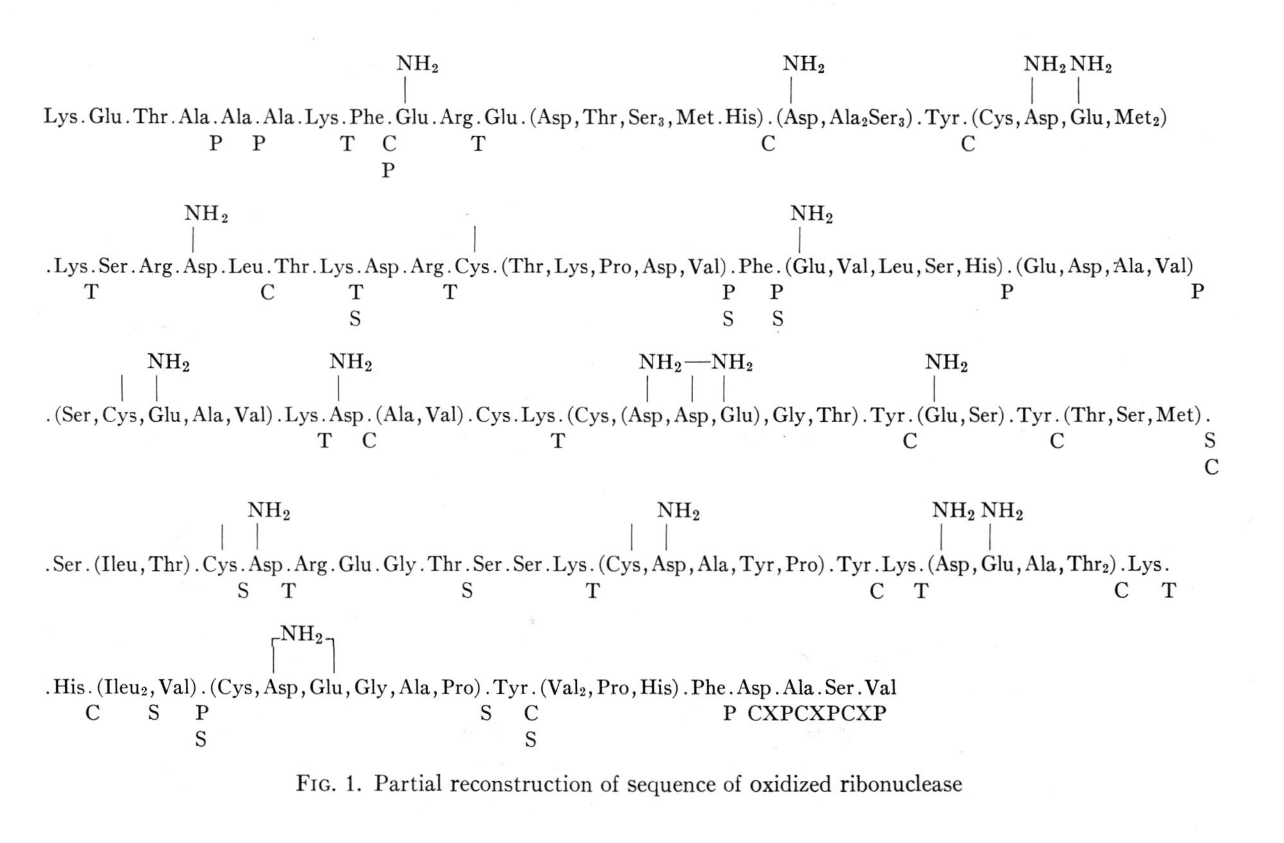

FIG. 1. Partial reconstruction of sequence of oxidized ribonuclease

The studies I wish to discuss this morning are concerned with the enzyme, ribonuclease, an enzyme which possesses very favorable structural and enzymatic properties for investigations of this sort. The detailed sequence of ribonuclease has been under investigation both in our own laboratory and by Drs. Hirs, Moore and Stein at the Rockefeller Institute in New York. The approaches to the structure of this protein used in the two laboratories have been quite dissimilar and it is very gratifying to all of us concerned that the present picture of the ribonuclease chain is compatible with both sets of results (Anfinsen, Redfield, Choate, Page and Carroll, 1954; Hirs, Moore and Stein, 1956; Redfield and Anfinsen, 1956; Hirs, Moore and Stein, 1956). A discussion of the research involved in establishing this structural picture is beyond the scope of the present discussion. Therefore, I can do no more at this time than to show Fig. 1, which gives the alignment of amino acids in the ribonuclease molecule according to our own data at the present time (revised as of May 1, 1956). I could equally well have shown an illustration of the Rockefeller data which shows considerably more detail in some areas and less in others. While your attention is on this figure, I would like to indicate to you the following points which will be of interest in the subsequent discussion. Ribonuclease consists of a single peptide chain containing 124 amino acid residues. It contains eight half-cystine residues, all of which are joined in disulphide bonding (Anfinsen *et al*, 1954; Rabinovitch and Barron, 1955). Inspection of the formula indicates that the N-terminal end of the molecule contains a long non-disulphide linked "tail", and as is more apparent from the structure as drawn from the data of Hirs, Moore, and Stein, a fairly long C-terminal "tail" as well.

The physical properties of ribonuclease are of particular interest in our present discussion. Ribonuclease has a molecular weight of 14,000 and from measurements of its diffusion constant and sedimentation constant, as well as its intrinsic viscosity, one can state that the molecule exists in solution as a rather compact, globular, protein (Anfinsen *et al*, 1954). Osmotic pressure studies carried out by Dr. Donald Kupke (personal communication) at the Carlsberg Laboratories have established that the protein is monodispersed under a variety of conditions, giving it a distinct advantage over insulin in studies relating structural and physical properties since the polymerization of insulin is strongly dependent both on pH and concentration. Oxidation of ribonuclease with performic acid, which leads to the rupture of the S—S bridges, results in the production of an inactive, oxidized derivative (Anfinsen *et al*, 1954) having the predicted molecular weight (i.e., slightly larger than the native enzyme), thus indicating the presence of only a single chain. The amino acid analysis of the oxidized derivative agrees with that of the native molecule according to both the Rockefeller Institute studies and to our own.

Fig. 2 shows data obtained by Harrington and Schellman (1956) on the concentration dependence of sedimentation constants for both native and oxidized

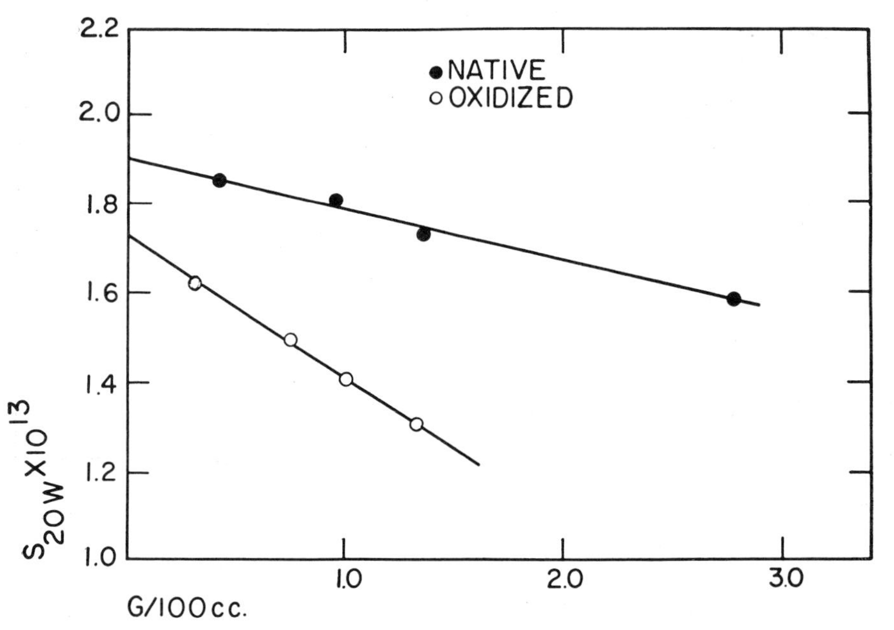

Fig. 2. Sedimentation studies on ribonuclease and oxidized ribonuclease.

ribonuclease, the oxidized molecule being much more dependent on concentration changes.

Careful viscosity studies have also been carried out by Harrington and Schellman (1956), at the Carlsberg Laboratories, on native and oxidized ribonuclease, both in 0.1 ionic strength buffer and in 8 M urea. Fig. 3 summarizes these viscosity studies. Of particular interest here is the fact that the intrinsic viscosity of native ribonuclease is greatly increased in 8 M urea, going from 3.3 to almost 9, and that the intrinsic viscosity of oxidized ribonuclease, which is now presumably completely free of covalent cross-linkages, is not a great deal larger, being about 11.5. These studies suggest that the folding of the native ribonuclease chain, although restricted by four disulphide bridges, is arranged in such a way that rupture of hydrogen bonds can lead to extensive disorientation, nearly approaching that of the oxidized chain which presumably exists as a random coil in solution. Among the hydrogen-bonded linkages which must be present in native ribonuclease, one may certainly list those of the type described by Pauling, Corey and Branson (1951), and perhaps further hydrogen bonds of the sort originally suggested by Crammer and Neuberger (1943) involving linkages between hydroxyl groups of tyrosine side-chains and free

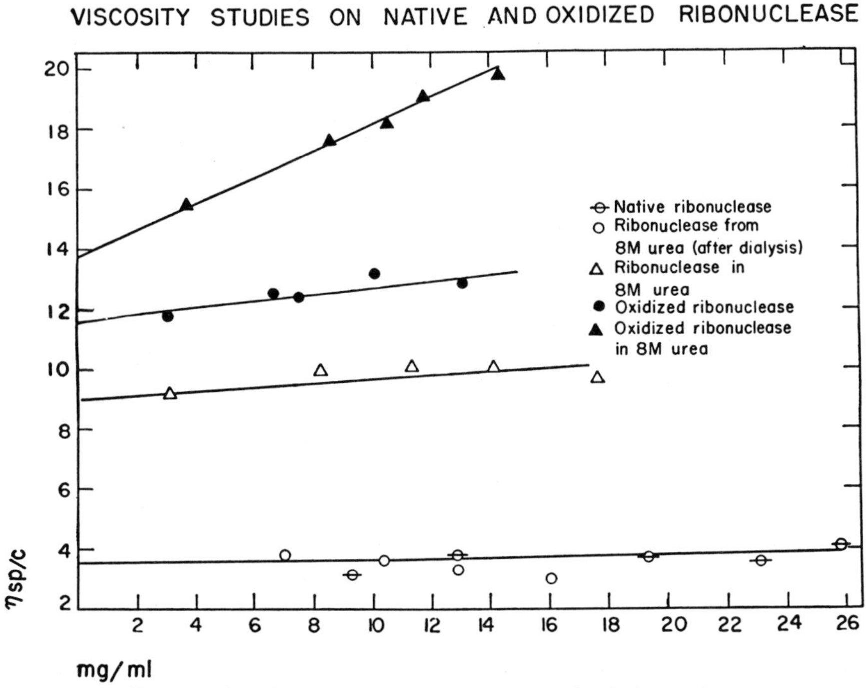

FIG. 3. Viscosity studies on native and oxidized ribonuclease.

carboxyl groups present in other side chains along the protein structure. Indeed, evidence for the latter type of hydrogen bond in ribonuclease has been presented by several workers, including Shugar (1952), Harrington and Schellman (1956), and Tanford and collaborators (1955), all of whose studies suggest the presence of two or three such hydrogen-bonded tyrosines out of the six tyrosine residues present in the molecule. In passing, one should also mention the careful studies of Linderstrøm-Lang and Hvidt (1955) on the hydrogen exchange of peptide bond linked hydrogens, in which they have found that the rate of exchange of a large percentage of these exchangeable hydrogen atoms becomes almost instantaneous in guanidine chloride or urea containing solutions.

One can fix, approximately, the positions of the various half-cystine residues along the peptide chain of ribonuclease by an examination of the partially reconstructed molecule shown in the first figure (and particularly in the molecule as derived from the data of Hirs, Moore and Stein). By the utilization of the spacing between such cystine residues and by studies which we are now carrying out on the problem of assignment of half-cystine sequences to specific disulfide bridges, one may construct a fanciful diagram which accounts in principal, at least, for the viscosity behavior summarized in the last figure. It should be emphasized that the specific cross-linking of half-cystine residues shown in this

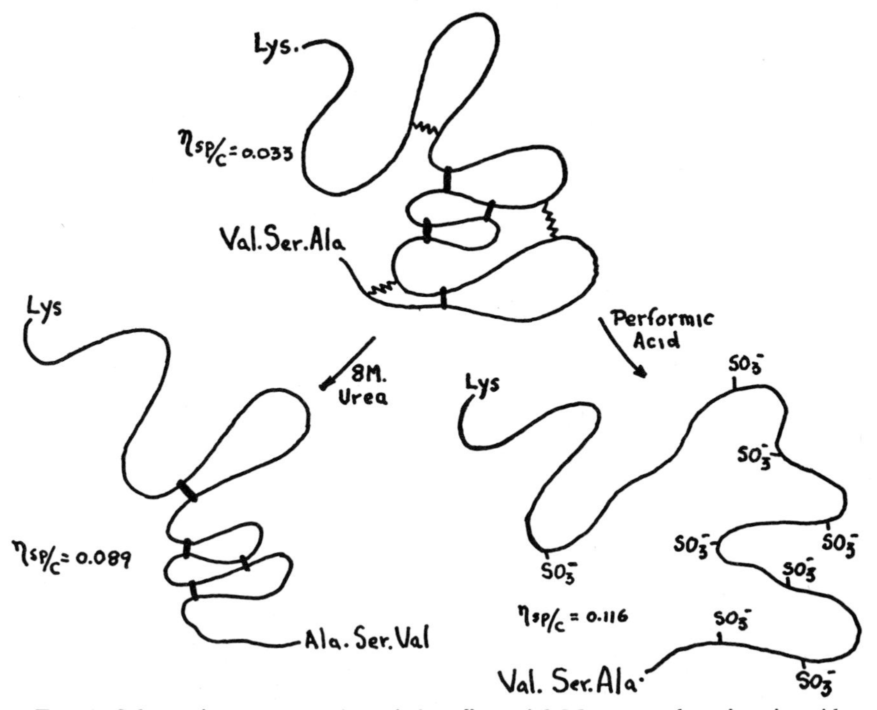

FIG. 4. Schematic representation of the effect of 8 M urea and performic acid on ribonuclease.

figure is by no means the final story. In general, however, bonding between half-cystines located near the beginning and end of the chain is indicated.

In Fig. 4 we have also introduced, for conversational purposes, three tyrosine carboxyl interactions as suggested by the studies of Shugar and others. Upon treatment of the native molecule with 8 M urea, the structure of the molecule may become extensively disoriented, much more, perhaps, in a relative way than shown here, since the partial unfolding of the helical coiling which undoubtedly exists in certain spatially restricted areas of the molecule may add considerable to this disorientation. Upon oxidation of the native molecule a somewhat greater, but not necessarily much greater, disorientation can take place.

In view of the dramatic changes in structure which appear to occur in strong urea solutions, tests were made on ribonuclease for enzyme activity in which the activity measurements were carried out in 8 M urea. To our considerable surprise the molecule appeared to be as active and perhaps more active, than the native molecule under these circumstances (Anfinsen *et al*, 1955).

Fig. 5 shows a first order reaction plot of data taken from experiments in

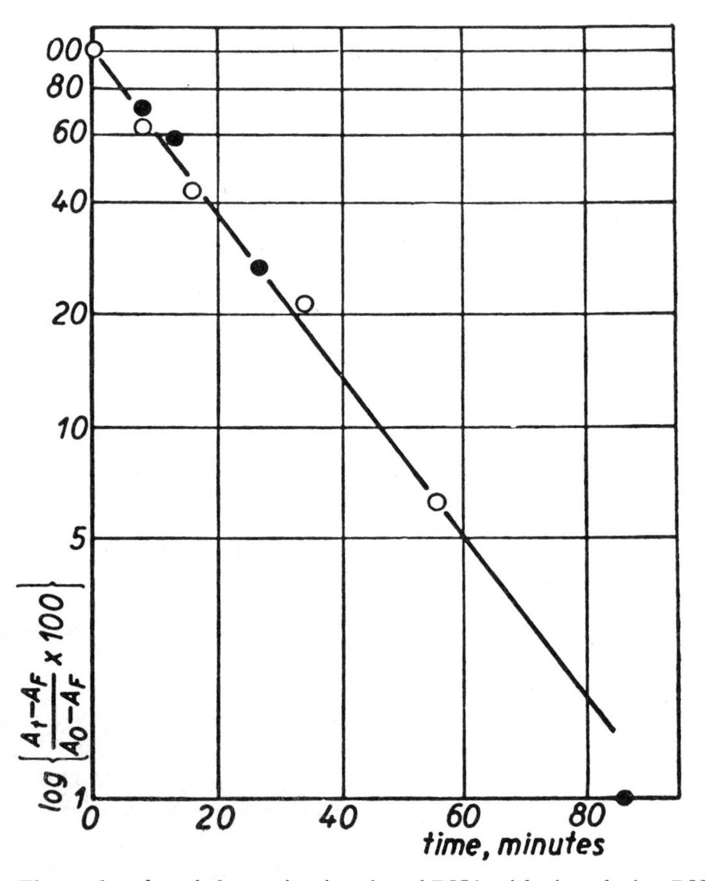

FIG. 5. First order plot of change in viscosity of RNA with time during RNase action in presence and absence of 8 M urea. RNA (2% in 8 M urea, pH 5.0, 20°C) + RNase (2.6/ml, 8 M urea, pH 5.0): Same without urea. A_0 = initial viscosity; A_f = final viscosity.

which the change in the viscosity of yeast ribonucleic acid was measured during ribonuclease action both in the presence and in the absence of urea. Under both conditions, similar first order kinetics appear to be followed. Further evidence was obtained by other approaches to the problem.

Fig. 6 shows the production of dialyzable nucleotides from ribonucleic acid in the presence and absence of 8 M urea. Production of such fragments is unimpaired. It was found also that the hydrolysis of the synthetic substrate, uridine 2′3′ diphosphate, could proceed in 8 M urea solutions.

We must conclude from these enzyme experiments and from the previous studies on the degree of disorientation of ribonuclease in urea, that the catalytic

Production of dialyzable nucleotides from RNA by RNase in the presence and absence of 8 M urea

Vessel	RNA	Urea	ϵ_{260}	Corrected for Blank
1	0.6%	8 M	0.091	—
2	0.6%*	8 M	0.198	0.107
3	2.0%	8 M	0.230	—
4	2.0%*	8 M	0.705	0.475
5	2.0%	—	0.180	—
6	2.0%*	—	0.611	0.431

* Incubations contained RNase.

FIG. 6. Production of dialyzable nucleotides from RNA by RNase in the presence and absence of 8 M urea.

activity of this enzyme is not dependent on an intact, hydrogen-bonded secondary structure. The experiments further suggest that the active center of the molecule may be localized in a very restricted area of the chain.

Further attack on the problem of function in relation to structure has been made through the study of limited proteolysis of ribonuclease. As mentioned previously, carboxypeptidase treatment does not appear to result in activity loss under circumstances where the C-terminal sequence, -ala.ser.val, is removed.

In another study, carried out by Richards (1955), ribonuclease has been digested with the bacterial proteolytic enzyme, subtilisin. From such digests Richards has been able to isolate a modified derivative as shown in Fig. 7, by chromatography on XI-64 resin columns. This derivative, possessing full enzyme activity, appears to contain one, or possibly more, new N-terminal amino groups. That is to say, subtilisin has cleaved one or more peptide bonds somewhere in the interior of the native molecule. The new peptide chain which is formed appears to be attached to the rest of the molecule by a stable cross-linkage. This latter conclusion is based on physical measurements made by Richards on native ribonuclease and on the active derivative following performic acid oxidation.

Fig. 8 shows, for example, that the sedimentation constant of the oxidized derivative is somewhat lower than that of oxidized native ribonuclease.

We have recently carried out further proteolytic studies on ribonuclease using pepsin (Anfinsen, 1955). We found several years ago that extremely restricted digestion with pepsin (Anfinsen, 1952) resulted in the complete inactivation of ribonuclease long before the detectable structural changes could be observed. The course of this digestion has now been examined in greater detail, using, once again, XE-64 columns.

Fig. 9 shows the progressive appearance of an inactive derivative of ribonuclease at the expense of the native molecule in a pattern of increasing production

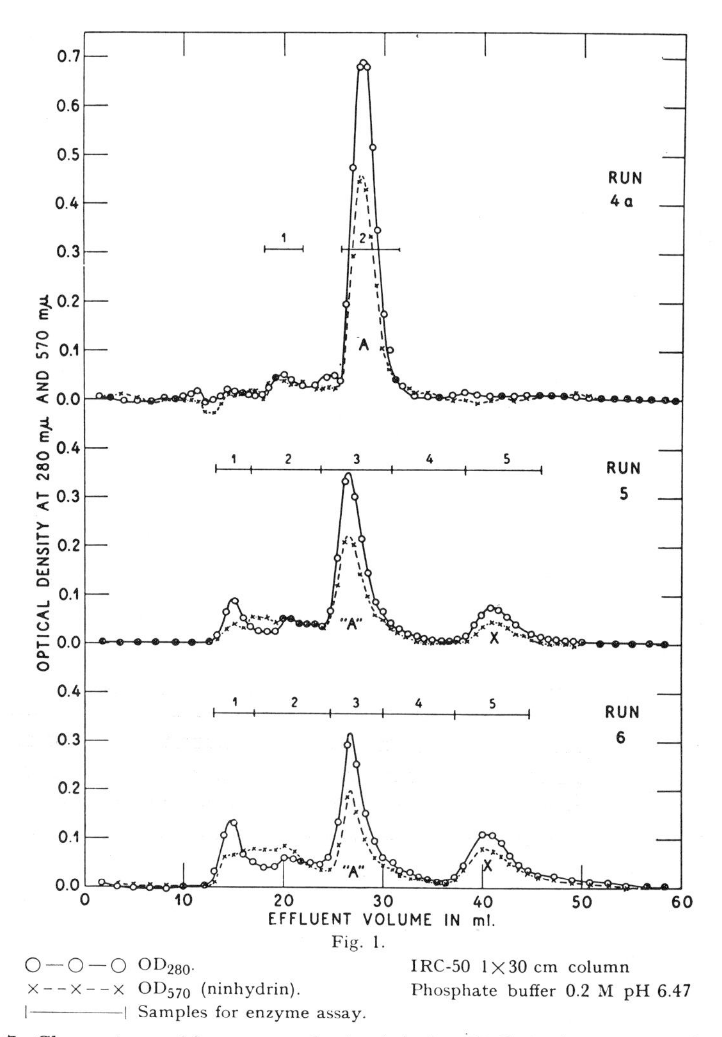

FIG. 7. Chromatographic pattern obtained during IRC 50 chromatography of subtilisin digests of native ribonuclease (from Richards, 1955).

of derivative with time. To further characterize this inactive derivative, we have separated workable amounts by large-scale chromatography as shown in the next figure (Fig. 10). The material isolated in this way still contains lysine as the N-terminal amino acid, but no new N-terminal amino residues have been found. The intrinsic viscosity of the inactive derivative, both before and after oxidation, is identical with that of control values for the native enzyme before and after oxidation.

The sedimentation constant of the derivative (Fig. 11) is also identical with

Sedimentation constants

Sample	Source	$S_{20,w}$	Literature Value
Unoxidized			
Peak A undigested	N.I.L.	1.93	1.88 (18)
Peak A isolated from digest	N.I.L.	1.92	
Peak X isolated from digest	N.I.L.	1.89	
Oxidized			
RNase whole initial sample	Armour	1.37	1.35 (18)
Peak A isolated from digest	Armour	1.33	
Peak X isolated from digest	Armour	1.18	

FIG. 8. Sedimentation studies on native ribonuclease and on the enzymatically active derivative obtained by subtilisin digestion (after Richards, 1955).

that of native ribonuclease although after oxidation one observes somewhat less concentration dependence, though the value at infinite dilution appears to be the same as that found for oxidized native ribonuclease. In further attempts to account for the inactivation of ribonuclease by pepsin in the absence of serious structural change, we have studied the production of small non-protein nitrogen fragments during this rapid process. By such techniques it has been found that the tetrapeptide, -asp.ala,ser.val, is produced at a rate quantitatively correlated with the rate of inactivation of the enzyme (Anfinsen, 1956). The possibility exists that peptide fragments other than this tetrapeptide (Fig. 12) also appear during the rapid inactivation, although the detection of such further materials has not as yet been possible. It seems likely, however, that pepsin has not attacked the protein at some internal point since the physical properties of the inactive derivative, following oxidation of S—S bridges, are extremely similar to those of the oxidized native molecule.

In summary, we must conclude that pepsin has inactivated ribonuclease by an extremely restricted modifying action which does not at first sight appear to involve internal cleavage of the protein chain.

It was shown earlier by Shugar (1952) that pepsin digestion of ribonuclease led to changes in the ultraviolet absorption spectrum of the molecule which are characteristic of the rupturing of hydrogen bonds of the sort which appear to exist between tyrosine hydroxyl groups and aspartyl or glutamyl carboxyl groups. These observations prompted an examination of the UV spectrum during the extremely restricted pepsin treatment described above. It has been found that a shift does indeed occur which is of the order to be expected for the rupture of one such bond (Anfinsen and Tritch, unpublished experiment). This spectral change occurs at a rate which parallels both the rate of appearance of the tetrapeptide fragment and the rate of ribonuclease inactivation. Whether or not the indicated hydrogen bond plays a role in the workings of the active center is, of

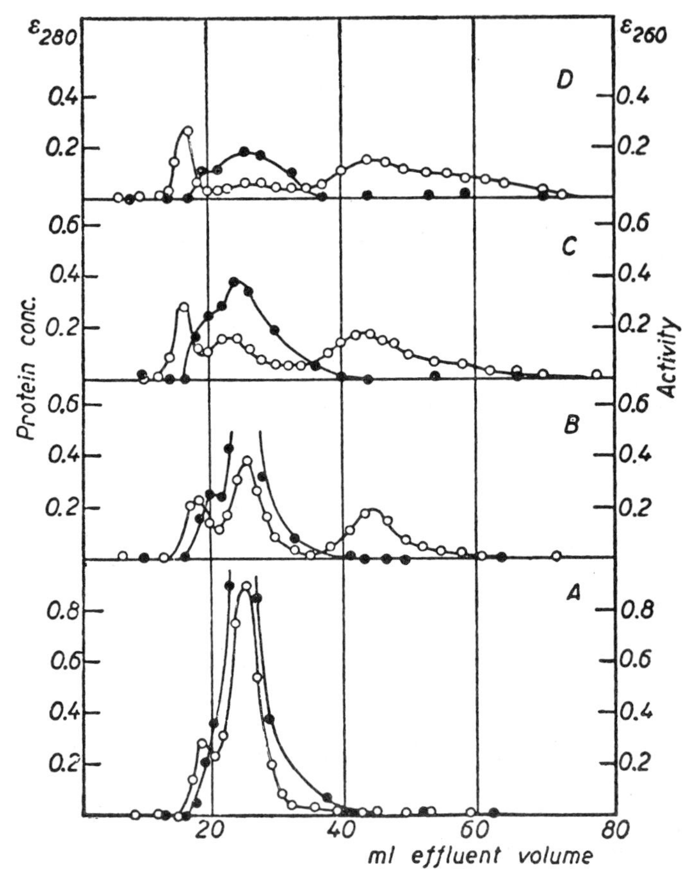

FIG. 9. Chromatography of 10 mg. samples of native and pepsin-digested ribonuclease on IRC-50 columns, 9 x 30 mm. Eluting buffer, phosphate, 0.2 M, pH 6.45. Digestion conditions: ribonuclease 0.92%; pepsin (Armour crystallized ca. 0.002%; 37°C, pH 1.8. Remaining ribonuclease activity (I): Curve A, 100%; B, 60% (5 min); C, 40% (10 min); D, 15% (16 min). Solid points, enzyme activity. Open circles, protein concentration. (The peak appearing at 18–19 effluent ml. is a ninhydrin-negative artefact, uniformly seen with this preparation of resin.)

course, quite beyond consideration at the present time. It is of interest, however, that the alkali-catalyzed rupture of tyrosine hydroxyl hydrogen bonding in ribonuclease indicated by the spectrophotometric experiments of Tanford, Hauenstein and Rands (1955), also has been found to parallel the loss in enzymatic activity (Anfinsen and Tritch, unpublished data).

The next figure (Fig. 13) shows the results of a crude attempt to schematize and summarize some of the approaches to the basis of ribonuclease function. It

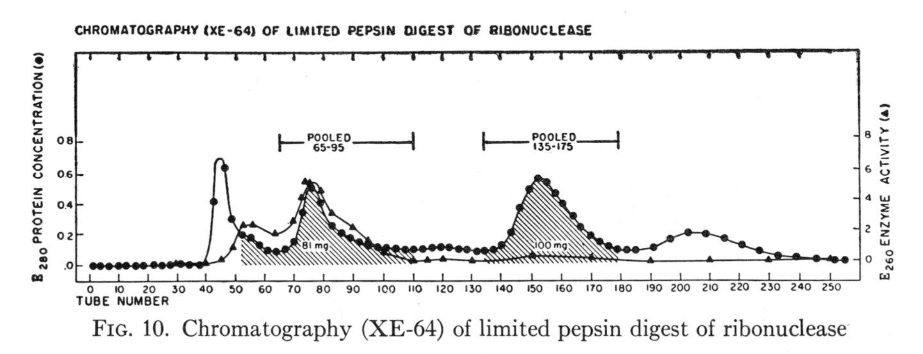

FIG. 10. Chromatography (XE-64) of limited pepsin digest of ribonuclease

has been observed by Weil and Seidles (1955) that the photodestruction of a single histidine residue leads to inactivation. Since two of the four histidine residues of ribonuclease are located within the last fifth of the molecule and in view of the present studies on pepsin digestion and urea treatment of ribonuclease, we must tentatively conclude that part of the active center of ribonuclease is located near the C-terminal end of the molecule and may involve a relatively simple constellation of amino acids. It is important, however, to emphasize that activity cannot be due to a simple amino acid sequence alone in view of the inertness of the oxidized enzyme. Our present picture of the arrangement of S—S bridges suggests that the active center may involve peptide sequences located in two or more positions along the protein chain which are separated in

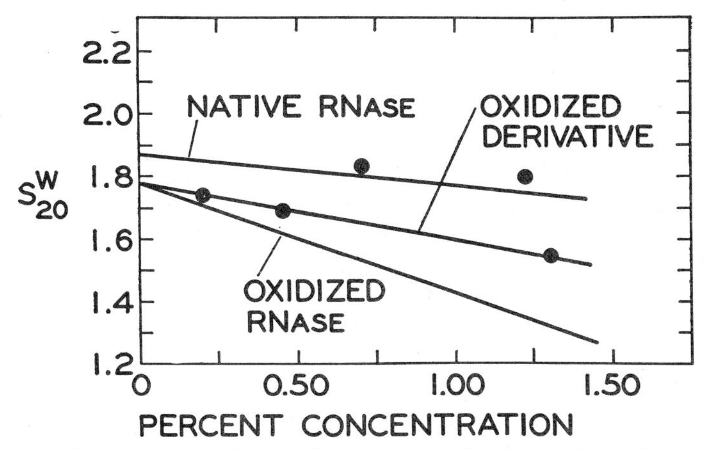

FIG. 11. Sedimentation studies on the inactive derivative of ribonuclease produced by pepsin digestion before and after oxidation of the disulphide bridges. The experimental points on the upper curve were obtained on the derivative before performic acid oxidation. The experimental points from the center curve are from studies on this derivative after oxidation.

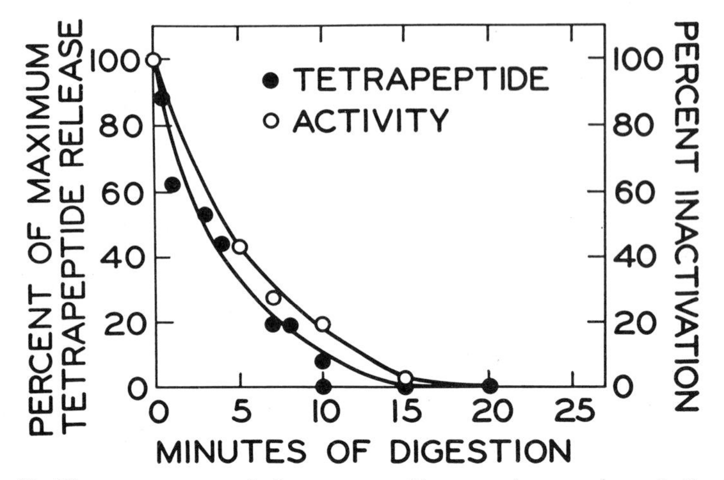

FIG. 12. The appearance of the tetrapeptide, -asp.ala,ser.val, and the loss in enzyme activity during the digestion of native ribonuclease with pepsin.

the linear polypeptide sense but not in terms of the three-dimensional picture. Whether the pepsin activation brings about changes not related to peptide bond rupture, such as the so-called "denaturase" action suggested by Linderstrøm-Lang and his colleagues (1950), cannot be answered without further study.

In conclusion, the question might be raised as to the biological significance of the complex, highly restricted chain structure which accompanies what appears to be a relatively more simple catalytic core. One may speculate whether urea-insensitive, "simple" enzymes, such as ribonuclease might not represent a class

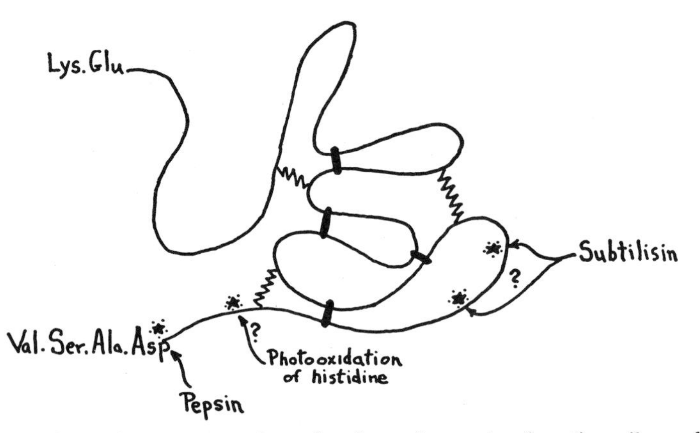

FIG. 13. Schematic representation of points of attack of native ribonuclease by various reagents.

of relatively primitive catalysts, embellished and modified by nature during the evolutionary development of cell metabolism to the present highly complex state.

References

Anfinsen, C. B. 1952. The peptic digestion of ribonuclease. J. Biol. Chem. *196:* 201–208.

Anfinsen, C. B. 1955. The inactivation of ribonuclease by restricted pepsin digestion. Biochim. et Biophys. Acta *17:* 593–594.

Anfinsen, C. B. 1956. On the structural basis of ribonuclease activity. J. Biol. Chem. In press.

Anfinsen, C. B., W. F. Harrington, Aa. Hvidt, K. Linderstrøm-Lang, M. Ottessen, and J. Schellman. 1955. Studies on the structural basis of ribonuclease activity. Biochim. et Biophys. Acta *17:* 141–142.

Anfinsen, C. B. and R. R. Redfield. 1956. Protein structure in relation to function and biosynthesis. Advances in Protein Chemistry. Academic Press. New York. In press.

Anfinsen, C. B., R. R. Redfield, W. L. Choate, J. Page, and W. R. Carroll. 1954. Studies on the gross structure, cross linkages, and terminal sequence in ribonuclease. J. Biol. Chem. *207:* 201–210.

Crammer, J. L. and A. Neuberger. 1943. The state of tyrosine in egg albumin and in insulin as determined by spectrophotometric titration. Biochem. J. *37:* 302–310.

Evans, M. G. and J. Gergely. 1949. A discussion of the possibility of bands of energy levels in proteins. Electronic interaction in non-bonded systems. Biochim. et Biophys. Acta *3:* 188–197.

Geissman, T. A. 1949. A theory of the mechanism of enzyme action. Quart. Rev. Biol. *24:* 309–327.

Gladner, J. A. and H. Neurath. 1954. Carboxyl terminal groups of proteolytic enzymes. II. Chymotrypsins. J. Biol. Chem. *206:* 911–924.

Harrington, W. F. and John Schellman. 1956. Compt. rend. trav. lab. Carlsberg. In press.

Harris, J. I. and C. A. Knight. 1955. Studies on the action of carboxypeptidase on tobacco mosaic virus. J. Biol. Chem. *214:* 215–237.

Harris, J. I. and C. H. Li. 1952. The biological activity of enzymatic digests of insulin. J. Am. Chem. Soc. *74:* 2945–2946.

Harris, J. I. and C. H. Li. 1955. Corticotropins (ACTH) IV. The action of carboxypeptidase on alpha-corticotropin, and the C-terminal amino acid sequence. J. Biol. Chem. *213:* 499–507.

Hill, R. L. and E. L. Smith. 1955. Action of leucine aminopeptidase on proteins and polypeptides. (Abs.) Federation Proc. *14:* 226.

Hill, R. L. and E. L. Smith. 1956. Biochim. et Biophys. Acta. In press.

Hirs, C. H. W., S. Moore, and W. H. Stein. 1956a. Peptides obtained by tryptic hydrolysis of performic acid-oxidized ribonuclease. J. Biol. Chem. *219:* 623–642.

Hirs, C. H. W., S. Moore and W. H. Stein. 1956b. J. Biol. Chem. In press.

Hvidt, Aa. 1955. Deuterium exchange between ribonuclease and water. Biochim. et Biophys. Acta *18:* 306–307.

Kalnitzky, G. and W. I. Rogers. 1956. In press.

Kupke, D. Personal Communication.

Linderstrøm-Lang, K. 1949. Structure and enzymatic break-down of proteins. Cold Spring Harbor Symposia Quant. Biol. *14:* 117–126.

Pauling, L., R. B. Corey, and H. R. Branson. 1951. The structure of proteins: two hydrogen-bonded helical configurations of the polypeptide chain. Proc. Nat. Acad. Sci. U. S. *37:* 205–211.

Rabinovitch, M. and E. S. G. Barron. 1955. The effect of —SH reagents on the activity of ribonuclease. Biochim. et Biophys. Acta *18:* 316–317.

Redfield, R. R. and C. B. Anfinsen. 1956. The structure of ribonuclease. II. The preparation, separation, and relative alignment of large enzymatically produced fragments. J. Biol. Chem. In press.

Richards, F. M. 1955. On an active intermediate produced during the digestion of ribonuclease by subtilisin. Compt. rend. trav. lab. Carlsberg *29:* 329–346.

Ryle, A. P., F. Snager, L. F. Smith and R. Kitai. 1955. The disulphide bonds of insulin. Biochem. J. *60:* 541–556.

Sanger, F. and E. O. P. Thompson. 1953. The amino-acid sequence in the glycyl chain of insulin. Biochem. J. *53:* 353–374.

Sanger, F. and H. Tuppy. 1951. The amino acid sequence in the phenylalanyl chain of insulin. Biochem. J. *49:* 463–490.

Shugar, D. 1952. The ultraviolet absorption spectrum of ribonuclease. Biochem. J. *52:* 142–149.

Szent-Gyorgyi, A. 1941. Towards a new biochemistry? Science *93:* 609–611.

Tanford, C., J. D. Hauenstein and D. Rands. 1955. Phenolic hydroxyl ionization in proteins. II. Ribonuclease. J. Am. Chem. Soc. *77:* 6409–6413.

Weil, L. and T. S. Siebles. 1955. Photoöxidation of crystalline ribonuclease in the presence of methylene blue. Arch. Biochem. and Biophys. *54:* 368–377.

Wirtz, K. 1947. Hydrogen linkage, structure and energy transport in proteins. Zeits. fur Naturforsch. *2b:* 94–98.

Professor Klotz: With respect to your last remark, Dr. Anfinsen, I may say that I believe that hemoglobin, which dissociates into halves in urea still picks up oxygen in urea just as well as before. I know that this is true also of hemocyanin but with respect to hemoglobin I think there are no disulfide bridges. All the sulfur can be shown to be in the form of sulfhydryl groups.

Would you care to comment on how you visualize a structure like that? Particularly, I wonder if it is fair to limit your comment just to small molecules like ribonuclease and pepsin?

Dr. Anfinsen: I am sorry I introduced that point at all. It is not what I wanted to say. Perhaps the first catalyst was simply the heme.

Professor Klotz: I did not want to go into that so much as into the assumption that in urea the molecules really unfold. Again I raise the question with with respect to the hemoglobin and the general question of what happens in urea. In this case, in hemoglobin, you cannot say that the disulfide bonds are holding the structure together, because there are not any, so the hydrogen bonds must be holding it together. Can we be sure then that in urea you are really breaking these hydrogen bonds—that the inactivation presumably occurs by the breaking of hydrogen bonds?

DR. ANFINSEN: I think the point that we both missed is that hemoglobin may not need much more than the heme and a few amino acids. It does transport oxygen in urea.

CHAIRMAN PAULING: I might comment here that I do not think that the attack of urea or other agents of this sort on hydrogen bonds should be talked about in this "all or none" sense. There are, no doubt, certain hydrogen bonds in a protein molecule that are pretty effectively attacked at a certain concentration of urea and others that are not. In hemoglobin the attack is enough to permit molecules to split into two halves, 6 normal urea, but apparently the activity is not great enough to break up these two halves in such a way as to destroy the activity.

Molecular Shapes, Especially Orientation around Single Bonds

K. S. Pitzer

University of California, Berkeley, Calif.

MY REMARKS ARE OF THE SAME SORT as a number of the other papers in referring to small and model substances that are only indirectly applicable to the sort of problems we are really interested in. I know relatively little about the big molecules. On the other hand, I suspect that it was felt that a continuous dose of fundamental principles would be just a little bit too much so I am scheduled today to be diluted by the more biological papers.

I believe the subject of internal rotation about single bonds must be kept under consideration when structures are postulated for the sort of substances that we are all interested in here. I was particularly reassured in this regard by the Chairman's remark yesterday that a tenth of a kilocalorie was about as large a distortion in certain other types of angular orientation as has been actually observed. Since the potential energy change restricting rotation or varying with angle in ethane is about 30 times a tenth of a kilocalorie, this gives me a factor of safety of about 30, in the significance of what I am talking about.

Another general remark I might make is that with all of their advantages these scale model sets that we buy and use are nevertheless misleading in that they take no account of barriers to internal rotation about single bonds. If you try to judge them by just looking at the sizes of the groups attached you will almost certainly come to the wrong answer. Instead one must maintain a parallel set of information about potential effects associated with torsion about single bonds and apply these pieces of information as supplementary and extraneous conditions to the angular orientation which the models may take.

I do not blame the model makers in the slightest in this respect. If I knew how to produce models that would take this into account, I can assure you I would have gone ahead and done something about it. I do not have any idea as to how this can be done feasibly, but one of the things to remember is that the models exaggerate the rigidity of angles—for example, the tetrahedral angles around the four single bonds of carbon. In other words, they are not flexible enough at this point and they are much too flexible with respect to the twisting orientation about single bonds.

I am not going to try to say anything about what you might call first principles, i.e., quantum mechanical theory of these potential barriers. A number of us have played with the problem and I know most of my calculations are still in the file drawer or in the waste basket and I think that is where they belong. We do know a great deal about this subject from the interpretation of experimental data; initially, mostly from thermodynamic measurements and then statistical-mechanical interpretations of them, and now more recently from molecular spectroscopy, particularly in the microwave range. We know a great deal about the potential energy effects with respect to internal rotation and it is that information that I will be mentioning this morning.

I am afraid I will not be able to give due credit at all points to the proper authors, but I would like to mention at this time that Professor Aston and his group at Pennsylvania State University, Professor Yost at the California Institute of Technology, Professor Gwinn on our staff at Berkeley, Professors Wilson and Kistiakowsky at Harvard and others, in addition to many graduate students who worked with me, have contributed to the sort of information I am going to mention.

To come down to specific cases, let us consider the parent substance for this problem, namely, ethane, with just a single bond between two carbon atoms and with only hydrogen atoms attached.

There are two configurations we will consider at length, and these are best visualized by sighting down the line connecting the carbon atoms of ethane. The internal rotation problem is concerned with the orientation of the hydrogen atoms of one CH_3 group relative to those of the other CH_3 group. If the H atoms are superimposed (sighting down the carbon-carbon bond), the configuration is called "eclipsed." If the H atoms of one end fall just between the atoms at the other end (as viewed down the carbon-carbon bond), the configuration is called "staggered."

Now, we know that this so-called staggered orientation about the single bond is the low energy one. Notice that rotating one methyl group relative to the other restores this low energy configuration after a rotation of either 120° or 240°. Hence this low potential energy form corresponds to the angles of zero, 120°, 240°, if we plot energy against this rotation angle. The eclipsed configuration is about 3 kilocalories higher and corresponds to angles of 60°, 180°, and 300° on this plot.

Connecting these high and low energy points with a smooth curve, we obtain a potential energy plot of the energy of the molecule with respect to this angle of rotation. As nearly as we can tell, this curve is well represented by a simple sine curve. Those efforts which have been made to expand this in Fourier series and find higher terms, show that the higher terms are zero within experimental error, so that I am sure there is little error in using just the sine curve for this purpose. This is just a starting point. Let me discuss a few other simple modifications of this structure which may represent units that are at least of a type to be of interest in the biologically important substances.

If we substitute, say, an additional carbon atom at one end of the molecule, the other end still has a methyl group on it and has three-fold symmetry and the potential barrier gets a little higher but it doesn't change much. If you extend the carbon chain to four and sight down the middle carbon-carbon bond in normal butane, you see that the presence of the two terminal methyls introduces new complexity to the potential curve. The three potential minima are no longer identical but rather correspond to rotational isomers. When the methyl at one end is in the same plane and on the opposite side as the one at the other end, the conformation is called trans. Then there are two forms which are optically related to one another as D and L forms with a 60 degree angle between methyl groups.

I think the organic chemists have decided that these rotational isomers are going to be called conformations. There has been considerable confusion in the terminology, but I am perfectly willing to go along with this. The potential energy curve still retains the three minima but two of them are at a different energy than the others. We know this energy difference to be a little less than one kilocalorie, maybe eight-tenths of a kilocalorie. There are two potential maxima about the same height as in ethane, 3 kilocalories or a little more, and one which is considerably higher but I do not think we know very well how high it is. This position corresponds to the methyl groups being lined up with one another (cis) but I am sure there is some additional strain there and I do not think any of our present methods of investigation give any good measure of it.

Fig. 1 is a model of normal butane. There is the trans-conformation and skew or gauche conformation. The eight-tenths of a kilocalorie of strain presumably arises from the repulsion between the hydrogen atoms of the methyl groups.

Fig. 2 is the Raman spectrum of normal butane at two different temperatures. At the lower temperature one of the doublet of bands near 800 cm^{-1} is much

FIG. 1

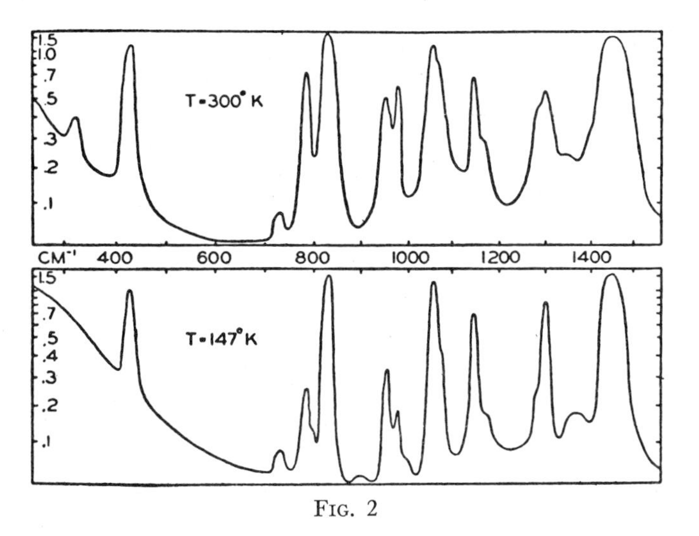

FIG. 2

more intense while at the higher temperature they are nearly equal. The intense band at the lower temperature corresponds to the trans conformation and the other one to the skew conformation. In the spectrum of the solid the bands corresponding to the skew conformation disappear completely.

This is a type which appears in principle in many molecules. The methyl group is purely a sample that does not involve any new types of atoms; if you put two chlorines on ethane you get the same type of curve. The energy difference between minima is about 1.3 kilocalories for dichlorethane in the gas state.

In the case of dichlorethane there is a large solvent effect on that energy term. It goes from practically zero in the liquid to 1.3 or 1.4 kilocalories in the gas, whereas, for normal butane, there is practically no difference.

Since we are not primarily interested in molecules that have only carbon atoms in them, let us ask what happens when you put in other atoms. In general, the same qualitative picture holds but the potential barriers are usually somewhat diminished. For example, in methyl alcohol where you have an oxygen at one end and carbon at the other end of the single bond, the barrier is down to about one kilocalories. This is quite accurately known now, but I do not remember the precise figure. With an NH_2, the value is intermediate.

In dimethyl ether, where you put methyl groups on both bonds of oxygen, the interference between the methyl groups is appreciable and the potential barrier goes back up to about 3 kilocalories. Thus one has potential energy effects associated with single bond rotation with first row elements in the one to three kilocalorie range with the atoms other than carbon giving a somewhat lower figure. As you go down the periodic table the barriers tend to become even smaller.

Now let us turn to some molecules with double bonds. It does not matter very much whether we have oxygen or another CH_2 group. We take one of our end-on diagrams in which we now look axially along the single bond. On the far end we have the double bond coming down to the oxygen or CH_2 and the single one up to a hydrogen. Then, on the near end we still have our triangular methyl group. There is quite convincing evidence that the stable orientation is staggered with respect to the single bond at the far end and opposed with respect to the double bond.

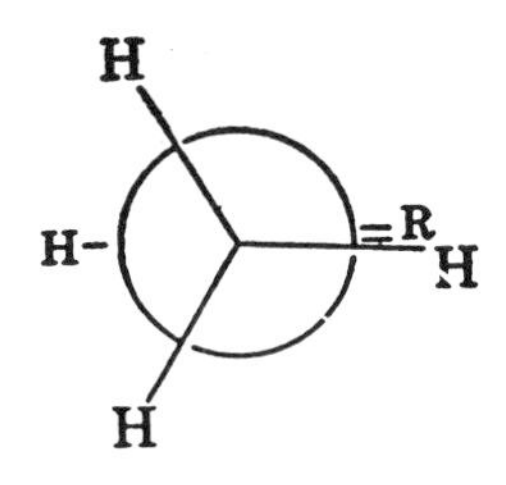

The values of the potential barrier, that is, the maximum range of potential, are about 2 kilocalories for the propylene with the CH_2 and about 1 for acetaldehyde with the oxygen.

If other atoms or radicals are substituted for the hydrogen and the oxygen or CH_2 the barrier will still be about the same unless the new atoms are very large or have other special properties.

On the other hand, in nitromethane or toluene the situation is a bit different. We still have the methyl group, but now we have something that is not only flat but precisely symmetrical at the other end of the bond. Both of these cases are the same by symmetry and the potential barrier is known to be small. As far as the older methods were concerned, it was within experimental error zero but this only meant less than a few tenths of a kilocalorie.

My colleague, Professor Gwinn, in Berkeley recently studied nitromethane with the micro-wave method. His answer for this molecule was 6 small calories and not just 6, but 6.00 small calories plus or minus a few hundredths. This is smaller than the level of significance of a tenth of a kilocalorie which we were mentioning by at least one order of magnitude. Thus, for our purposes, we can say that in these cases the potential barrier is simply zero.

Another case that gives truly free rotation, although probably of trivial interest, is the acetylene case. Dimethyl acetylene, or its derivatives, where the rotation can occur across a three-bond length linkage in a linear structure has zero potential barrier.

I might remark at this point that in my experience I have never found a case where the solid failed to accommodate the low energy conformation of a molecule. It is a wonderfully complex subject but apparently there is always some crystal structure, some arrangement which satisfactorily accommodates the low energy form of the molecule without enough difference in crystal energy to

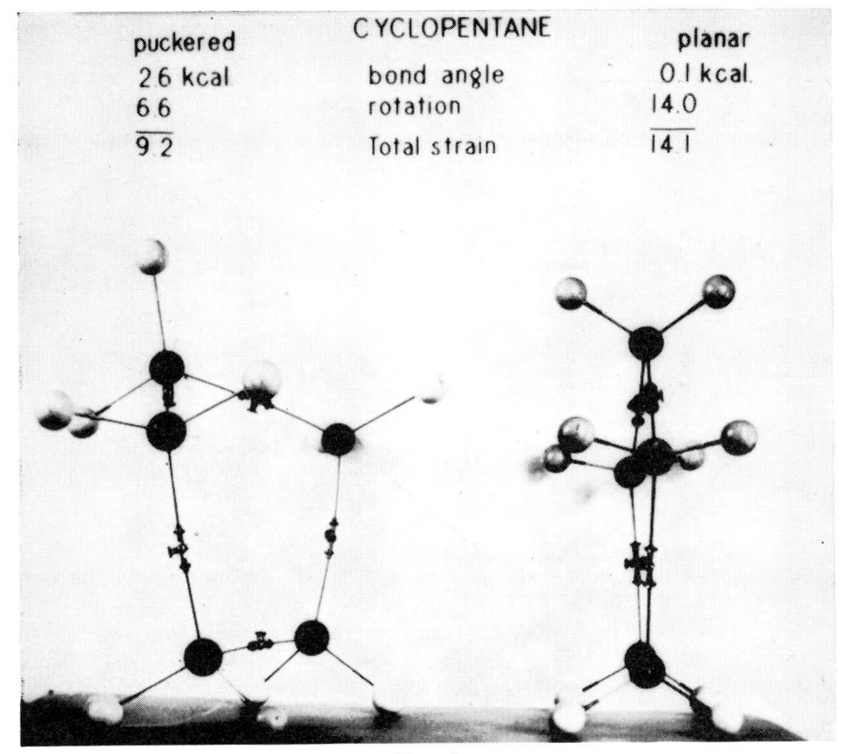

CYCLOPENTANE
puckered
2.6 kcal
6.6
9.2
bond angle
rotation
Total strain
planar
0.1 kcal
14.0
14.1

FIG. 3

force the molecule into some other form. This is probably not a completely general conclusion but we have enough information to make it a pretty safe generalization. One should be, I think, very cautious about postulating a change in structure of the molecule in order to accommodate the lattice arrangement.

I want to talk a little about rings. Fig. 3 is cyclopentane, and you will recall that all the older books indicate that the five carbon atoms are in a single plane. So far as the bond angle strain is concerned, that is the optimum orientation. On the other hand, cyclopentane does not exist in this geometry and the reason is simply the torsional forces about the single bond. In this case all five single bonds are in the worst possible orientation and you have about 14 or 15 kilocalories strain, if we may take the ethane value for the potential. This is a large strain.

What happens, of course, is that nature finds the compromise between the various forces which yields the minimum net energy. By puckering the rings somewhat at least some of the bonds can twist to near their potential minimum. By accepting as much as 2½ kilocalories bond angle strain you can lower the torsional strain much more and gain an appreciably lower energy.

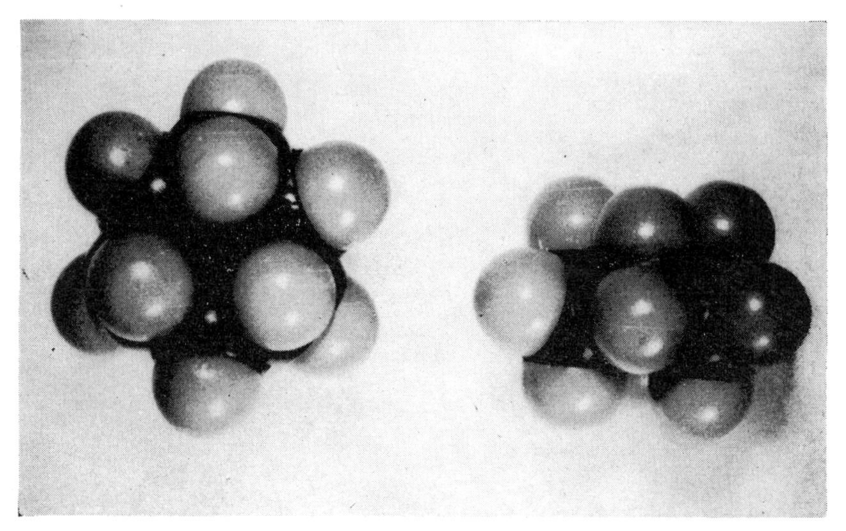

FIG. 4

The balance, even in the four-membered ring which is of much less interest, seems to be in favor of a little distortion from the plane, although there it is very small. As I said before, if you put atoms other than carbon into the ring, the torsional forces are usually reduced and the balance will therefore move from this back toward a planar ring.

Likewise, if you put double bonds in a five membered ring the torsional forces favor a flatter ring because the portion of the molecule aroung the double bond tends to be planar. Cyclopentadiene is no doubt flat. Cyclopentane is just on the verge. The energy is substantially the same for a flat or slightly distorted ring.

In the six-membered ring (Fig. 4) the books in the older literature always showed both a boat and chair conformation. If you look into those structures in the same manner that we just did for cyclopentane, you find that the chair structure is just ideal; it could not have been better. It staggers all the orientations of the single bonds and it gives tetrehedral bond angles at the same time. So chair cyclohexane is a strain free structure for the molecule.

The boat conformation has two of the C—C bonds in opposed orientation and therefore presumably has a strain energy in the vicinity of 5 to 6 kilocalories. No one has found any evidence whatsoever for cyclohexane itself in the boat conformation. Some highly substituted derivatives have been postulated as having the boat form, but that arises from a compromise of other forces. There is no evidence in the spectrum for any boat cyclohexane at room temperature or at the temperature in which the spectra were measured. I have no doubt that it does appear at high temperatures and in fact included such heat capacity terms in our own calculations, but this is not of interest in the general area that we are discussing.

Six-membered rings can ordinarily be assumed to be chair-like and, if you will notice cyclohexane more closely, there are two types of hydrogen locations. The three atoms above the ring are equivalent and there are three below that are the same and form one group of six. Then there are six around the middle that are all equivalent geometrically. There has been some confusion of nomenclature but we now have a four-nation treaty that was published in *Science* and *Nature* not long ago in which Hassel, Prelog, Barton and I recommended the terms axial and equatorial, respectively, for the two groups. The organic chemists seem to be happy with this system and are now putting the labels throughout the literature.

I will not go through all the cyclohexane conformational work, but it should be kept in mind generally that almost any group can be put into an equatorial position without getting into steric difficulties. But if you try to put substituents into the axial position, you find that even one methyl group is crowded, and two big groups would be impossibly strained. This on the other hand, is a strain that the molecular models will show quite clearly.

We do have some energy data on cyclohexane conformations. A methyl group located equatorially is free of strain. But a methyl group located axially is strained at two points and it turns out that the geometry here is just the same at each point as occurred in normal butane in the gauche conformation. Thus we can double that energy value. This is confirmed by experiments for the dimethylcyclohexanes.

I might just take a moment to discuss two big molecules and indicate how differences in these single bond potentials have quite an effect on the general properties. Again, this is an example that is probably remote from biological interests, but I think it illustrates the sort of thing that might arise. Suppose we take a straight paraffin chain. It would presumably have a CH_3 on each end of it. This is essentially an infinite chain.

Then we compare this with the chain which occurs in the inner tube of your tire, assuming you do not have a tubeless tire, namely, polyisobutylene.

Offhand, you would think that the paraffin chain would have less interference, and, therefore, that the normal paraffin ought to be the more flexible chain. That is precisely wrong. The polyisobutylene is much more flexible chain which makes it a rubber—that is the reason you can make an inner tube out of it if you want to. The long paraffin chain is polyethylene, which, of course, is a much harder material.

Also, if you dissolve these materials in a solvent the paraffin is a much more extended chain than the polyisobutylene. You can see this easily if you look down one of the C—C bonds (Fig. 5). Suppose we take a methyl substituted carbon atom at the far end and we have then CH_3 groups in two positions and

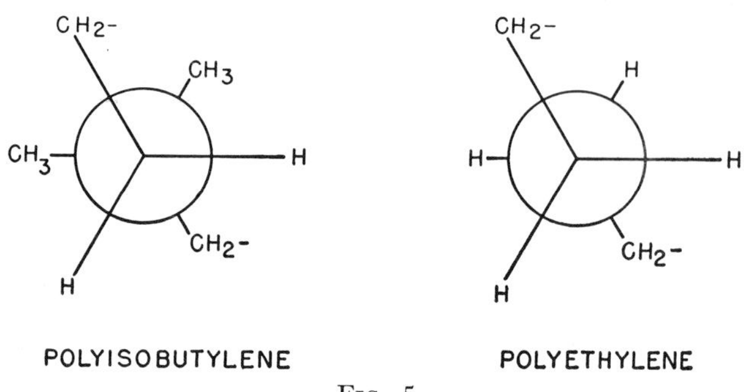

FIG. 5

in the third position we have a CH_2 and some more of the chain. At the near end we have two hydrogens and some more chain.

If you look at it this way you will see that the far end of this unit is practically symmetrical because there are two methyl groups, a methylene group that looks like a methyl group so far as the other end of this bond is concerned. Therefore, you can turn this bond by 120 degrees without any appreciable change in the potential energy. If, on the other hand, these methyl groups are replaced by hydrogen in the paraffin, then the situation is like that in n-butane where the potential minima differ in energy about one kilocalorie.

If you have for each bond in polyisobutylene, not free rotation, but three evenly spaced potential minima, then a long chain has practically as much flexibility as if there were free rotation. The chain can get into practically any position. If there is a difference in energy between the three potential minima, then the chain will be in the low energy position for most bonds, and the chain will be much less flexible. Thus in many cases you get the effect of free rotation, not by having the potential barrier zero, but by having several potential minima of equal energy.

I believe I should say a word about partial double bond systems, although I am sure you are quite familiar with them already. Since these are still mostly single bonds we ought to put it in this frame of reference. Let us take, 1,3-butadiene, and again it does not matter very much if oxygens or other groups are substituted for the terminal CH_2 groups. There is enough double bondedness in the central bond to favor a planar configuration—either cis or trans. The work of Aston, Brickwedde and others on 1,3-butadiene indicates that the trans is the low energy conformation. If the central bond is twisted by 90 degrees there is a potential maximum of about 5 kilocalories. In other words, the barrier is a little higher than in ethane, but not much different. If you let it go back down into the cis potential minimum you get a rotational isomer, or a conformer—which has a higher energy than trans by around 2 to 2½ kilocalories. Here again is a structural unit which, with other groups than CH_2's may be of interest to you. You can take the normal geometry as planar with respect to the single bond between double bonds as well as the double bonds themselves. Also the trans orientation with respect to the largest, most bulky groups is usually more stable than the cis.

CHAIRMAN PAULING: I think that I agree with Professor Pitzer that this aspect of molecular structure, the restriction of rotation around single bonds, is the one that is most overlooked, especially by people who make use of molecular models in the correlation of experimental results. I can emphasize another point that he made that is an interesting commentary on the role of quantum mechanical calculations in this field of chemistry. Eighteen years after Pitzer and Kemp discovered this phenomenon of restricted rotation around single bonds there still is no valid theory, at any rate, there is no theory that Professor Pitzer and I are willing to stand up for. Almost all of our knowledge about molecules is chemical in origin. It has been obtained empirically by chemical experiment and by generalizations, that the theories that exist are essentially inductive theories that have been obtained by chemists by analysis of chemical information.

DR. SIDNEY BERNHARD: I would like to ask Dr. Pitzer whether, with reference to enzymes and specific sites in general, when a molecule is twisted in order to fit a specific site, one empirically makes some guess as to how much these distortion effects are going to work against you or for you?

PROFESSOR PITZER: Yes, I think that in most cases we have the component information such that if you distort a molecule into other than its natural lowest energy conformation, you can calculate within possibly about 20 per cent the strain energy that would be required.

I have been amazed at the way these numbers can be transferred. The number that started out in normal butane is good to within 20 per cent in calculating the energy difference between cis and trans decahydronaphthalene. Thus as long as you have the energy values for good model substances I am sure they can be applied to other substances with quite high accuracy.

DR. G. B. M. SUTHERLAND (University of Michigan): I made an excursion into this field a long time ago, looking at the structure of hydrogen peroxide and hydrazine where it seemed that there was, from the spectroscopic data, very restricted rotation; in fact, only one form. I cannot remember the height of the barrier that we calculated. It seems to me, as a generalization, that all of the first row ones would be around about one to three kilocalories, but this, perhaps, was not true in the case of hydrogen peroxide and hydrazine.

PROFESSOR PITZER: I am glad you brought that up. I will have to stretch my range a little. Dr. Giguere in Quebec has been working on hydrogen peroxide by the same general methods and he finds a barrier somewhat higher than that in ethane. I think that it is four and a half kilocalories. In other words, it is not grossly different, but it is higher than the figure I gave.

I do not believe there is really good value for hydrazine, but I have no doubt that it will turn out to be about the same.

The principle that you and Penney brought out in your paper about unshared pairs of electrons as compared to the bonding ones is, I think, quite valid, and that is the reason why this barrier is a bit higher. On the other hand, your calculations may have put it a little on the high side; I have forgotten just what your numbers were.

CHAIRMAN PAULING: I think that with respect to proteins it may be of interest to mention a paper that I wrote two or three years ago about sulfur-sulfur single bonds in which it was shown that the dihedral angle determined by a sequence of three bonds is observed to be usually around 100° and that there is a theoretical reason for expecting 90° for this dihedral angle. Just as in hydrogen peroxide, the unshared electron pair on each of the two oxygen atoms or sulfur atoms in pi orbitals should set themselves at right angles to one another.

This disulfide configuration is really significant to the problem of protein structure.

PROFESSOR HIRSCHFELDER: I would like to ask Dr. Pitzer whether there are any good review articles or sources of data such as he has been talking about?

PROFESSOR PITZER: Not as good as one would like. I summarized the hydrocarbon data in the Discussion of the Faraday Society in 1951 and the hydrocarbons had been fairly well worked out at that time.

Mizushima has a small book on internal rotation which summarizes quite well the work on conformational energy differences, which is his principal subject, but gives relatively little information about the potential barriers between these potential minima. Also there is the chapter by Dauben and myself in the book "Steric Effects in Organic Chemistry" edited by M. Newman.

Specificity and Inhibition of Fumarase

Robert A. Alberty

University of Wisconsin, Madison, Wis.

There are two aspects of the specificity of an enzyme, the specificity with respect to the substrate and the specificity with respect to inhibitors. Some enzymes, such as chymotrypsin, have many substrates. For others, like fumarase, no additional substrates have been found. In the case of enzymes such as the latter there is some question as to how much information is forthcoming from the fact that a large number of other compounds are not substrates, and this increases the interest in the inhibition constants for competitive inhibitors.

Competitive inhibition constants are of special interest because they are believed to apply to the site at which the substrate combines. However, there are a number of difficulties involved in the interpretation of competitive inhibition constants. Today I want to talk primarily about one of them, the complication that is introduced by the fact that the kinetics of most enzymatic reactions, like protein reactions in general, depend upon the pH.

The effect of pH upon the binding of oxygen by hemoglobin (Wyman, 1948), the binding of antigen by antibody (Singer, Eggman and Campbell, 1955) and the binding of competitive inhibitors by cholinesterase (Wilson and Bergmann, 1950) have been studied. Such effects may result from the ionization of vicinal groups for which the ionization constants are altered by the presence of the inhibitor or the substrate. The effect of pH may be more subtle, but this simple interpretation has been quite satisfactory as a theoretical basis in a number of instances.

While I am going to use this sort of picture in discussing the data for fumarase, the discussion of Professor Kirkwood (1956) of an alternative interpretation of the effect of pH changes should be kept in mind. We prefer the interpretation which I am going to present because it brings together several aspects of the behavior of fumarase. However, we must keep in mind the fact that the force due to charge fluctuation may have an important effect. Perhaps experiments can be devised which will give decisive answers to the relative importance of these two effects.

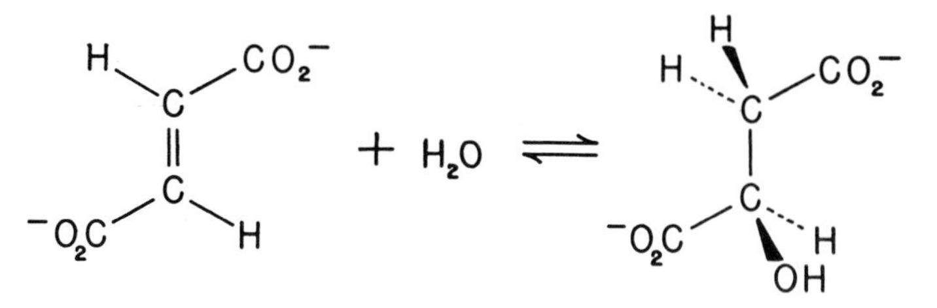

Water is added to the double bond of fumarate to form the *l*-isomer of malate. At equilibrium there is about four times as much *l*-malate as fumarate so that the kinetics of both the forward and the reverse reactions may be studied. This is of interest in checking certain conclusions as may be seen later.

The catalysis is stereospecific at the hydroxyl carbon, and experiments by Dr. Fisher (Fisher, Frieden, McKee and Alberty, 1955) using heavy water show that it is stereospecific in addition at the methylene carbon atom. When the reaction is carried out in deuterium oxide a single atom of deuterium is introduced into *l*-malate, and when this monodeutero-*l*-malate is dehydrated enzymatically, the deuterium is lost and no deuterium is incorporated into the fumarate.

Fumarase crystallized (Massey, 1951; Frieden, Bock and Alberty, 1954) from pig heart muscle has a molecular weight of 220,000 and appears to be a simple protein. Fumarase has a turnover number of the order of 10^5 min.$^{-1}$ which depends upon the pH and buffer.

A number of compounds have been tested as possible substrates for fumarase, and none have been found to react. The list (Massey, 1953) includes *d*-malate, *dl*-thiomalate, maleate, *cis* and *trans*-aconitate, citrate, mesaconate (which is the methyl substituted fumarate), citraconate (which is the methyl substituted maleate), *d,l* and *meso*-tartrate, *L*-ethane-1-hydroxy-1-carboxylic-2-sulphonic acid and mono- and diesters of fumarate. Thus fumarase has a very high degree of substrate specificity. A number of other compounds of interest remain to be tested when they have been freed of fumarate and malate to a sufficient extent.

Dependence of Kinetics upon pH

The kinetics of the fumarase reaction are markedly dependent upon pH (Massey, 1953; Alberty, Massey, Frieden and Fuhlbrigge, 1954; Frieden and Alberty, 1955) and the composition of the buffer. The anions in the buffer are apparently responsible for the buffer effects which are both of an activating and inhibiting nature. Phosphate buffers present an additional complication in that as we go from low pH values to high pH values we go from a buffer which contains primarily monovalent phosphate ions to one that contains primarily divalent phosphate ions. Since these ions have quite different activating and inhibiting effects on fumarase this complicates the elucidation of the ionization of the enzyme itself. It appears that in the case of fumarase these difficulties may be largely avoided by using buffers of the uncharged base, uncharged acid type, such as *tris*-(hydroxymethyl)-aminomethane acetate, because the ionic composition of the buffer medium may be held constant over a very wide range of pH.

At low substrate concentrations the initial steady state velocity v for the fumarase reaction depends upon the substrate concentration according to the Michaelis equation,

$$v = \frac{V_S}{1 + K_S/(S)}$$

The maximum initial velocity is represented by V_S and the Michaelis constant by K_S. At high substrate concentrations further terms have to be added to this equation to represent substrate activation and inhibition. The effect of pH on the kinetics of the forward and reverse reactions at low substrate concentrations can be summarized by showing the variations of V_S and K_S with pH. Such data are presented in Fig. 1. It is of interest to note that the pH optima for the forward and reverse reactions differ by 1.5 pH units.

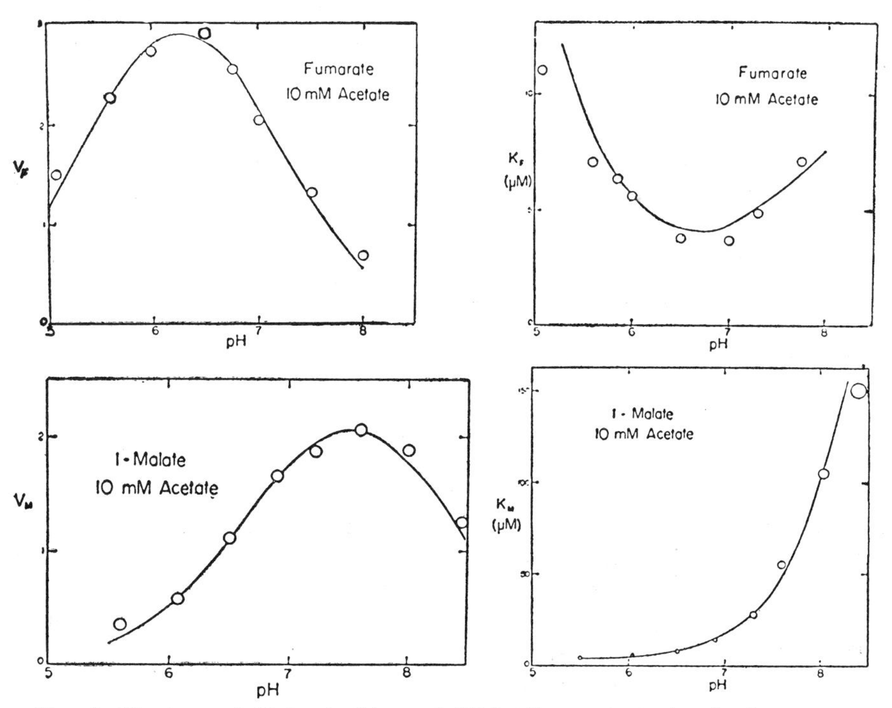

FIG. 1. Maximum initial velocities and Michaelis constants for the fumarase reaction at 25° for 0.01 M *tris*-(hydroxymethyl)-aminomethane acetate buffers (Frieden and Alberty, 1955). The curves have been calculated using equations (3) and (4).

The pH dependence of the kinetic constants may be represented by equations of the type

$$V_S = \frac{V_{S'}}{1 + (\mathrm{H}^+)/K_{aES} + K_{bES}/(\mathrm{H}^+)} \tag{3}$$

$$K_S = K_{S'} \frac{1 + (\mathrm{H}^+)/K_{aE} + K_{bE}/(\mathrm{H}^+)}{1 + (\mathrm{H}^+)/K_{aES} + K_{bES}/(\mathrm{H}^+)} \tag{4}$$

where V_S' and K_S' are "pH-independent" maximum velocities and Michaelis constants and K_a and K_b are acid dissociation constants. The plot of V_S versus pH is a symmetrical bell-shaped curve and K_{aES} is readily calculated (Alberty and Massey, 1954) from the hydrogen ion concentration at the inflection points of the acidic, $(\mathrm{H}^+)_a$, and basic, $(\mathrm{H}^+)_b$, branches of this curve by use of the equation

$$K_{aES} = (\mathrm{H}^+)_a + (\mathrm{H}^+)_b - 4\sqrt{(\mathrm{H})_a(\mathrm{H})_b} \tag{5}$$

The second ionization constant K_{bES} is then calculated from the relation

$$K_{aES}\, K_{bES} = (\mathrm{H}^+)_{\mathrm{max}}^2 \tag{6}$$

where $(\mathrm{H}^+)_{\mathrm{max}}$ is the hydrogen ion concentration at the optimum pH.

Equations (3) and (4) are obtained from the following mechanism in which the enzymatic site is considered to be a dibasic acid and the intermediate ionized form of the enzyme-substrate complexes to be the catalytically-active species.

$$\begin{array}{ccccccccc}
 & E & & EF & & EM & & E & \\
 & K_{bE}\updownarrow & & K_{bEF}\updownarrow & & K_{bEM}\updownarrow & & K_{bE}\updownarrow & \\
F\ + & EH & \underset{k_2}{\overset{k_1}{\rightleftharpoons}} & EHF & \underset{k_4}{\overset{k_3}{\rightleftharpoons}} & EHM & \underset{k_6}{\overset{k_5}{\rightleftharpoons}} & EH & +\ M \\
K_{HF}\updownarrow & K_{aE}\updownarrow & & K_{aEF}\updownarrow & & K_{aEM}\updownarrow & & K_{aE}\updownarrow & \updownarrow K_{HM} \\
HF & EH_2 & & EH_2F & & EH_2M & & EH_2 & HM
\end{array} \tag{75}$$

where the ionization constants are all acid dissociation constants.

In order to obtain equations (3) and (4) it is necessary to assume that the steps with rate constants k_3 and k_4 are rate determining when substrate is in excess and to ignore the ionization of the substrate.

The kinetics of the forward and reverse reactions are not independent as shown by Haldane (1930) for two simple mechanisms for reversible reactions. The equilibrium constant for the over-all reaction given above is

$$K = \frac{(M)eq}{(F)eq} = \frac{V_F K_M[1 + (\mathrm{H}^+)/K_{HF}]}{V_M K_F[1 + (\mathrm{H}^+)/K_{HM}]} \tag{8}$$

Thus, once theoretical curves have been drawn through the plots for V_F, V_M and K_M we are no longer at liberty to draw an independent theoretical curve through the points for K_F. The theoretical line in the K_F plot of Fig. 1 may be considered to come from the other three plots.

The Michaelis constant is represented by equation (4) which has five parameters, but two of these parameters, the ionization constants for the enzyme-substrate complex, are determinable from the pH variation of the maximum velocity. Since K_S' has nothing to do with the pH dependence, the nature of this dependence is represented by two additional parameters, K_{aE} and K_{bE}. The values of K_{aE} and K_{bE} may be obtained from a plot of V_S/K_S versus pH since

$$\frac{V_S}{K_S} = \frac{V_{S'} K_{S'}}{1 + (\mathrm{H}^+)/K_{aE} + K_{bE}/(\mathrm{H}^+)} \tag{9}$$

We now have an opportunity to test the theory since the same values of K_{aE} and K_{bE} should be obtained whether we are studying the forward reaction or the reverse reaction. Such a plot is shown in Fig. 2. The correction terms $[1 + (\mathrm{H}^+)/K_{HF}]$ and $[1 + (\mathrm{H}^+)/K_{HM}]$ are required at low pH values to allow the secondary ionizations of the substrates in the case of the fumarase reaction. The equilibrium constant for the over-all reaction under the conditions used is 4.4. The values of pK_{aE} and pK_{bE} are calculated from this bell-shaped plot.

The pK values for the active site of fumarase obtained in this way are summarized in Table I (Frieden and Alberty, 1955). It is of interest to note that the

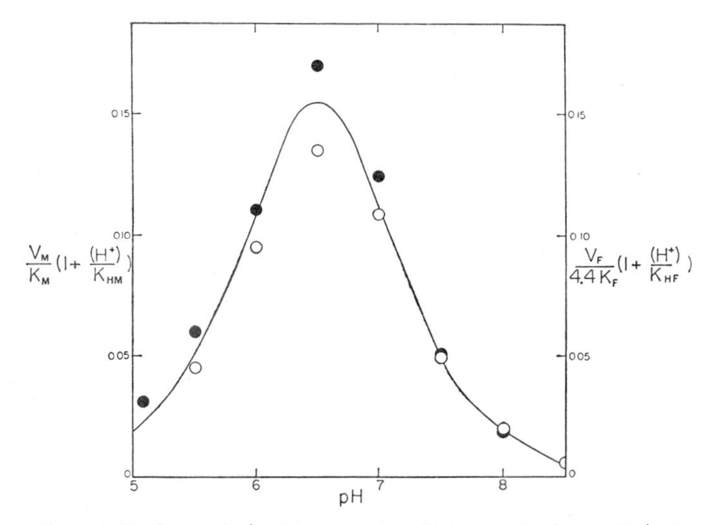

FIG. 2. Plot of V_F $[1 + (\mathrm{H}^+)/K_{HF}]/4.4\ K_F$ (●) and $V_M[1 + (\mathrm{H}^+)/K_{HM})/K_{HM}$ (○) versus pH at 25° for 0.01 M *tris*-(hydroxymethyl)-aminomethane acetate buffers (Frieden and Alberty, 1955). The curve has been calculated using equation (9).

TABLE I

pK values for groups in fumarase and in fumarase-substrate complexes in 0.01 M acetate buffer at 25°

	E	*EF*	*EM*
pK_a	6.2	5.3	6.6
pK_b	6.8	7.3	8.4

ionization constants for the groups in the free enzyme differ by a factor of 4, which is the statistical factor for a dibasic acid with two independent groups.

Now, the simple electrostatic effect of bringing a divalent negative ion into the vicinity of an acid group would be to raise the *pK* value. Malate does this but in the case of fumarate some other effect predominates since one of the *pK* values is actually reduced.

Now, why do two ionizable groups exert a total effect on the activity and why, of the three ionized forms of the enzyme-substrate complex, is it the intermediate one which is catalytically active? We believe the answer is that these two groups are actually involved in donating and accepting protons in the catalytic process. This sort of mechanism has been suggested by Nachmansohn and Wilson (1951) for the cholinesterase reaction and by Swain and Brown (1952) for the catalysis of the mutarotation of tetramethylglucose by *o*-hydroxypyridine.

Fig. 3 indicates the kind of mechanism that we imagine for this reaction. Only the step in which the enzyme-fumarate complex is converted into the enzyme-malate complex is shown. The shaded portion represents our ignorance about the structure of the enzyme except for the fact that it contains two groups, R and R′, which are involved in the catalytic process. The form of the enzyme-substrate complex which can yield enzyme-product complex is the one in which

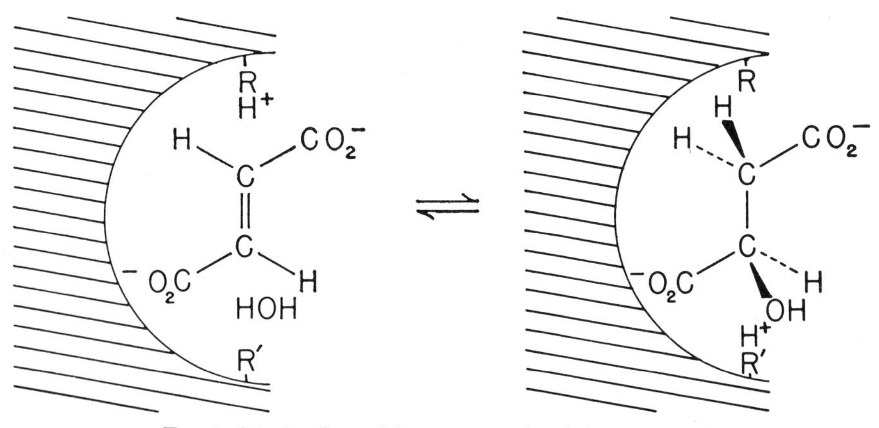

FIG. 3. Mechanism of fumarase action (Alberty, 1956)

one group is in its acid form so that it can serve as a proton donor and the other group is in the basic form so that it can serve as a proton acceptor. The enzyme-malate complex is cocked to catalyze the reverse reaction. Thus, we believe that the enzyme works essentially by an acid-base catalysis, but the reaction occurs rapidly in neutral solutions because the acidic and basic groups are located at exactly the right positions in space. This sort of picture helps us to understand many things about the fumarase reaction. For example, the activity is low in strongly acidic solutions because the group which has to serve as a proton acceptor spends a very small fraction of the time in the basic form. A single optical isomer of malate is obtained because group R′ determines the side on which the hydroxyl group is added. Similarly, the mechanism helps us understand why monodeuteromalate is formed when the reaction is carried out in deuterium oxide and why no deuterium is found in the fumarate.

Competitive Inhibition of Fumarase

The inhibition constant K_I for a competitive inhibitor I is obtained by use of the equation

$$v = \frac{V_S}{1 + K_S[1 + (I)/K_I]/(S)} \tag{10}$$

In contrast with the Michaelis constant, which is not to be interpreted as an equilibrium constant, the inhibition constant may be interpreted as a dissociation constant for the enzyme-inhibitor complex. However, K_I may depend strongly upon the pH (Massey, 1953). If the active site may be considered to be a dibasic acid, the dissociation of the enzyme-inhibitor complex may be represented by

$$\begin{array}{ccc} EI & & E \\ K_{bEI} \upharpoonleft\downharpoonright & & \upharpoonleft\downharpoonright K_{bE} \\ EHI & \overset{K_I'}{\rightleftharpoons} & I + EH \\ \upharpoonleft\downharpoonright & & \upharpoonleft\downharpoonright K_{aE} \\ K_{aEI}\, EH_2I & & EH_2 \end{array} \tag{11}$$

where $K_{aEI} = (H^+)\,(EHI)/(EH_2I)$, $K_{bEI} = (H^+)\,(EI)/(EHI)$, $K_{aE} = (H^+)\,(EH)/(EH_2)$, and $K_{bE} = (H^+)\,(E)/(EH)$. It is assumed that the inhibitor does not ionize in the region under investigation, although provision could readily be made for such ionization if necessary. The inhibition constant which is obtained by use of the equation (10) is given by

$$K_I = K_{I'} \frac{1 + (H^+)/K_{aE} + K_{bE}/(H^+)}{1 + (H^+)/K_{aEI} + K_{bEI}/(H^+)} \tag{12}$$

where K_I' is the dissociation constant for the complex with a particular ionized form of the enzyme

$$K_{I'} = \frac{(I)(EH)}{(EHI)} \tag{13}$$

Thus the experimentally-determined dissociation constant K_I depends not only upon the affinity of the inhibitor for a particular ionized form of the enzymatic site, but also upon the effect of the bound inhibitor on the ionization constants of the two dissociable groups. As shown by Massey's data (1953) different inhibitors have very different effects on the ionization constants of the two groups in fumarase. In other words, inhibitors with the same K_I' value might have quite different K_I values at a given pH. Thus, if inhibitions are arranged in the order of their inhibition constants at an arbitrarily chosen pH and a structural interpretation of the data is developed, very likely some agonizing reappraisals would be required when additional studies are made at another pH value.

By comparison of equations (3), (4) and (12) it is seen that the calculation of K_{aEI} and K_{bEI} may be facilitated by plotting $K_I V_S / K_S$ versus pH since a symmetrical bell-shaped plot should be obtained. Preliminary data on the competitive inhibition of fumarase bears out this expectation (Frieden, 1955). The best inhibitor that has been found for the fumarase reaction is *meso*-tartrate (Frieden, 1955).

In order to illustrate the nature of the pH variation of K_I which is permitted by equation (12), plots of log (K_I/K_I') versus pH are given for two hypothetical cases in Fig. 4. The plot on the left might be considered to be that expected for an anionic inhibitor which causes the pK values for both groups in the enzyme to be increased one unit. The plot on the right illustrates the case in which one pK value (pK_{aEI}) is decreased one unit and the other (pK_{bEI}) increased one unit by the bound inhibitor. When this occurs the apparent inhibition constant will not have a value at any pH which is equal to K_I'. The direction of the electrostatic effect of an ionic inhibitor on the ionization constant of a neighboring group may be predicted (Kirkwood and Westheimer, 1938a.) (Westheimer and Kirkwood, 1938b.) but other effects, such as the formation of hydrogen bonds (Laskowski and Scheraga, 1954), may be involved.

Another aspect of the effect of bound inhibitor upon the ionization constants of groups in the enzymatic site is that acid will be produced or consumed in the reaction. The number, $\Delta\bar{X}$, of equivalents of acid produced per mole of enzymatic sites in the dissociation reaction is given by (Alberty, 1955)

$$\Delta_{\bar{X}} = \frac{1 + 2(\mathrm{H}^+)/K_{aEI}}{1 + (\mathrm{H}^+)/K_{aEI} + K_{bEI}/(\mathrm{H}^+)} - \frac{1 + 2(\mathrm{H}^+)/K_{aE}}{1 + (\mathrm{H}^+)/K_{aE} + K_{bE}/(\mathrm{H}^+)} \tag{14}$$

This equation is different from that derived by Wyman (1948) but actually involves the same dependence on hydrogen ion concentration. This is the equation

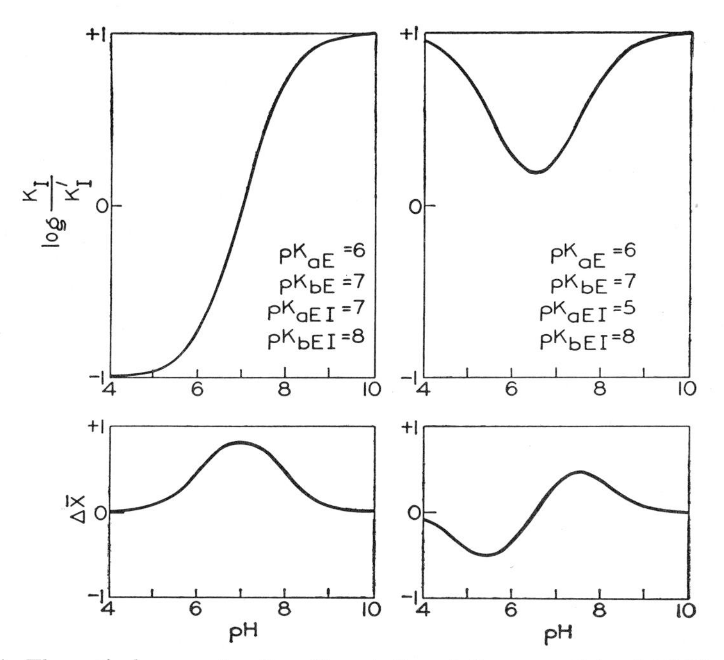

FIG. 4. Theoretical curves for the pH variation of the competitive inhibition constant for two hypothetical cases. The lower curves give the number of equivalents of acid produced per mole of enzymatic sites in the dissociation reaction.

for the differential titration curve of the enzyme in the presence and absence of the competitive inhibitor. When the number of enzymatic sites per molecule is unknown, such a differential titration offers the means for determining the number of sites. Differential titrations would also provide a check upon the interpretation of the pH dependence of the kinetically-determined inhibition constants.

In comparing the plot of log (K_I/K_I') versus pH with the corresponding one for $\Delta\bar{x}$, it will be seen that when acid is produced the dissociation of the EI complex increases with pH, and that when acid is consumed the dissociation decreases with increasing pH.

At extreme pH values (pH 8.5 at 0.01 ionic strength) there are deviations from the simple equations described above. These deviations are in the direction to be expected for electrostatic effects from the rest of the protein molecule (Alberty, 1956). It is to be expected that they will be less important at higher ionic strength values.

Conclusion

This discussion has been designed to bring out some of the complications which may be encountered in the interpretation of enzyme kinetic data and to show how these are being handled in the case of fumarase. The prospects are encouraging, but quite a bit remains to be done before information about the catalytic site will be obtained by the study of inhibitors. However, the studies of the effect of pH on the fumarase reaction have shown that the enzymatic site may be considered to be a dibasic acid. The fact that it is the intermediate ionized form which is catalytically active suggests that the enzymatic action involves the donation of a proton by one of these groups and the acceptance of a proton by the other. What is needed in the study of inhibitors is kinetic data over a range of pH so that it will be possible to discuss the affinity of a particular ionized form of the enzyme for the inhibitor and to compare inhibitors with respect to their effects upon the ionization of groups in the catalytic site.

References

Alberty, R. A. 1953. The relationship between Michaelis constants, maximum velocities, and the equilibrium constant for an enzyme-catalyzed reaction. J. Am. Chem. Soc. *75:* 1928–1932.

Alberty, R. A. 1954. Some mechanisms for the interpretation of the effects of pH and buffer salts on a simple enzymatic reaction. J. Am. Chem. Soc. *76:* 2494–2498.

Alberty, R. A. 1955. The ionization constants of the heme-linked groups of hemoglobin. J. Am. Chem. Soc. *77:* 4522–4524.

Alberty, R. A. 1956. Kinetic effects of the ionization of groups in the enzyme molecule. J. Cell. and Comp. Physiol. In press.

Alberty, R. A. and V. Massey. 1954. On the interpretation of the pH variation of the maximum initial velocity of an enzyme-catalyzed reaction. Biochim. et Biophys. Acta *13:* 347–353.

Alberty, R. A., V. Massey, C. Frieden, and A. R. Fuhlbrigge. 1954. Studies of the enzyme fumarase. III. The dependence of the kinetic constants at 25° upon the concentration and pH of phosphate buffers. J. Am. Chem. Soc. *76:* 2485–2493.

Fisher, H., C. Frieden, J. S. McKinley McKee and R. A. Alberty. 1955. Concerning the stereospecificity of the fumarase reaction and the demonstration of a new intermediate. J. Am. Chem. Soc. *77:* 4435.

Frieden, C. 1955. Kinetic studies of the enzyme fumarase. Ph D. Thesis. University of Wisconsin.

Frieden, C. and R. A. Alberty. 1955. The effect of pH on fumarase activity in acetate buffer. J. Biol. Chem. *212:* 859–868.

Frieden, C., R. M. Bock and R. A. Alberty. 1954. Studies of the enzyme fumarase. II. Isolation and physical properties of the crystalline enzyme. J. Am. Chem. Soc. *76:* 2482–2484.

Haldane, J. B. S. 1930. Enzymes. New York. Longmans, Green and Company.

Kirkwood, J. G. 1956. The influence of fluctuations in protein charge and charge configuration on the rates of enzymatic reactions. Faraday Soc. Discussions. In press.

Kirkwood, J. G. and F. H. Westheimer. 1938. The electrostatic influence of substituents on the dissociation constants of organic acids. I. J. Chem. Phys. *6:* 506–512.

Laskowski, M., Jr. and H. A. Scheraga. 1954. Thermodynamic considerations of protein reactions. I. Modified reactivity of polar groups. J. Am. Chem. Soc. *76:* 6305–6319.

Massey, V. 1951. The crystallization of fumarase. Biochem. J. *51:* 490–494.

Massey, V. 1953a. Studies on fumarase. II. The effects of inorganic anions on fumarase activity. Biochem. J. *53:* 67–71.

Massey, V. 1953b. Studies on fumarase. IV. The effects of inhibitors on fumarase activity. Biochem. J. *55:* 172–177.

Nachmansohn, D. and I. B. Wilson. 1951. The enzymatic hydrolysis and synthesis of acetylcholine. Adv. in Enzymol. *12:* 259–339.

Singer, S. J., L. Eggman and D. H. Campbell. 1955. Physical chemical studies of soluble antigen-antibody complexes. VI. The effect of pH on the reaction between ovalbumin and its rabbit antibodies. J. Am. Chem. Soc. *77:* 4855–4857.

Swain, C. G. and J. F. Brown. 1952. Concerted displacement reactions. VIII. Polyfunctional catalysis. J. Am. Chem. Soc. *74:* 2538–2543.

Westheimer, F. H. and J. G. Kirkwood. 1938. The electrostatic influence of substituents on the dissociation constants of organic acids. II. J. Chem. Phys. *6:* 513–517.

Wilson, I. B. and F. Bergmann. 1950. Studies of cholinesterase. VII. The active surface of acetylcholinesterase derived from effects of pH on inhibitors. J. Biol. Chem. *185:* 479–489.

Wyman, J. Jr. 1948. Heme proteins. Advances in Protein Chem. *4:* 407–531.

Specificity in the Interaction of Sickle Cell Hemoglobin Molecules

Harvey A. Itano

National Institute of Arthritis and Metabolic Diseases, National Institutes of Health, Bethesda, Md.

STUDIES OF THE PHYSICAL PROPERTIES of the human hemoglobins have provided much information concerning how a specific molecular interaction in a living organism can cause a particular group of inherited anemias. The normal hemoglobins of man are fetal (F), present in fetal life and in early infancy, and adult (A). Electrophoretic studies have disclosed the existence of a number of abnormal forms which are inherited modifications of the adult hemoglobin (Pauling, *et al.*, 1949; Itano, 1955). The adult form and its modifications are probably determined by a series of allelic genes (Itano, 1953a), so that a person can have either one or two of these forms, depending upon whether he is homozygous in one of the genes or heterozygous; he can have no more than two since an individual can have only one pair of genes at any allelic site. The production of hemoglobin F is under separate genetic control, and this form may be present in addition to the adult forms, not only during infancy but also in later life in certain chronic anemias (Singer, *et al.*, 1951; Itano, 1953b).

Hemoglobin S, the hemoglobin of sickle cell anemia, has the striking property, not possessed by the other forms, of aggregating and of becoming very insoluble when deoxygenated (Harris, 1950; Perutz and Mitchison, 1950). The specific structural abnormality which causes hemoglobin S to aggregate, and to do so only when deoxygenated, is not known. The tendency to aggregate cannot be correlated with any of the other known properties of the molecule. In spite of an abnormal net charge (Pauling *et al.*, 1949), its amino acid composition (Schroeder, *et al.*, 1950; Huisman, *et al.*, 1955) and antigenic behavior (Goodman and Campbell, 1953; Chernoff, 1953) are very similar to those of hemoglobin A. Its solubility when oxygenated is the same as that of oxyhemoglobin A (Perutz and Mitchison, 1950), and its oxygen equilibrium behavior is normal, even in the presence of aggregates of its deoxygenated form (Allen and Wyman, 1954). The second abnormal hemoglobin, hemoglobin C, is more abnormal in electrophoretic mobility (Itano and Neel, 1950) and amino acid composition than is hemoglobin S (Huisman, *et al.*, 1955); but its solubility when deoxygenated is closer to that of A (Itano, 1953c). Hemoglobin D has the electrophoretic mobility of hemoglobin S and solubility of hemoglobin A (Itano, 1951). A number of other abnormal hemoglobins have been found with use of the electrophoretic method; however, hemoglobins C and D are the only abnormal forms known to be associated with sickle cell disease.

It seems reasonable to assume that the ultimate origin of the abnormal hemoglobins were mutations in the gene which determines the structure of hemoglobin A. The mutations resulted in changes in amino acid sequence or composition, or both; and these changes produced the alterations in net charge and surface configuration manifested by abnormalities in electrophoretic mobilities and solubilities. The alterations were not sufficient to alter the ability of the abnormal hemoglobins to combine reversibly with oxygen since each of the known forms functions as an oxygen carrier in blood.

In this paper I shall discuss the ways in which the aggregating property of hemoglobin S has been observed and measured. The sickling behavior of red cells was studied long before the discovery that an abnormal hemoglobin occurs in sickle cell anemia. It was known that the removal of oxygen causes sickling in the cells of certain individuals (Hahn and Gillespie, 1927) and that the ease with which sickling could be induced varies in different individuals (Emmel, 1917). In those whose sickling cells are not accompanied by anemia, sickling occurs more slowly than in those with anemia. Even among those who have anemia with sickling cells, some have cells which sickle less readily than in the usual case of sickle cell anemia (Cooke and Mack, 1934). Moreover, there is a difference in the shape of the sickled cells from anemic and non-anemic individuals. In sickle cell anemia the typical sickled cells have the shape of slender, elongated crescents and spindles with filamentous extensions from each end. In the non-anemic carriers of the sickle cell trait the cells assume a more compact and multi-pointed form, and the filaments are not as prominent. The two types of sickling are called "filamentous" and "holly-leaf", respectively (Neel, 1951). Sickled cells are rigid (Murphy and Shapiro, 1944) and are birefringent (Sherman, 1940); in contrast, oxygenated cells containing sickle cell hemoglobin and normal cells, oxygenated or deoxygenated, are flexible and show no sign of hemoglobin aggregation or orientation. The cells in sickle cell trait do not sickle at the oxygen tension of venous blood; whereas in sickle cell anemia a high proportion of the cells in venous blood are partially or completely sickled (Sherman, 1940). When sickle cell anemia subjects are placed in an atmosphere with a high partial pressure of oxygen, the percentage of sickled cells in their blood and the rate of destruction of their red blood cells in the circulation diminish (Reinhard, *et al.*, 1944; Callender, *et al.*, 1949). Genetically, sickle cell anemia is due to homozygosity in the sickle cell gene (Neel, 1949). Normal adult hemoglobin is absent, and hemoglobin S is the only abnormal hemoglobin present. As in other chronic anemias, fetal hemoglobin may also be present. Sickle cell trait is due to the presence of one allele each for sickle cell hemoglobin and normal adult hemoglobin, and hemoglobins S and A are present (Pauling, *et al.*, 1949). Apparently the gene-controlled mechanism for the synthesis of hemoglobin A is more efficient than that for S; sickle cell trait blood invariably contains more hemoglobin A than S (Itano, 1953a).

Sickle cell hemoglobin C disease and sickle cell hemoglobin D disease are genetic analogues of sickle cell trait in which the gene for an abnormal non-sickling hemoglobin replaces the normal allele. The existence of these variants of sickle cell disease was brought to light as a result of electrophoretic and solubility studies of hemoglobin in cases which did not fit the classical descriptions of sickle cell anemia and trait (Itano and Neel, 1950; Itano, 1951). As shown by the solubility studies, to be described, the hemoglobin mixtures in these two diseases form more stable aggregates than do the A-S mixture of sickle cell trait. Sickling is of the filamentous type, but the cells show less intravascular sickling than those of the anemia (Kaplan, *et al.*, 1951; Sturgeon, *et al.*, 1955). In sickle cell thalassemia disease one sickle cell gene and one thalassemia gene, which blocks partially or completely the synthesis of normal hemoglobin, are present (Sturgeon, *et al.*, 1952). The red cells produce more hemoglobin S than A, and the net effect is to increase the ability of the cells to sickle. Hematologic observations which reflect differences in sickling tendency have been summarized in Table I. Although the results are given in qualitative terms, the differences are usually quite evident to the trained observer.

Recent observations at high altitudes have illustrated dramatically the effect of oxygen tension and of hemoglobin composition on sickling (Smith and Conley, 1955). The pathological effects of sickle cell disease can be ascribed to the presence of sickled cells in circulating blood. As an apparent effect of their

TABLE I

Relationship of the sickling properties of red blood cells to their hemoglobin content and solubilities

Condition	% Hb S[1]	Total Solubility[2]	Type of Sickling	Sickled Cells in Venous Blood
Sickle cell trait	23–47	1.26–2.17	holly-leaf	None
Sickle cell Hb C disease	41–50	1.11–1.22	filamentous	Few
Sickle cell Thal. disease	61–84	0.44–0.90	filamentous	11% (1 case)
Sickle cell Hb D disease	not known	1.77–0.98	filamentous	20–25% (2 cases)
Sickle cell anemia	60–97	0.10–0.95	filamentous	30–75% (many cases)

[1] These figures are for samples which correspond to the solubilities shown. Percentages of Hb S falling a few per cent outside these ranges have been reported.

[2] The solubilities in grams per liter of amorphous ferrohemoglobin were determined in 2.24 molar phosphate buffer at 25°C. (Itano, 1953c).

shape and rigidity, sickled cells tend to block off small blood vessels and cause tissue destruction. The spleen is a common site of occurrence of this phenomenon in sickle cell anemia. The amount of intravascular sickling in sickle cell hemoglobin C disease is small, and the incidence of splenic infarction under normal conditions is low. Several instances of splenic infarction in sickle cell hemoglobin C disease have been observed in previously well subjects at altitudes of 4000–6000 feet in unpressurized airplanes. In sickle cell trait splenic infarctions have occurred only at higher altitudes of 10,000–15,000 feet.

The discovery that the hemoglobin in sickling cells has abnormal electrophoretic behavior suggested further investigation of its physical properties. Gellation and solubility studies showed differences in the interactions of hemoglobin S and the other abnormal hemoglobins. In gellation studies the behavior of concentrated hemoglobin solutions prepared by the lysis of red blood cells was examined. These solutions contain other soluble constituents of the red cell and are relatively low in salt concentration. It was discovered by Harris (1950) that if a solution of oxyhemoglobin S of greater than 10 per cent concentration were deoxygenated, a rise in viscosity occurred; below 10 per cent concentration no change in viscosity occurred. The viscous solutions prepared in this manner contain birefringent, spindle-shaped aggregates of hemoglobin S. Harris also observed that solutions of higher concentration became gels when deoxygenated. By testing progressive dilutions of concentrated mixtures containing hemoglobin S, Singer and Singer (1953) determined the minimum concentration at which gellation occurs. For the S-F mixtures of sickle cell anemia the minimum concentration for gelling was 19–25 per cent. The minimum concentrations for the A-S mixtures of sickle cell trait and the S-C mixtures of sickle cell hemoglobin C disease were 30–33 and 26–28 per cent, respectively. In terms of the hemoglobin S concentration at least 19 per cent was required to cause sickle cell anemia samples to gel. In sickle cell trait and sickle cell hemoglobin C disease the minimum hemoglobin S concentrations for gel formation were 10–16 and 9–13 per cent, respectively. Thus, although hemoglobins A and C do not form gels in the absence of hemoglobin S, they can take part in gel formation in the presence of S and reduce the concentration of S required for gellation to occur.

The determination of hemoglobin solubility in concentrated salt solutions provides a quantitative measure of interactions in mixtures and is more readily controlled than sickling or gellation studies. Landsteiner and Heidelberger (1923) compared solubilities of the oxyhemoglobins of different mammals. They found that the solubilities of mixtures prepared from different species had additive solubilities but that a mixture of donkey and horse hemoglobins interacted to yield an intermediate solubility. Kunitz and Northrop (1938) studied the solubility behavior of protein mixtures in salt solutions and applied the phase rule to the interpretation of their data. In a typical experiment increasing amounts of a protein mixture were added to aliquots of a salt solution of fixed composition at a given temperature and pressure. After equilibrium was attained, the amount of protein in solution was measured and was plotted against the total protein added. Characteristic curves were obtained for a homogeneous protein, a two-phase protein mixture, and a solid solution of two proteins. I have shown by use of this technique that the solubility behavior of a mixture of hemoglobins A and S corresponds to that of a solid solution (Itano, 1953c). The solubility curve does not have any sharp breaks that would indicate the appearance of a new phase, and the solubilities lie between those of A and S. 50 mg of hemoglobin A dissolves completely in 10 ml of 2.24 molar phosphate buffer. However, if a mixture containing 30 mg of hemoglobin and 20 mg of hemoglobin S is equilibrated with the same volume of buffer, the total hemoglobin in solution is only 14 mg. This result indicates that a stabilizing interaction in the solid phase prevents more than half of the available hemoglobin A from going into solution.

Kunitz and Northrop calculated the solubilities of solid solutions on the assumption that the solubility of each component was proportional to its solubility in its pure state multiplied by its mole fraction in the solid phase and obtained fairly good agreement with theory when they tested two different chymotrypsin mixtures. I have carried out calculations based on the same assumption for hemoglobin mixtures for which comparable data were available. The results are summarized in Table II. A mixture of hemoglobins A and C behaves according to the criterion of Kunitz and Northrop. Both the A-S and S-C mixtures are less soluble than expected on the basis of the same criterion. Moreover, although hemoglobin C is more soluble than A, the S-C mixture

TABLE II

Calculated and observed solubilities of amorphous ferrohemoglobin

Mixture	Buffer Concentration[1]	Total solubility in g/l		Observed / Calculated
		Calculated[2]	Observed[3]	
30% C, 70% A	2.58 M	1.9	1.9	1.0
30% S, 70% A	2.24 M	3.3	1.7	.52
40% S, 60% A	2.24 M	2.8	1.4	.50
40% S, 60% C	2.24 M	3.0	1.2	.40
50% S, 60% C	2.24 M	2.5	1.1	.44

[1] Potassium phosphate buffer at 25° C was used. The mole fraction of K_2HPO_4 was 0.58 (Itano, 1953c).

[2] The calculations were based on the assumption that the solubility of each component is equal to its solubility as a homogeneous protein multiplied by its mole fraction in the solid state. (Kunitz and Northrop, 1938). Data for the calculations are from Itano (1951, 1953c).

[3] The observed solubilities shown here are means of several samples having the same approximate compositions (Itano, 1953c).

with 40 per cent hemoglobin S is less soluble than the corresponding A-S mixture. The last result is consistent with observations that the cells of sickle cell hemoglobin disease sickle more readily than those of sickle cell trait and that S-C mixtures gel at a lower total concentration than A-S mixtures containing the same percentage of hemoglobin S.

The composition of the hemoglobin mixture in sickle cell hemoglobin D disease cannot be determined since hemoglobins S and D have the same electrophoretic mobility. The hemoglobin in this disease has a total solubility in phosphate buffer that is less than that in sickle cell hemoglobin C disease and greater than that in sickle cell anemia. Hemoglobin D has not been obtained in the homogeneous state; naturally occurring mixtures of hemoglobins A and D have nearly the same solubility as hemoglobin A alone. Thus, there is insufficient information to decide whether the relatively low solubility of S-D mixtures is due to a stabilizing interaction in the aggregated phase or to the presence of a high percentage of hemoglobin S.

Briefly summarized, the basic factor in the production of sickle cell disease is the presence of an abnormal hemoglobin molecule which aggregates when deoxygenated and produces a rigid, distorted cell. The sickled cell is more susceptible to destruction and is capable of causing tissue damage by blocking blood vessels. The effectiveness of the abnormal molecule in causing disease is modified by several factors. When an individual has only genes for hemoglobin S, a severe anemia called sickle cell anemia occurs. When genes for hemoglobins A and S are present, the resulting hemoglobin mixture always contains more A than S, and sickling is inhibited to such an extent that no anemia results. If, in addition, a gene for thalassemia is present, hemoglobin A synthesis is inhibited; consequently the red cells contain more S than A, and anemia occurs. In sickle cell hemoglobin C disease the average proportion of hemoglobin S is higher than the average in sickle cell trait; in addition, sickling is enhanced by the increased stability of S-C aggregates. On the other hand, the aggregates are not as stable as those of hemoglobin S alone, and the sickling tendency and anemia are less than in sickle cell anemia.

In conclusion, I wish to point out that in order to simplify the discussion and illustrate the basic factors which characterize the variants of sickle cell disease, the average findings in each variant have been considered. As is evident from Table I, the proportion of hemoglobin S varies in each of these conditions, and overlapping of values between different conditions occurs. Other factors which determine the final effect on the individual, such as the ability of his body to compensate for blood destruction by increasing blood formation, have not been discussed. The factors involved in any human disease are so numerous that we are indeed fortunate in having for study a group of conditions in which the actual molecules responsible for the disease process can be isolated in large quantities for controlled investigations.

References

Allen, D. W., and J. Wyman, Jr. 1954. Équilibre de l'hémoglobine de drépanocytose avec l'oxygène. Rev. Hematol. *9:* 155–157.

Callender, S. T. E., J. F. Nickel, C. V. Moore, and E. O. Powell. 1949. Sickle cell disease: studied by measuring the survival of transfused red blood cells. J. Lab. et Clin. Med. *34:* 90–104.

Chernoff, A. 1953. Immunologic studies of hemoglobins. I. Production of antihemoglobin sera and their immunologic characteristics. Blood *8:* 399–412.

Cooke, J. V., and J. K. Mack. 1934. Sickle cell anemia in a white American family. J. Pediatrics *5:* 601–607.

Emmel, V. E. 1917. A study of the erythrocytes in a case of severe anemia with elongated and sickle-shaped red blood corpuscles. Arch. Int. Med. *20:* 586–598.

Goodman, M., and D. H. Campbell. 1953. Differences in antigenic specificity of human normal adult, fetal, and sickle cell anemia hemoglobin. Blood *8:* 422–433.

Hahn, E. V., and E. B. Gillespie. 1927. Sickle cell anemia. Report of a case greatly improved by splenectomy. Experimental study of sickle cell formation. Arch. Int. Med. *39:* 233–254.

Harris, J. W., and S. J. Bunting. 1950. Studies on the destruction of red blood cells. VIII. Molecular orientation in sickle cell hemoglobin solution. Proc. Soc. Exptl. Biol. Med. *75:* 197–201.

Huisman, T. H. J., J. H. P. Jonxis, and P. C. van der Schaaf. 1955. Amino-acid composition of four different kinds of human hemoglobin. Nature *175:* 902–903.

Itano, H. A., and J. V. Neel. 1950. A new inherited abnormality of human hemoglobin. Proc. Natl. Acad. Sci. U. S. A. *36:* 613–617.

Itano, H. A. 1951. A third abnormal hemoglobin associated with hereditary hemolytic anemia. Proc. Natl. Acad. Sci. U. S. A. *37:* 775–784.

Itano, H. A. 1953a. Qualitative and quantitative control of adult hemoglobin synthesis—A multiple allele hypothesis. Am. J. Human Genetics *5:* 34–45.

Itano, H. A. 1953b. Human hemoglobin. Science *117:* 89–94.

Itano, H. A. 1953c. Solubilities of naturally occurring mixtures of human hemoglobin. Arch. Biochem. Biophys. *47:* 148–159.

Itano, H. A. 1955. Clinical states associated with alterations of the hemoglobin molecule; the Minot Lecture. A. M. A. Arch. Int. Med. *96:* 287–297.

Kaplan, E., W. W. Zuelzer, and J. V. Neel. 1951. A new inherited abnormality of hemoglobin and its interaction with sickle cell hemoglobin. Blood *6:* 1240–1259.

Kunitz, M., and J. H. Northrop. 1938. Solubility curves of pure proteins and of mixtures and solid solutions of proteins. Cold Spring Harbor Symposia Quant. Biol. *6:* 325–330.

Landsteiner, K., and M. Heidelberger. 1923. Differentiation of oxyhemoglobins by means of mutual solubility tests. J. Gen. Physiol. *6:* 131–135.

Murphy, R. C. Jr., and S. Shapiro. 1944. Sickle cell disease. I. Observations on the behavior of erythrocytes in sickle cell disease. Arch. Int. Med. *74:* 28–35.

Neel, J. V. 1949. The inheritance of sickle cell anemia. Science *110:* 64–66.

Neel, J. V. 1951. The inheritance of the sickling phenomenon, with particular reference to sickle cell disease. Blood. *6:* 389–412.

Pauling, L., H. A. Itano, S. J. Singer, and I. C. Wells. 1949. Sickle cell anemia, a molecular disease. Science *110:* 543–548.

Perutz, M. F., and J. M. Mitchison. 1950. State of haemoglobin in sickle cell anemia. Nature *166:* 677–679.

Reinhard, E. H., C. V. Moore, R. Dubach, and L. J. Wade. 1944. Depressant effects of high concentrations of inspired oxygen on erythrocytogenesis. Observations on patients with sickle cell anemia with a description of the observed toxic manifestations of oxygen. J. Clin. Investigation *23:* 682–698.

Schroeder, W. A., L. M. Kay and I. C. Wells. 1950. Amino acid composition of hemoglobin of normal Negroes and sickle-cell anemics. J. Biol. Chem. *187:* 221–240.

Sherman, I. J. 1940. The sickling phenomenon, with special reference to the differentiation of sickle cell anemia from the sickle cell trait. Bull. Johns Hopkins Hosp. *67:* 309–324.

Singer, K., A. I. Chernoff, and L. Singer. 1951. Studies on abnormal hemoglobins. I. Their demonstration in sickle cell anemia and other hematologic disorders by means of alkali denaturation. Blood *6:* 413–428.

Singer, K., and L. Singer. 1953. Studies on abnormal hemoglobins. VIII. The gelling phenomenon of sickle cell hemoglobin: its biologic and diagnostic significance. Blood *8:* 1008–1023.

Smith, E. W., and C. L. Conley. 1955. Sicklemia and infarction of the spleen during aerial flight. Electrophoresis of the hemoglobin in 15 cases. Bull. Johns Hopkins Hosp. *96:* 35–41.

Sturgeon, P., H. A. Itano, and W. R. Bergren. 1955. Clinical manifestations of inherited abnormal hemoglobins. I. The interaction of hemoglobin-S with hemoglobin-D. I. The interaction of hemoglobin-E and thalassemia trait. Blood *10:* 389–404.

Sturgeon, P., H. A. Itano and W. N. Valentine. 1952. Chronic hemolytic anemia associated with thalassemia and sickling traits. Blood *7:* 350–357.

Specificity in Cholinesterase Reactions

I. B. Wilson

Columbia University, New York City, N. Y.

IN TALKING ABOUT THE SPECIFICITY of cholinesterase reactions, I will have to include older work and I want to apologize to those of you who will have to listen to this again. The substrate for cholinesterase is acetylcholine. It is a quaternary amonium ion and it is also an ester. The reaction is a hydrolysis to form the quaternary amino alcohol choline, and acetic acid.

$$(CH_3)_3\overset{+}{N}C_2H_4O{-}\overset{\overset{O}{\|}}{C}CH_3 + H_2O \rightarrow (CH_3)_3\overset{+}{N}C_2H_4OH + CH_3COOH.$$

The way one usually writes an enzyme catalyzed reaction is

$$E + S \underset{k_2}{\overset{k_1}{\rightleftharpoons}} E\cdot S \xrightarrow{k_3} E + \text{ products}$$

so that, assuming a stationary state in E.S.,

$$v = \frac{K_3 E^0}{K_m + S}$$

where

$$K_m = \frac{k_2 + k_3}{k_1}$$

Now, when we say that a compound is a good substrate, we mean that it is hydrolyzed at a high rate, at a low substrate concentration. That means that besides having a good value for k_3, the Michaelis-Menten constant, K_m, must be quite small.

The first thing is to find out from the specificity of the reaction what forces, what factors, are involved in making K_m small. Now, this interpretation of the Michaelis-Menten constant includes both an equilibrium term and a kinetic term in which k_2 over k_1 is the equilibrium dissociation constant for the enzyme substrate complex. It is clear that K_m has to be greater than or equal to the dissociation constant and, since we want K_m to be small, we have to have a small dissociation constant.

From the structure of this substrate, I think one would suspect that if the forces of nature had designed a protein to combine with such a molecule it certainly would have taken advantage of ionic forces and I would suspect that one should look for what we have called an anionic site in the protein molecule; some negative site which by ionic forces helps to bind this group. The role of ionic forces in hapten-antibody reactions has been studied by Pressman and Pauling and presented in this volume. With enzymes, this question can be investigated in several ways.

One method we have used a good deal (Wilson and Bergmann, 1950a ; Bergmann, Wilson and Nachmansohn, 1950), has been with competitive inhibitors. These are inhibitors which produce an inhibition which decreases with increasing substrate concentration, so that one can interpret that they are competing for the same site. It is often apparent, however, just from their structure that they are competing for the same site. Prostigmine,

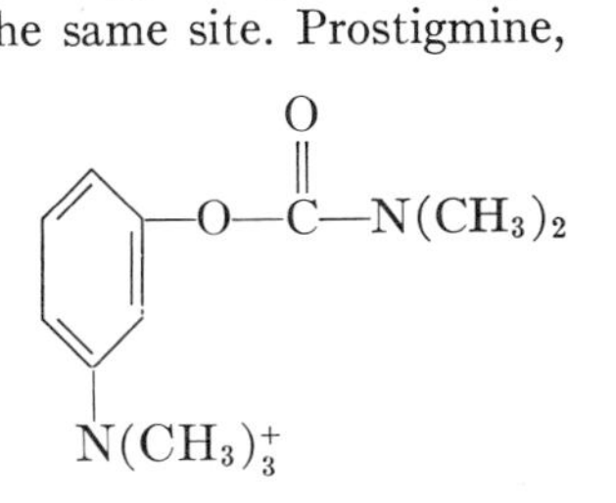

for example, clearly resembles acetylcholine.

The tertiary compound eserine is related to prostigmine. Both are very good inhibitors of cholinesterase, effective at about 10^{-6} M concentration. The pertinent difference between these inhibitors is that while prostigmine is a quaternary ion and is therefore always positively charged no matter what the pH, eserine is a tertiary compound and is therefore positively charged in acid solution but uncharged in alkaline solution.

By acid or alkaline I mean with respect to its pKa, which is about 8.5.

Fig. 1 shows the inhibition of these compounds as a function of the pH. Inhibition by prostigmine (black circles) does not vary with pH. Now, that is of importance in our interpretation because it shows that within this range of pH, those changes that may occur in the protein do not affect the inhibition.

However, eserine, which at pH less than 8.5 is mainly cationic and at pH greater than 8.5 is mainly neutral, shows a very marked change; the inhibition decreases in alkali (▲). So, we can measure the binding constants for the uncharged and charged forms.

There are other ways we can make similar measurements. For example—nicotinamide which is uncharged in neutral solution (nicotinamide is also an inhibitor for this enzyme) can be compared to its N methyl derivative, which, of course, is a quaternary ion, and is positively charged.

And, to take still another case, one can compare carbon and nitrogen analogues as inhibitors (as was done by Whitaker and Adams for substrates). For example, isoamylalcohol can be compared with dimethyl amino ethanol. The latter compound is cationic at neutral pH.

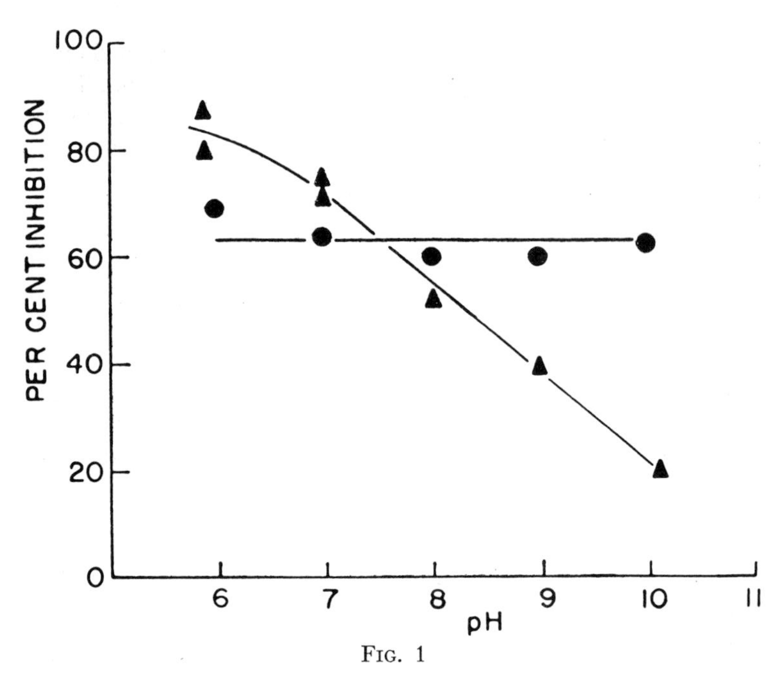

FIG. 1

In each case the positively charged member of the pair is the better inhibitor. The results are shown in Table I.

What one would like to do, I suppose, is to see how this compares to a simple equation for the Coulombic potential energy of two charges, Z_A and Z_B, separated by a distance, R.

$$U = \frac{-Z_A Z_B}{DR^2}$$

The dielectric constant involves some difficulties, but Schwartzenbach has indicated a way of handling that problem (Pressman and Pauling have used this method) by selecting an effective dielectric constant in accordance with empirical observations relating D to R.

TABLE I

The effect of positive electrical charge on the potency of inhibition

	K^0/K^+	$-\Delta$Fe (KCal/mole	R	R (corrected for salt)
N-Methylnicotinamide-nicotinamide............	8	1.2	7.7	5.8
Eserine cation-eserine.........................	16	1.7	6.7	5.4
Dimethylethanolammonium ion-isoamylalcohol...	30	2.0	6.3	5.0

Assuming unit negative charge for the anionic enzymic site and equating the extra free energy of binding of the cationic member of each pair to the potential energy we may calculate R.

The effective dielectric constant is calculated to be approximately 20.

I would like to mention, as Dr. Pressman mentioned earlier, that there is an approach to the closest contact possible for a quaternary methylated ammonium ion and some negative grouping, because the quaternary structure has about 3.5 Angstrom radius and, if we take one and a half Å for the other group—oxygen or whatever it may be—that bears the negative charge, the closest approach is 5 Å.

There are several other ways of checking ionic binding, but I would just like to briefly mention one other. We can change the ionic strength of the medium and that is a useful procedure because the expected variation is independent of the distance of approach, except in a correction term. It has been found that the Michaelis-Menten constant which we will temporarily assume is the enzyme-substrate dissociation constant, decreases quite rapidly as the ionic strength decreases. Again assuming that the anionic site charge is one electronic unit, the effective dielectric constant comes out to about 25.

So one can make the story fit with a single ionic charge for the anionic site. It does not have to be so; it might be the summation of many charges at different distances with different effective dielectric constants, but at any rate, the data fit a single charge satisfactorily, and there is little doubt that there is an anionic site.

There is one other type of experiment which I should like to mention, which pertains to this anionic site story. So far we have compared charged and uncharged inhibitors. This can also be done with substrates. Whitaker and Adams compared acetylcholine with its carbon analogue, 3,3 dimethyl butyl acetate (Adams and Whitaker, 1950). We have compared acetylcholine with its tertiary analogue, dimethylaminoethyl acetate, as a function of pH (Wilson and Bergmann, 1950a). The pKa of this compound is 8.3, so that by going to the acid side or the alkaline side we can make a positively charged or an uncharged substrate. In Fig. 2 the velocity is given as a function of pH. Just as one might anticipate, a curve is obtained that drops between pH 8 and 9, indicating that the cationic species is much more readily hydrolyzed.

So we have, I think, established rather well that there are ionic forces of attraction between the substrate and the enzyme which play an important role in the binding and catalysis.

Next one might ask whether there are binding forces associated with the methyl groups of the cationic head. It might be suspected that there would be van der Waals forces of attraction between these groups and hydrocarbon portions of the protein.

Rather than go into this too far, I might just explain that one can take any

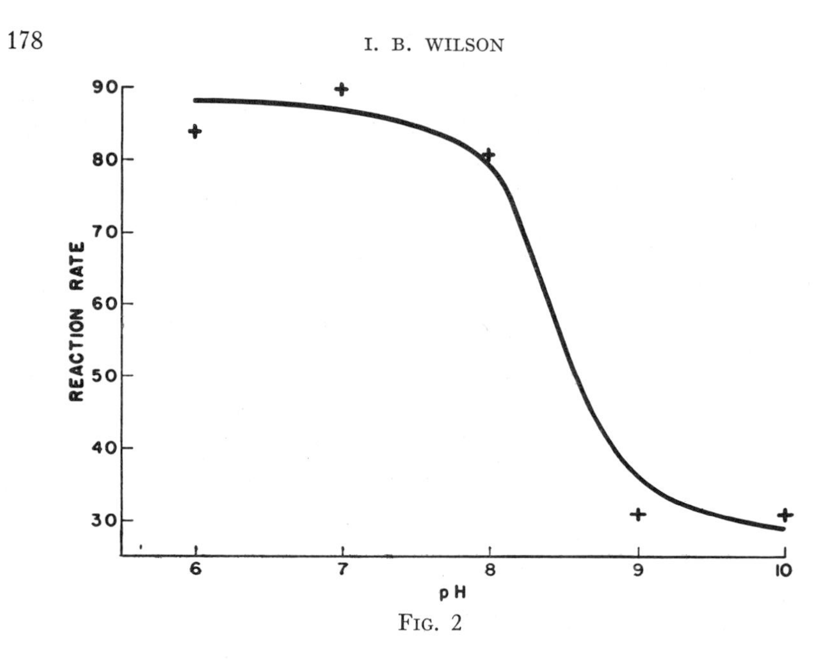

FIG. 2

number of series of compounds but the series I took are derivatives (Table 2) of choline and tetramethyl ammonium ion (Wilson, 1952). We have gone down the line and removed one methyl group each time to see the effect of replacing a methyl group with a hydrogen atom.

, The first thing we notice in both series is that whether one has the full complement of methyl groups or whether one group is removed makes very little, if any, difference in the binding.

However, as one proceeds further, large differences occur. One methyl group on the average makes a change of a factor of about 7 in the binding. That the presence of four groups or three groups makes no difference in binding can be interpreted in the following way:

The quaternary ammonium ions have a tetrahedral structure, that is, they

TABLE II

Inhibitory potency of methylated ammonium ions

The concentration necessary to produce 50 per cent inhibition when the acetylcholine concentration is 4×10^{-4} M.

Methyl Groups Replaced by H Atoms	—N— (M)	—NC₂H₄OH (M)
0	0.018	0.005
1	0.015	0.005
2	0.12	0.07
3	0.70	0.28

are more or less spherical and one group must stick out into the solution unless the protein wraps itself around this group. If we assume that the protein does not undertake such an envelopment, then the group must stick out into the solution and be without binding properties. In that case, we would expect that it would make no difference whether there were four or three. However, as we further decrease the number of groups, binding properties are lost.

Obviously, there are going to be questions of hydration and dehydration but, neglecting them for the moment—they have been considered by others—we can derive an order of magnitude here. A factor of 7 is worth about 1.2 kilo calories/mole binding energy and when we can compare that with the latent energy of evaporation of methane, which is about 2 kilocalories/mole, we come out with about the right order of magnitude for substituting a methyl group for hydrogen.

I do not want to go into this question further, but prefer to discuss what other sources of binding could be involved.

Another important feature is the carbonyl group. Chemists in the early days used to write this group with a negative and a positive charge, but now it is considered to be a resonance structure in which this form contributes about equally with a pure double bond. If we leave it in this dipolar form, we have a carbon atom which is looking for electrons. We believe a weak covalent bond is formed between this atom and some basic group in the active site of the enzyme.

We have used a number of series to investigate this prospect, but I will give the data for only one series. That series is ethyl acetate, ethylchloroacetate and acetic anhydride, which are presented in Table 3 with the Michaelis-Menten constants (Wilson, 1952). I might just mention that, of course, it is not surprising that acetic anhydride should be hydrolyzed by this enzyme. This compound is not much different from an ester. But the organic chemist will right away know that in going down this series he is making a tremendous increase in the electron-seeking properties of the carbonyl carbon atom, in the electrophilic properties. The Michaelis-Menten constants also decrease rapidly. These changes correspond to from 3 to 5 kilocalories and I think the only way one can account for this large difference in binding is to assume that in fact

TABLE III

Substrate	K_m	Relative k_3*
Ethyl acetate	5×10^{-1}	12
Ethyl chloroacetate	6×10^{-3}	13
Acetic anhydride	2×10^{-4}	13

* Acetylcholine = 100.

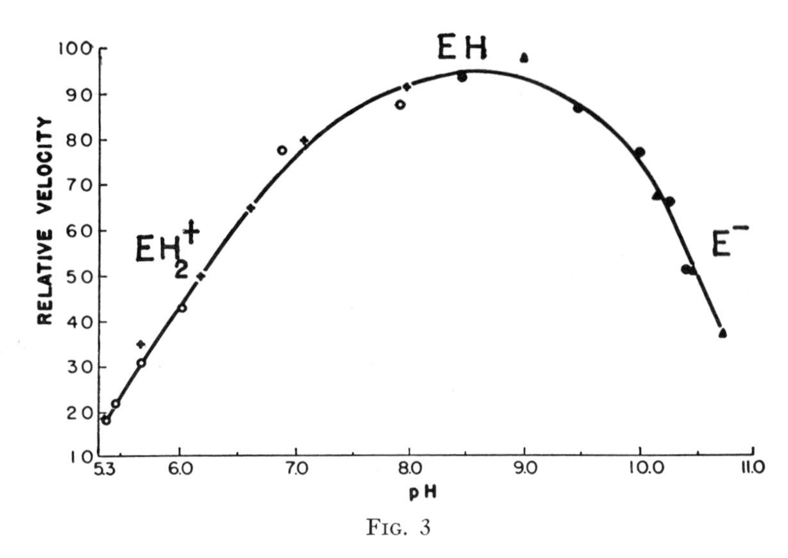

Fig. 3

there is some sort of a weak covalent bond formed between the carbonyl carbon atom and some basic group in the protein.

There is specificity associated with the acid portion of the substrate, but I will not go into that (Augustinsson and Nachmansohn, 1949).

The pH velocity curve of this enzyme (Fig. 3) is what one usually finds (Wilson and Bergmann, 1950b). We assume there is an active form which we represent as EH, an inactive E^- form in alkaline, and an inactive EH_2^+ form in acid. These last members either do not form the complex with the enzyme or, if they do form the complex with the enzyme, the complex is not active. Actually we know that EH_2^+ does not form the complex. E^- forms the complex but the complex is inactive.

We have interpreted the pH dependence then in terms of an acidic and basic group, both of which are necessary for activity. We could assume (if we were bold enough) that this basic group is the one that forms the covalent bond with the carbonyl carbon atom of substrates, and we have gone on that basis and have written our esteratic site, as shown in Fig. 4. We thus recognize two subsites, an anionic site which reacts with the cationic head by ionic and van der Waal's forces, and an esteratic site which combines with the ester part of the substrate by a weak covalent bond between its basic group and the carbonyl carbon atom. We have used the symbol $\underset{\cdot\cdot}{G}H$ where H represents the necessary acid group and the pair of electrons represent the necessary basic group. G may be a number of atoms. We do not specify its chemical identity. This is our picture of the ES complex.

The hydrolytic process which we propose (Wilson, Bergmann and Nach-

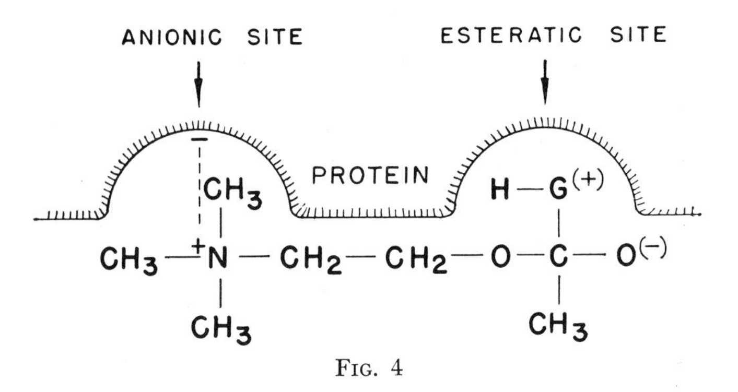

FIG. 4

mansohn, 1950) is an acid base catalysis. We have left out the anionic site and only

$$\mathrm{RCOOR'} + \mathrm{H{-}\ddot{G}} \rightleftharpoons \mathrm{R{-}\ddot{O}{-}\underset{R}{\overset{H-G^+}{C}}{-}O^-} \rightleftharpoons \mathrm{\underset{R}{\overset{G^+}{\overset{\|}{C}}}{-}O^-} + \mathrm{R'OH}$$

$$\mathrm{H_2O} + \mathrm{\underset{R}{\overset{G^+}{\overset{\|}{C}}}{-}O^-} \rightleftharpoons \mathrm{HO{-}\underset{R}{\overset{H-G^+}{C}}{-}O^-} \rightleftharpoons \mathrm{H{-}\ddot{G}} + \mathrm{RCOOH}$$

consider the hydrolytic site, the esteratic site. We have first a complex between the ester and the esteratic site and we imagine an electronic cycle as indicated and in which the acidic hydrogen starts moving over to the ether oxygen, with, perhaps, the intermediate formation of a hydrogen bond. Finally, the alcohol is split out and what is left you will recognize as a resonance form of an acylated enzyme.

Next, the acetyl enzyme reacts with water and forms again a complex but this time an acetic acid enzyme complex. This complex dissociates to yield the free enzyme and acetic acid.

I cannot go into this at length but we have, I think, very good evidence for this theory. The algebra of this two step process is as follows (Wilson and Cabib (1956)). ES′ is the acetyl enzyme.

$$\mathrm{EH} + \mathrm{S} \underset{k_2}{\overset{k_1}{\rightleftharpoons}} \mathrm{EHS} \xrightarrow{k_3} \mathrm{ES'} + \mathrm{ROH}$$

$$\mathrm{ES'} + \mathrm{H_2O} \xrightarrow{k_4} \mathrm{EH} + \mathrm{CH_3COOH}$$

$$v = \frac{kE^0 S}{(k_2/k_1 + k_3/k_1)/(1 + k_3/k_4) + S} = \frac{V_m S}{K_{m'} + S}$$

where

$$\frac{1}{k} = \frac{1}{k^3} + \frac{1}{k_4}$$

We have two successive processes that change the meaning of the Michaelis-Menten constant. That, I think, is the trouble with the Michaelis-Menten constant. Its meaning is highly susceptible to the particular model you pick.

For example, I have not included any pH terms but according to the model we have picked and Dr. Alberty has indicated, there are also pH terms in this constant.

I would now just like to indicate what kind of Arrhenius plot could be expected in a two-step process. The logarithm of the rate constant is plotted as a function of the reciprocal temperature. Suppose that each step follows the Arrhenius law (Fig. 5).

The question is: What type of curve would we expect? It is clear that we are going to measure something smaller than the slower step. Only if one rate is much larger than the other, will we get a straight line.

We have made a series of substrates based on the structure of acetylcholine, the purpose of which was to try to find out something about the specificity in k_3. We have talked about specificity in binding and now we come to the question of specificity in the hydrolytic process.

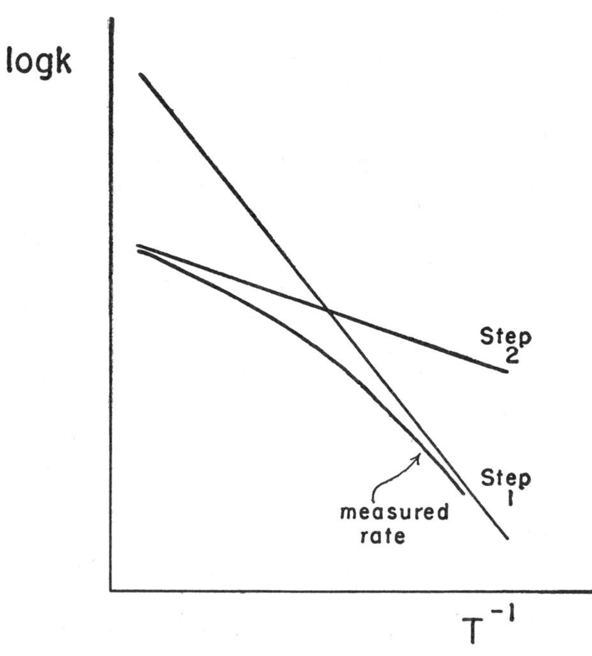

FIG. 5

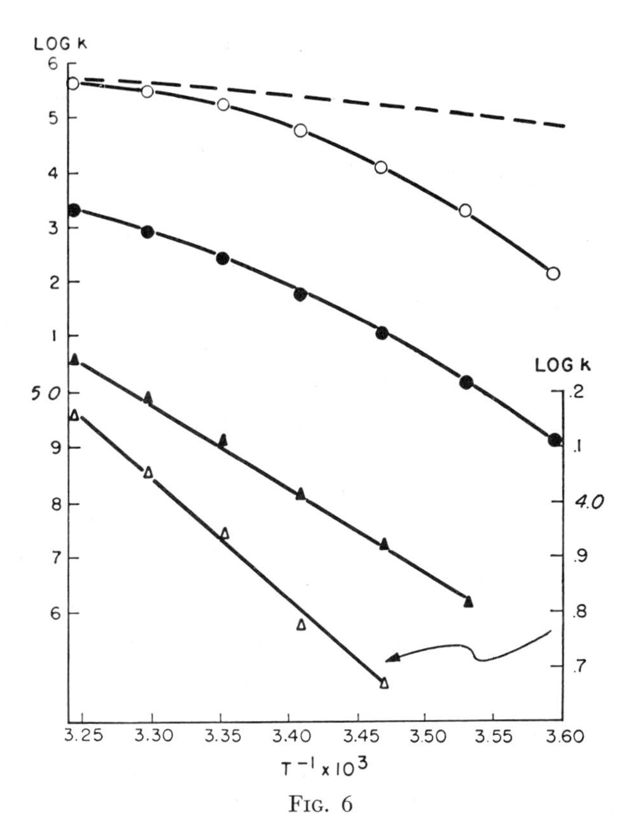

FIG. 6

Each substrate differs from the next by having one fewer methyl group, thus acetylcholine, dimethylaminoethyl acetate, monomethylaminoethyl acetate, and aminoethyl acetate. All are positively charged at neutral pH.

The Arrhenius plots for these substrates are shown in Fig. 6 (Wilson and Cabib, 1956). It will be noted that the fewer the methyl groups the lower the hydrolytic activity.

In the case of the poorer substrates we have straight lines, but in the case of the better substrates the loci are very markedly curved.

Now, if we had an infinite series of substrates, one better than the next, and there was in fact a two step process in which the second step was always the same, the first process must become faster and faster and eventually catch up with—and possibly exceed—the second process. That is what I think has happened here. With the two poorest substrates the first step is rate controlling, but with the better substrates both steps are rate controlling.

If we accept this interpretation as correct we can evaluate the entropies and enthalpies for step one by using the above equations provided, we can derive a good value for the specific rate constant of step two by drawing an asymptote

TABLE IV

Values of k_3, $\Delta H^{\ddagger}$ and $\Delta S^{\ddagger}$ at 25° and pH 7

	k_3	$\Delta H^{\ddagger}$	$\Delta S^{\ddagger}$
Acetylcholine	$1.5–3.4 \times 10^6$	$14–19 \times 10^3$	(16–34)
Dimethylaminoethyl acetate	$3.3–3.5 \times 10^5$	6.7–8	−(6.5–10.5)
Methylaminoethyl acetate	1.1×10^5	8.0	−9
Aminoethyl acetate	9.0×10^3	9.5	−9

to the acetylcholine curve as indicated in the figure. These values are presented in Table 4.

The energy of activation data is interesting because acetylcholine, which is the best substrate, has by far the largest energy of activation. The others do not differ too much.

When we turn to the entropies of activation as calculated from the absolute rate theory formulas, we see that acetylcholine is a much better substrate than the others because the entropy of activation is much more favorable than for the other substrates. It appears that the interaction of a quaternary structure with the anionic site promotes the catalytic activity through the entropy of activation. The anionic site thus not only serves to bind the substrate and thereby make K_m small but also promotes the catalytic activity making k_3 large.

There are a number of inhibitors such as tetraethylpyrophosphate and diisopropyl fluorophosphate, which are called irreversible inhibitors. They phosphorylate the enzyme: they phosphorylate the same grouping which is

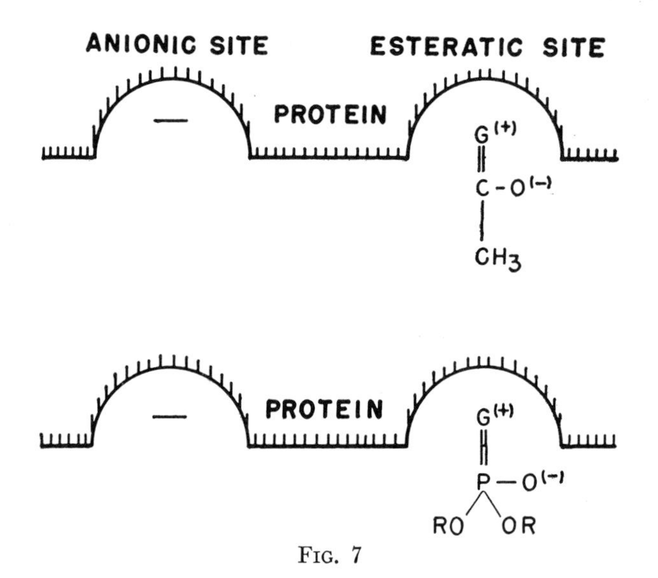

Fig. 7

normally acetylated, Fig. 7 (Wilson, 1951). But whereas the acetyl enzyme reacts with water in microseconds, the phosphoryl enzyme requires many hours and the enzyme is therefore inhibited.

If we want to reactivate such an inhibited enzyme, we have to use a nucleophilic agent, something which will displace the enzyme by making a nucleophilic attack on the phosphoryl phosphorus atom. Hydroxylamine is an active nucleophilic agent and it is interesting that hydroxylamine will reactivate enzyme inhibited by this material. Nucleophilic reagents will in general reactivate any enzyme which is inhibited by such materials. When I say "any", I take some liberty because I have tested only four, chymotrypsin, serum esterase, cholinesterase and liver esterase.

However, the anionic site is not affected, and since we have seen that it can contribute to the activity of this enzyme one would think that if we could combine a quaternary structure with a nucleophilic functional group, as for example in pyridine-2-aldoxime methiodide (Wilson and Ginsburg, 1955), a very active compound might result. This compound is, in fact, quite active and is on the order of 50,000 times as active as hydroxylamine. It will reactivate at 10^{-5} M in one minute. It is really a very potent reactivation agent, and interestingly enough it is good only for this enzyme. It is not good for liver esterase; it is not much good for serum esterase; nor for chymotrypsin. It just fits the special nature of this enzyme. It illustrates the promoting effect of the anionic site.

References

Adams, D. H. and V. P. Whittaker. 1950. The cholinesterases of human blood. II. The forces acting between enzyme and substrate. Biochim. et Biophys. Acta *4:* 543–558.

Augustinsson, K. B. and D. Nachmansohn. 1949. Distinction between acetylcholine esterase and other choline ester-splitting enzymes. Science *110:* 98–99.

Bergmann, F., I. B. Wilson, and D. Nachmansohn. 1950. Acetylcholinesterase. IX. Structural features determining the inhibition by amino acids and related compounds. J. Biol. Chem. *186:* 693–703.

Wilson, I. B. 1951. Acetylcholinesterase. XI. Reversibility of tetraethyl pyrophosphate inhibition. J. Biol. Chem. *190:* 111–117.

Wilson, I. B. 1952. Acetylcholinesterase. XII. Further studies of binding forces. J. Biol. Chem. *197:* 215–225.

Wilson, I. B. and F. Bergmann. 1950. Cholinesterase. VII. Active surface of acetylcholine esterase derived from effects of pH on inhibitors. J. Biol. Chem. *185:* 479–489.

Wilson, I. B. and F. Bergmann. 1950. Acetylcholinesterase. VIII. Dissociation constants of the active groups. J. Biol. Chem. *186:* 683–692.

Wilson, I. B., F. Bergmann, and D. Nachmansohn. 1950. Acetylcholinesterase. X. Mechanism of the catalysis of acylation reactions. J. Biol. Chem. *186:* 781–790.

Wilson, I. B. and E. Cabib. 1956. Acetylcholinesterase: Enthalpies and entrophies of activation. J. Am. Chem. Soc. *78:* 202–207.

Wilson, I. B. and S. Ginsburg. 1955. A powerful reactivator of alkylphosphate-inhibited acetylcholinesterase. Biochim. et Biophys. Acta *18:* 168–170.

Summary and Discussion

Linus Pauling, Chairman

California Institute of Technology, Pasadena, Calif.

I HAVE THE TASK of summarizing the work that has been reported by the speakers.

Since this symposium is on the subject of biological specificity, the first question that we ask is: What is biological specificity?

Electron micrographs and X-ray diffraction patterns of tobacco mosaic virus show that the rods that constitute the virus particles have the form of a cylindrical tube of protein, within which are strands of nucleic acid. The tube of protein is made up of small protein molecules, molecular weight of the order of 20,000, which are arranged in a helix. We conclude that certain protein molecules are manufactured that have the power of clamping onto one another in a specific way, so as to produce a tightly wound helix. The power that these protein molecules have, that of clamping onto identical molecules to produce a helix with well-defined diameter and pitch, represents one sort of biological specificity.

The ability that genes have to duplicate themselves and also to control the manufacture of protein molecules, such as those in tobacco mosaic virus, represents another sort of biological specificity. The action of enzymes, discussed by Drs. Wilson, Anfinsen, and Alberty, represents another special sort of biological specificity. Still another sort is represented by the interaction of antibodies and antigens.

This last aspect of biological specificity was discussed by Drs. Pressman and Haurowitz. A great deal of information about the specific interactions of antibodies and antigens has been obtained through the study of serological reactions; in particular, there have been extensive studies of the action of simple substances that act as inhibitors of serological reactions, by combining with antibodies. Serological systems may not be as good as enzyme systems for the study of biological specificity, because the antibodies present in an antiserum are not all identical: the antiserum is heterogeneous, whereas a preparation of an enzyme may be essentially homogeneous. Nevertheless a great deal of evidence about the nature of the specific interactions of antigens and antibodies has been obtained through the study of serological systems. It was as the result of the study of serological systems, especially by Landsteiner, that 25 years ago Professor Haurowitz and Dr. Breinl, and independently Stuart Mudd and also Jerome Alexander, simultaneously suggested the important idea of complementariness in structure as the basis of the specificity of interaction of antibodies and antigens. This idea represents a refinement of Ehrlich's lock-and-key concept. The idea is that weak intermolecular forces, which individually would not be enough to produce a significant bond, may cooperate between molecules that are complementary in structure in such a way as to produce a strong bond.

It is my opinion that the conclusions that have been reached through the studies of serological systems are completely reliable, that there is no doubt that the specificity of antibodies results from their having a structure complementary to that of the antigen, and that the forces that operate between molecules of antigen and molecules of antibody are weak intermolecular forces that individually are non-specific, but that become specific because of the spatial relationship of the different parts of the combining region of the antibody in relation to the surface structure of the antigen.

So far as I am aware there is only one alternative idea about specificity: that there is a special sort of interaction between identical molecules. According to this idea a gene can direct the manufacture of another gene because there is an interaction between two identical molecules that is different from that between one molecule and another molecule that is not identical with it. Professor Jehle talked about a theory of this sort. I must say that I am skeptical about the significance of Professor Jehle's theory. I do not doubt the correctness of his equations, but I think that the special terms in the expression for the energy of interaction of identical molecules have values so small in comparison with kT, the energy of thermal agitation, as to permit them to be ignored.

Professor Haurowitz raised the question of whether antibodies can be manufactured after the antigen is gone. The speakers here have, I think, agreed that it is likely that an antigen must be present in order to have continued production of antibodies. We were, perhaps, unfortunate at this symposium in not having somebody present to support the other point of view.

Dr. Pressman in his talk mentioned some of the evidence that shows that the antibody molecule fits tightly around the haptenic group of an antigen, the fit being better than an atomic diameter—within about an Ångstrom, whereas atoms are about 4 Ångstroms in diameter. Serious steric hindrance occurs if a methyl group is introduced in the hapten in place of a hydrogen atom, increasing the radius by less than 1 Å. Introduction of a chlorine atom, a bromine atom, or an iodine atom produces larger steric hindrances.

Dr. Pressman also mentioned the experiments that show that there is an electric charge of opposite sign to that in the haptenic group of the antigen within a couple of Angstroms of the minimum distance of approach. The ratio of combining powers of the charged and uncharged haptens was found to be about 15, which corresponds to about a 7 Å distance.

Dr. Wilson mentioned that in the measurements that he has made of the effect of replacing a methyl group by a hydrogen atom on the cholinesterase enzyme he got ratios of between 8 and 30, which correspond to distances between positive charge and negative charge between 5.8 Å and 5.0 Å. These are close to the minimum distance of approach of the charged groups, a trimethylammonium ion group and a carboxylate ion group.

The van der Waals interactions are important. We know a great deal about van der Waals interactions because of London's theory, and Professor Hirshfelder in his discussion based upon virial coefficients of gases pointed out that the theories of interaction of molecules involving not only the van der Waals attractions of molecules but also interactions of electric dipole moments and electric quadrupole moments are in good agreement with experiment, especially the experiments on transport phenomena in gases, and that we can have confidence in simple theoretical considerations based upon these ideas.

The differences in interaction energy that Dr. Pressman and Dr. Wilson reported corresponding to replacing a methyl group in a place where there is a hole big enough for it by a hydrogen atom, differences of about one kilocalorie per mole, are reasonable differences to interpret as resulting from the van der Waals attraction of the surrounding atoms for the hydrogen atom as compared with that for a methyl group.

Professor Kirkwood discussed a force due to fluctuations in electric charges on two protein molecules that can be significantly large under certain circumstances and can operate over a rather long distance. This is an interesting new kind of interaction of molecules that are, on the average, electrically neutral but, because of charge fluctuations in the ionization of ionizable groups, can show a significant electrostatic interaction, significant probably only when the molecules are essentially at their isoelectric points; otherwise the force is small compared with the larger forces of interaction of the permanent electric charges.

Of course, there are other kinds of forces that also need to be considered, some of which have not been discussed at all, or mentioned only very briefly. There can be significant forces operating between two big protein molecules rather far apart, a whole molecular diameter apart from one another in aqueous solution, if their polarizabilities, specific polarizabilities, differ significantly from those of the medium.

An interesting aspect of the theory is that if both of the two protein molecules have larger specific polarizability than the medium, they attract one another. If they both have smaller specific polarizabilities than the medium they also attract one another. That is, perhaps, not a result that one would have foreseen.

One more point about Professor Haurowitz' talk. He said that we know that the dimensions of the active region of an antibody molecule are only around a couple of hundred square angstroms, and that the region might represent only about four amino acid residues. If we say that each of these could be any one of 16 different amino acids, we get ten to the fourth power different possible combining regions, and we conclude that the specificity of antibodies should be far from perfect, that there would not be an infinite number of possible antibodies but only a finite number.

I might point out that even if we have the same four amino acid residues in the combining region, there is the possibility of backing them up differently. That is, by moving these four around to different positions, with the use of more protein material as structural material behind, we can produce, with these same four residues as the face plates, a very large number of different kinds of combining regions.

This gives us the possibility of an essentially infinite number of different kinds of combining regions, not ten to the fourth power. Ten to the fortieth would sound more reasonable.

PROFESSOR HAUROWITZ: I would like to talk quite briefly in self defense and then ask two questions.

Until a few years ago I would have agreed with Professor Pauling that there are perhaps ten to the fortieth antibody molecules. Peptide chains at that time were believed to exist in an infinite number of conformations. At present we know that they cannot be distorted beyond a certain limit and we know by the work of Pauling, Corey and others that there are preferential states of stability and states of least energy, for instance, the alpha helix or the pleated sheet. If we assume for the sake of simplification, that just alpha helixes can exist, then we find that there cannot be ten to the forty different arrangements for amino acids, but only about ten to the four.

There are two other questions. One of them is concerned with Dr. Itano's paper on hemoglobin. It is not surprising that normal hemoglobin and sickle-cell hemoglobin are different in solubility and therefore in crystalline shape but what is astounding is that the solubility should be so enormously dependent on one single CO or one single O_2 molecule bound to the hemoglobin molecule. The hemoglobin of the horse crystallizes in large platelets which are rather easily soluble. If we saturate it with oxygen, we get a needle-like shape which is much less soluble. Thus not only the crystal shape but also the solubility changes drastically on oxygenation. In some cases, as in normal adults, the solubility decreases on oxygenation. In the case of sickle-cell hemoglobin, the solubility increases in oxygenation. I would be happy if I knew any explanation for these changes. In no field of protein research are we so in the dark as in the problem of solubility. We cannot explain why certain globulins are soluble in water and other globulins are not, why some plant proteins are soluble in 80 percent alcohol and others are not. This is one of the main problems, I think, of protein chemistry.

I have another question which I would like to address to Dr. Anfinsen and, perhaps, Dr. Donohue. Dr. Anfinsen mentioned that tyrosine has a particular importance in forming hydrogen bonds with carboxylic groups. I wonder whether tyrosine has not another particular importance in proteins. Tyrosine has been accused, at least, for a long time of being responsible for the specificity of proteins. For instance, tyrosine-free gelatin is not antigenic. I wonder whether tyrosine actually has not a special strategic position in proteins because of its content of an aromatic ring. I suppose that Dr. Pressman's diagrams are over-simplifications and that he may mean that a benzene ring of the aromatic inhibitors may actually fit somehow and lie closely parallel to the benzene ring of tyrosine molecules. These would be London forces and not van der Waals forces.

CHAIRMAN PAULING: Perhaps I could say a word about the first question. Why does the solubility of proteins change so rapidly with small changes in structure? We might think that the solubility of a protein may be determined by complementariness in structure of one part of the surface to another part so that the molecules would tend to clamp onto one another and, since this complementariness in structure can be destroyed by such a small change as hydrogen to methyl, producing steric interference, the addition of oxygen atoms might well cause just as great an interference. We have thought that it was a special complementariness in structure of this sort that caused sickle-cell anemia hemoglobin to have such low solubility, and that it was interference with complementariness on oxygenation that caused the oxyhemoglobin to be soluble again. This seems to me to be a satisfactory explanation.

DR. ANFINSEN: I would like to say something about tyrosine. I did not mean to imply that tyrosine has been proved to be involved in the active center of ribonuclease. The only evidence for such involvement is the fact that 3 tyrosine hydroxyl-carboxyl interactions do seem to exist in this protein, and that one of them appears to be ruptured during limited pepsin digestion, at a rate paralleling both the loss of activity and the appearance of a free tetrapeptide fragment.

I suppose that I should also say a word about Dr. Pauling's earlier remarks. There is now considerable evidence that the complete native protein structure is not entirely essential in catalytic activity, not just in ribonuclease but in other proteins as well. Although the resonating, macromolecular picture is certainly intriguing and fun to think about, it seems worthwhile to consider the possibility that small regions of proteins might serve adequately as catalytic centers and that the size and complication of protein structure might have developed for evolutionary reasons other than purely catalytic ones.

CHAIRMAN PAULING: I think that in my discussion of enzymes I suggested that the active region of an enzyme might be about the same size as the combining region of one of the anti-haptenic antibodies, which is not very big. It is a very little spot on a protein molecule. Then we may ask: What is the need for the rest of the protein molecule? Some of it is needed in order to provide structural backing for these groups, to hold them in the right positions, but probably not more than ten per cent of even a small enzyme, such as ribonuclease, would be needed for this purpose.

I suggest that large size may be needed to keep the molecules from diffusing through tissues, through the pores. I agree with Dr. Anfinsen that in part large size may be just an evolutionary accident. Proteins are useful because their structures can be varied in many different ways, and a particular protein may undergo mutation, variation—a gene undergoes mutation to change one little region of a protein molecule so as to make it useful as an enzyme, and then it continues to be manufactured generation after generation for this purpose.

PROFESSOR KIRKWOOD: I would like to comment on the remark you made and on one of the remarks which Dr. Anfinsen made.

In regard to the role of the fluctuation force, I am emphasizing this, as I said, because I am working on it at the moment, but I do not maintain that it is a panacea for everything. However, I would like to disagree with you in the statement that this force is only important for isoelectric proteins.

It is true that in some experiments we were considering the contributions to essentially long-range interaction between protein molecules as a whole in isolating the pure charge fluctuation effect; that would be most important for isoionic proteins. However, in the discussion of the possible role of fluctuation force in the case of enzymes, one can imagine that the complementariness is concerned not only with a very local fit in which essentially short-range forces play a role, but that also one can have a more complicated peripheral pattern that could contribute, not only to the binding of the molecule which is being attached, say the substrate to an enzyme, but also to the free energy of activation.

Then there is another point that I think could be brought up here. It is not new, but has not been mentioned in our discussions. That has to do with the role of such forces as van der Waals forces. It was touched upon obliquely by Dr. Jehle when he was speaking of the bouyancy effect. When one is considering van der Waals forces between parts of two protein molecules or in a protein molecule, stabilizing the helical structures, I think that it is erroneous to speak of these forces as direct interactions between the non-polar groups which are coming into close contact, although very often this statement is made.

If one is working in aqueous solution, the direct interaction between methyl groups is virtually negligible in bringing them together in comparison with the energy that is gained by making more contacts between water. That is, if you bring two non-polar groups from infinity into contact, the gain is not so much due to the direct van der Waals interaction between these two groups as to the fact that in making the contact between the two non-polar groups you form more water contacts and gain your energy indirectly in this way.

Therefore, I think that Dr. Wilson's estimates of van der Waals energies are more-or-less fortuitous; I do not think that they have much relationship to what is actually happening.

However, this kind of interaction is well known. It is the kind of interaction which is responsible for the formation of soap micelles, detergent micelles particularly, where there is a carboxylate ion attached to a massive or long hydrocarbon chain. The aggregation is not really so much due to the fact that the hydrocarbons are fond of each other as that they are crowded together by the water and if one did not have the charged groups, of course, one knows what would happen. There would be a phase separation and then the hydrocarbon would simply separate as a separate phase. However, this process stops in the formation of a micelle because one gets the protective layer of ionic groups which interact with the water.

I think that in the case of protein structure one should not speak just about the stability of a helical structure being due to the direct hydrogen bond formation, although that is essential, but that the hydrogen bond can be reinforced by essentially the effect of water in squeezing side chains into contact. I think Linderstrøm-Lang recently has been thinking along these lines and I believe that it is well to think of the important role of the solvent in enhancing the strength of the primary bond in an indirect way.

There was one other thing I wanted to say in this connection; that the Hammacher relationship for likes always interacting more than unlikes in a binary mixture is limited to non-polar mixtures and that it can lead to very serious errors when one is considering one component such as water which is strongly hydrogen bonded to itself or a polar solvent, as the theorem applies only to mixtures of components which are interacting by van der Waals forces alone.

CHAIRMAN PAULING: I should like to emphasize the points that Professor Kirkwood has made. I think that people who have been talking about these things for fifteen years, like Dr. Pressman, forget that fifteen years ago or ten years ago they were careful to say that by the energy of the hydrogen bond between the antibody and the antigen we really mean the difference in energy of that hydrogen bond plus the new hydrogen bonds formed between water molecules and the energy of the hydrogen bonds that were formed with the water molecules in the system in its initial state. All of this was gone into in detail in the early papers.

There is a point that I should like to make about the matter of the water squeezing a hydrocarbon out. I think that this argument can be overdone, because you can fit a methyl group or, say, a methane molecule into water without breaking any hydrogen bonds. In the van der Waals calculation which Dr. Wilson referred to and which he took from Dr. Pressman's paper, the London expression was applied to the interaction energy of the group with water and then of the group with the antibody molecule but with no correction for the hydrogen bonds in the water.

The fact is that a little methane helps water to form hydrogen bonds, as in methane hydrate, $(CH_4)_8 (H_2O)_{46}$. Methane hydrate contains all of the hydrogen bonds that ice does and its melting point is above 0°C. The water molecules form hydrogen bonds in such a way that there is a big enough hole for the methane molecule to fit into.

DR. PRESSMAN: In connection with these last remarks, there is the experiment in which increased pressure will reverse an antigen-antibody reaction. Presumably, the antigen and antibody separately occupy a smaller space than the complex itself, plus the water which has been squeezed out during reaction. I was wondering if this might well not be pertinent to this argument in that the water which is squeezed out is low density.

CHAIRMAN PAULING: I think that this effect is due to electrostriction. The positive and negative charges on ionic groups compress the water around them because they attract the water molecules so strongly and if the positive and negative charges combine with one another during the reaction the electrostriction compression disappears and the water expands.

PROFESSOR KIRKWOOD: This brings up another point which is not new at all; it is not an idea that I have proposed but it has been floating around a long time. It has not been brought up in this discussion, although I am sure many of you are aware of it, certainly Dr. Pressman and Dr. Pauling.

Let us consider the forces between protein molecules or protein and a small molecule,—Dr. Pauling really hinted at this when he spoke about electrostrictions. Of course, one is interested in the change in free energy when one brings two molecules together and one knows that in the neighborhood of a protein molecule, having a number of polar side chains, one has a very severe hindrance of rotation of peripheral water molecules. This influence may extend out to several layers of water molecules.

These water molecules possess less entropy per molecule than water in bulk possesses, and when you bring up another molecule to the surface of a protein you free some water molecules whose rotation has been frozen or partially frozen and therefore you gain a considerable amount of entropy, and, this can contribute very appreciably to binding. Some interesting examples have come up in, I think, rather spectacular form from some of Dr. Sturtevant's thermochemical studies of interactions of proteins and in particular enzymes and substrates. Another instance in which this occurs is in, say, the formation of the mercury mercaptalbumin dimer.

CHAIRMAN PAULING: Thank you, Professor Kirkwood, for discussing this important matter.

PROFESSOR PITZER: I wish to come back to the matter of restricted rotation in the polypeptides. If you define an angle expressing internal rotation and then expand the appropriate potential, you get a three-fold term and a six-fold term. I believe we have shown that the six-fold term is negligible.

CHAIRMAN PAULING: That is in ethane.

PROFESSOR PITZER: Yes, also in nitromethane. In other words, we have no evidence for a six-fold term exceeding a few small calories. In nitromethane or any other molecule where the two sides of the planar group are the same, the potential is effectively zero.

Therefore, I think that the best approximation that we can make in the light of the known information is to neglect the six potential minima. In other words, if we can get potential minima and maxima in any significance in this case, it is going to be because the two sides of the planar group are different. If these two sides are different, then the significant potential term remaining is the three-fold term, not the six.

The first conclusion that we can reasonably draw is that there should be three minima rather than six. Secondly, the three-fold term arises from the difference between the sides of the molecule and whichever has the weaker interaction will line up and whichever has the stronger interaction will stagger between the three bonds at the other end.

I also wish to make a remark about the solubility question. Repeating just about what Pauling said, the solubility changes by roughly a factor of 10 if you change the energy term by a kilocalorie or $T\Delta S$ by a comparable amount. It does not make any difference whether it is a big molecule or a little molecule, the relation between energy and solubility product is the same.

Consider two large molecules which fit together nicely. If an oxygen atom is added and the molecules do not fit, the energy may change so as to decrease the solubility considerably. Or similarly, the energy might change by a kilocalorie the other way.

On the other hand, here we have an example of the failure of a crystal structure to accommodate itself to the molecular geometry. We were remarking earlier that it always did seem to accommodate itself and that we never find crystals in which molecules are in strained configurations. But within, now, an even finer scale, we do find appreciable shifts in solubility because in one case the molecule accidentally, as it were, fits better with the oxygen in and in another case it fits a little better with the oxygen out.

CHAIRMAN PAULING: Thank you for pointing this out. If I understand correctly, you think that only if the double bond is in the cis position to one of the single bonds of the other group in the peptide do you have stability.

PROFESSOR PITZER: Yes, and I think that it is almost certain that the carbonyl lines up with the bond at the other end.

CHAIRMAN PAULING: Then if I remember the alpha helix correctly, the orientation around the C—C single bond is right, and that around the alpha carbon to nitrogen bond is wrong. I shall have to examine that point.

PROFESSOR JEHLE: A somewhat different problem which puzzled me often is the question of the structure of the DNA when it is incorporated into a small compact virus particle. One might think of it as being composed of chopped-off pieces, or one might think of the helix as having distinct kinks which permit an extended helix to be fitted into a small compact region. Electronmicrographs have shown the DNA molecules a few seconds after they escaped from a virus, and neither chopped-off pieces or kinks have been seen; so that poses the question: What could have been the overall structure of the DNA inside the virus? I do not know whether this problem has a direct counterpart in the problem of the folding of proteins.

CHAIRMAN PAULING: I suppose that it may be related to the question of how the alpha helix is fitted into the hemoglobin molecule, and how it bends around a corner, and nobody, so far as I am aware, has detailed information about these matters.

Now we have come to the end of our symposium. First, let me say that all of the speakers have done an excellent job of exposition. I should like to take this opportunity to thank the Office of Naval Research and the American Institute of Biological Sciences, and the individuals: Dr. P. Hopper, Mrs. V. Bolton, Dr. K. Heumann, Dr. I. Fuhr, Dr. G. Livingston, Mr. I. Mohler, Dr. O. Reynolds and Mr. L. Shinn for having arranged this symposium, which I myself have found very interesting. I hope that you all agree with me that we are indebted to them for having taken the initiative and brought us here.